P9-AFH-749

HYPNOSIS THROUGHOUT THE WORLD

HYPNOSIS THROUGHOUT THE WORLD

Edited by

F. L. MARCUSE, Ph.D.

Professor, Department of Psychology
Washington State University
Pullman, Washington

With Contributions From

Brazil, Canada, Czechoslovakia, Denmark, Finland, Germany,
Great Britain, Hungary, India, Israel, Italy, Japan, Netherlands,
Norway, Sweden, Union of Soviet Socialist Republics, and the
United States of America

With a Foreword by

Bernard B. Raginsky, M.D.

The International Society for Clinical
and Experimental Hypnosis

CHARLES C THOMAS • **PUBLISHER**
Springfield • *Illinois* • *U.S.A.*

Published and Distributed Throughout the World by

CHARLES C THOMAS • PUBLISHER

BANNERSTONE HOUSE

301-327 East Lawrence Avenue, Springfield, Illinois, U.S.A.

NATCHEZ PLANTATION HOUSE

735 North Atlantic Boulevard, Fort Lauderdale, Florida, U.S.A.

© *1964, by* CHARLES C THOMAS • PUBLISHER

Library of Congress Catalog Card Number: 63-19582

*With THOMAS BOOKS careful attention is given to all details of
manufacturing and design. It is the Publisher's desire to present books
that are satisfactory as to their physical qualities and artistic possibilities
and appropriate for their particular use. THOMAS BOOKS will be true
to those laws of quality that assure a good name and good will.*

Printed in the United States of America

D-1

FOREWORD

THE COLLECTION of various scattered scientific material, in order
to simplify, to clarify and to organize is always commendable. It
often leads to a better understanding of material so correlated.
Hypnosis Throughout the World represents such an attempt in
one of the most difficult areas of knowledge. The added difficulties arise from the fact that hypnosis is an all-embracing subject,
almost without borders; that its nature and theory have never
been adequately defined; that its use is not restricted to a single
discipline but that it can properly be carried out by physicians,
dentists and psychologists within the field of their competence;
that because the induction techniques are rather simple it is not
uncommonly misused not only by the laity but also by some professional persons; and finally, that solid information about the
subject is hard to come by.

At a very considerable expenditure of time and energy, not to
mention personal discomfort and expense, Professor Marcuse
was able to visit personally most of the countries and authors
mentioned in this book. The results have been most rewarding.
Hypnosis Throughout the World, the first such attempt, will do
much to clarify important areas of methodology and theory. It
brings researchers in different parts of the world closer together,
stimulates further research and helps the clinician to make better
use of this modality.

Differences of opinion concerning theories and methodology
often arise from the fact that some countries have a limited access
to world literature on the subject. For example the "reflexology"
concept of hypnosis prevalent in the South American countries
stems from the simple fact that numerous Russian texts have been
promptly translated into Spanish and Portuguese while American
and British texts are seldom translated. When they are, the cost

is almost always prohibitive for the average reader. An attempt to correct this state of affairs is being made.

For somewhat similar reasons, European workers tend to use the authoritarian methods almost exclusively, and simple symptom removal is the most common objective. It is hoped that *Hypnosis Throughout the World* will give us a better overall picture of the many possibilities inherent in hypnosis.

The absence of a chapter on France makes a point it is well to remember. In countries where the use of hypnosis spreads explosively in an uncontrolled fashion, it results in an ebb of interest equal to its uncontrolled usage. The intense interest in hypnosis in France during the early years of this century was followed by an almost completely "silent" period of about four decades. At the present time a more rational interest is once again spreading through France.

For the serious workers in hypnosis and for those whose interest is only academic, this volume is a veritable fountain of hard-to-get facts. Professor Marcuse is to be congratulated for conceiving and executing this monumental task. It is to be hoped that future editions will include reports from an increasing number of countries.

BERNARD B. RAGINSKY, M.D.
Founding President
The International Society for Clinical
and Experimental Hypnosis

PREFACE

F. L. Marcuse; born 1916, Montreal, Canada; Ph.D. Cornell University U.S.A.; Vice-President S.C.E.H.; Fellow American Division I.S.C.E.H., Susan Linn Sage Fellowship, Medal in Psychology, President and Diplomate (Clinical) American Board of Examiners in Professional Hypnosis, Past-president Washington State Psychological Association; Member American Psychological Association, Sigma Xi; Areas of Psychology, 1954, Harper, N. Y., U.S.A., Hypnosis, Fact and Fiction, 1959, Penguin, Harmondsworth, England; *present position, Professor of Psychology, Washington State University, Pullman, Washington, U.S.A.*

HYPNOSIS as interpreted and utilized in any one country has a broad spectrum, and paradoxically it is only by seeing its still broader spectrum throughout the world that we may hope to narrow down its theory and practice to a more meaningful size. The International Society for Clinical and Experimental Hypnosis (I.S.C.E.H.) is attempting to achieve this objective. That is, it is attempting to comprehend the various manifestations of hypnosis over and beyond the bounds set by any one particular country. In this way, they believe that a more complete realization of what can and what cannot be done with hypnosis may result. That there is interest internationally is attested to by many different facts, e.g., the annual meetings of the I.S.C.E.H., the publication in different countries of various journals concerned with hypnosis, the certification of the legitimate use of hypnosis in medicine by different international bodies, personal contact, as well as the presence of I.S.C.E.H. divisions in many different lands.

Large differences in the evenness of style, length, inclusiveness, etc., of the various contributions might have been avoided if instead of being edited, this book were authored. To do this, however, would have, in the editor's opinion, been highly presumptuous, for it is difficult enough to write about the state of hypnosis even in one's own country. Differences in the emphasis given to various topics, as contrasted with the differences mentioned above (length, etc.) depend upon the specific interest of the particular contributor.

A suggested outline was given to each contributor in the endeavour to elicit from each country the following information: history (past and present), attitudes (medical, dental, legal, psychological, clerical, and public), teaching and research, misconceptions, laws, additional considerations, future possibilities, plus a restricted number of selective references (*such references may be both in the body and at the end of the chapters.*) The interpretation and use made of this outline varied considerably among contributors. One contributor, for example, gave an autobiographical account of incidents that occurred in his work with hypnosis. It is included inasmuch as the history of hypnosis in a particular country is sometimes tied in with the events that befall a particular individual. Material under the different headings also varied. For example, what belongs under the past, the recent past, or the present depends on many factors such as, editing, age (both the readers' and the writers') and the particular country in question. While no hard and fast decision was made, the editorial rule of thumb was as follows: before 1900- past; 1900-1950, recent past; 1951-on, present. There has been an attempt, on the part of the editor, to make the headings and contents in the various chapters both uniform and sequential. One may wonder what dictated the choice of countries included in this book. This was decided, in part, by the availability of a given contributor, by the desire to obtain as broad a representation as possible, and by the arbitrary decision of the editor. A brief biographical note about each contributor indicating his age, education, honours, professional affiliations, publications, and present position, is also included.

Contributors to this book are among the leading, if not the foremost, individuals in the field of hypnosis in their own country. The majority are members of the I.S.C.E.H., over seventy percent have published books of their own on some phase of the theory or practice of hypnosis, and three of the contributors are past, present, or future (president-elect) presidents of this organization. The Foreword, as well as the chapter on Hypnosis in Canada, has been written by the founding president of the I.S.C.E.H.—Bernard B. Raginsky, M.D. Approximately one-half of the manuscript has been written by medically trained individuals and one-half by psychologically trained persons.

Communication even when language is not a barrier, often presents a difficulty. Communication together with translation poses even greater difficulties. If to this is added editing, then the problem becomes most difficult. Inasmuch as the editor, by his changes, might have inadvertently suggested a different meaning than that originally intended by the contributor, a copy of the revised (edited) manuscript, *before publication* was sent to each of the contributors for his final approval.

The description of the use of hypnosis throughout the world contained in this book suggest that one should guard against speaking of hypnotist-psychologists and hypnotist-physicians, etc. Rather, it would clearly appear, there are psychologists and physicians, etc., who, *in addition* to possessing knowledge about their own specific field, *also* know about the nature of hypnotism. Hypnosis rarely supplants, it supplements; it seldom is used *per se* but generally as an adjuvant. Apart from the panorama and perspective provided the reader of the variety of ways in which hypnosis has been used—and misused—the names mentioned by the contributors of individuals from different countries who have played an important role in the history of hypnosis are most significant. Such information by implication cautions the reader, especially from the Western culture, to guard against scientific ethnocentrism.

A few years ago the present editor concluded a book on hypnosis with the statement "to be continued." It would appear logical that a fitting continuation would be a book concerned with uses and misuses and the attempt to cull fact from fiction in the practice of hypnosis in different parts of the world. It is the hope, and was the intent, of the editor to achieve this goal by this book.

CONTENTS

HYPNOSIS THROUGHOUT THE WORLD

INTERNATIONAL COMMUNICATION AND ORGANIZATION IN HYPNOSIS

By

JOHN G. WATKINS, PH.D.

John G. Watkins; born 1913; Ph.D. Columbia University; President-elect I.S.C.E.H., Past-president American Board of Examiners in Psychological Hypnosis; Member, American Psychological Association, American Association for the Advancement of Science, Academy of Psychosomatic Medicine, American Academy of Psychosomatic Medicine, American Academy of Psychotherapists, Council of Psychoanalytic Psychotherapists; Hypnotherapy of War Neuroses, N. Y., Ronald, 1949, General Psychotherapy, Springfield, Thomas, 1960, etc.; present position, Chief Psychology Service Veteran Administration Hospital, Portland, Oregon, U.S.A.

CONTRIBUTIONS to the field of hypnosis have come from many different countries. At various times France, England, India and the United States, as well as other nations, have been centers of research and publication. No single country can take exclusive credit for the progress in hypnotic development. However, until recently the communication between workers in different areas has been minimal. Studies were often carried on in one country by investigators who were completely uninformed about advances made by co-workers studying the same problem in other areas. Books were seldom translated into other languages, and journal articles were rarely available outside of the country of the contributor.

INTERNATIONAL PUBLICATIONS IN HYPNOSIS

In 1950, the *British Journal of Medical Hypnotism* under the editorship of Dr. S. J. van Pelt made its first appearance. This quarterly, published in the English language, presented papers of contributors from a number of different countries and developed a circulation extending throughout a large part of the world, especially in Europe and in the English-speaking regions. Until 1953, it served as the only available medium for the international publication of hypnosis papers. This *Journal* was listed as being the official organ of the British Society of Medical Hypnotists, and a number of distinguished foreign contributors were invited to join this "organization." It still continues to be published as such. However, no membership list for this Society has been published or register of officers posted.

In 1953, the *Journal for Clinical and Experimental Hypnosis,* under the editorship of Dr. Milton V. Kline, began publication and started accepting contributions from other countries as well as the United States. This quarterly, as the official journal of the Society for Clinical and Experimental Hypnosis, has maintained continuous publication with Kline as its editor until 1960. In 1960, the editorship was assumed by Dr. Frank B. Kirkner, Chief Clinical Psychologist for the Veterans Administration Hospital in Long Beach, California and in 1961, Dr. Martin Orne, of the Psychiatric Department of Harvard University Medical School, became its Editor. In 1959, as a consequence of the organization of the International Society for Clinical and Experimental Hypnosis (I.S.C.E.H.) the name of this Journal was changed to the *International Journal for Clinical and Experimental Hypnosis,* and a number of contributors from countries other than the United States were added to its editorial board.

Journals in other countries include the *Japanese Journal of Hypnosis* published by The Japanese Society of Hypnosis under the editorship of Dr. Gosaku Naruse, Psychologist at Kyushu University. This periodical publishes original research papers in Japanese with occasional titles and summaries in English. In South America several journals have had widespread circulation. The *Acta Hipnologica Latinoamerica* in Spanish is published by the Confederacion Latinoamericana de Hipnosis Clinica Y Experimental, an organization of Latin-American hypnosis societies. Its editor is Dr. Marcelo Lerner, psychiatrist, of Buenos Aires, Argentina.

Also published in Spanish is the *Revista Latino-Americana de Hipnosis Clinica* edited by Dr. Isaac Gubel. It is the official organ of the Federacion Latino-Americana de Hipnosis Clinica. The Brazilian National Division of the I.S.C.E.H. in 1959 began publication of its *Boletim* in Portuguese. This Journal, under its editor, Prof. Dr. Enzo Azzi, Director of the Institute of Psychology, of the Pontifical Catholic University of São Paulo, Brazil first began as a part of the *Revista de Psicologia Normal E Patologica* and then was published as a "Separata" of the *Revista*.

A few journals devoted primarily to dental hypnosis have appeared. These include the *Journal of the American Society of Psychosomatic Dentistry and Medicine,* and *Hipnologia,* the official organ of La Asociacion Cientifica Argentina de Hipnodoncia.

The American Journal of Clinical Hypnosis has enjoyed substantial international distribution through foreign societies affiliated with its publisher, the *American Society of Clinical Hypnosis.* Most of the above journals have begun publication since 1958, which indicates the considerable increase in publishing media now available to writers and researchers in the field.

THE INTERNATIONAL SOCIETY FOR CLINICAL AND EXPERIMENTAL HYPNOSIS (I.S.C.E.H.)

It had always been an objective of the Society for Clinical and Experimental Hypnosis (SCEH) to establish an international forum which would bring into communication scientists and clinicians throughout the world. Accordingly, in the summer of 1958 Bernard B. Raginsky, then SCEH President, appointed an informal "Organizing Committee" consisting of John G. Watkins, Milton V. Kline, Jacob H. Conn and Jerome M. Schneck which was given the assignment of establishing The International Society for Clinical and Experimental Hypnosis.

The task undertaken by this Committee was a prodigious one. In this rapidly expanding field there were many discordant voices, with workers in different countries speaking different languages and holding different theoretical views about the nature of hypnosis. Professional jealousies between leading workers were common. The goals of this Committee were: to bring together into one international association the leading scientists and clinicans in all countries who represented the best in research, clinical practice, and ethical standards, to establish under a single international constitution national division organizations within all countries which possessed contributing workers, and to secure the acceptance and recognition of workers in hypnosis by world scientific bodies.

Leading hypnosis contributors on all continents were contacted by the Organizing Committee and invited to become members of an International Board of Directors, to act as official "Representatives" for their countries, and to assume the responsibility of developing within their own nations "National Divisions" which would consist of clinicians, scientists, and professional societies actively and reputably engaged in work in the field of hypnosis.

Its first Constitution, adopted unanimously by all Representatives in 1958, states the purposes of this organization as follows: "The object of The International Society shall be to stimulate and to improve professional research, discussion and publications pertinent to the scientific study of hypnosis. It shall be to encourage co-operative relations among scientific disciplines with regard to the study and applications of hypnosis, and it shall be to bring together persons using hypnosis and setting up standards for professional adequacy and training in the field."

Membership was open to physicians, dentists and psychologists who demonstrated the completion of adequate training courses and who were actively using hypnosis in their research or clinical practices. Membership requirements in all national divisions were comparable but were subject to the legal regulations regarding the use of hypnosis in the respective countries. In 1959, SCEH became the U. S. Division of I.S.C.E.H.

The International Society held its first, and organizing, meeting in conjunction with the annual SCEH convention in Chicago in October 1958. Representatives from six different countries attended. Its Second International Congress was held in Rio de Janiero, Brazil, in July 1961 in conjunction with the meetings of the Brazilian Society for Medical Hypnosis. There was a widespread attendance by Latin-American delegates. The Third International Congress was held in Portland, Oregon, in August 1962 in conjunction with the Fourteenth Annual Convention of SCEH. At this time it had divisional organizations in the following countries: Argentina, Australia, Austria, Brazil, Canada, Chile, Cuba, Denmark, Finland, France, Germany (West), Great Britain, Hungary, Israel, Italy, Japan, Mexico, New Zealand, Netherlands, Norway, Sweden, Turkey, Union of South Africa, United States, and Venezuela. In 1960 it became an Affiliate Society of the World Federation for Mental Health and a member of the Union of International Associations, indicating the change in acceptance of the status of hypnosis by that date. Since the World Federation for Mental Health was an affiliate of UNESCO, a division of the United Nations, the path was opened for workers in hypnosis to communicate their contributions directly to world health organizations.

Bernard B. Raginsky, M.D., from Montreal, Canada, became the First and Founding President of the International Society, serving in that capacity from 1958 to 1960. John G. Watkins, Ph.D., of Portland, Oregon, U.S.A., was elected as the First Executive Secretary and served two terms in that office, from 1958 to 1962. Aaron A. Moss, D.D.S., of New York City, the Society's First Treasurer, also served two terms, from 1958 to 1962.

Initially the Society established three Vice-Presidencies, filled respectively by Ainslie Meares, M.D., Psychiatrist from Australia, A. C. deMoraes Passos, M.D., Professor of Phthisiology in the São Paulo Medical School, São Paulo, Brazil, and Berthold Stokvis, Chief of the Psychiatric Clinic at the Leyden State University in Netherlands. Following a constitutional reorganization in 1960 the three Vice-Presidencies were abolished and the position of President-Elect established. Dr. Meares served as the Society's second president (1960-1962) and Dr. Passos became its third administrative head (1962-1964).

The International Society has published biennial directories of its officers, representatives, its board of directors, committee members and editors, and has made its services available to facilitate the travel and lecturing of authoritative workers in the field. In collaboration with SCEH, its U. S. Division, it publishes a Newsletter which contains items about activities in many different countries. It has sponsored the publication of research bibliographies and the broader dissemination of pertinent literature. Through its offices there has been an interchange of publications and materials for teaching courses.

Global channels of communication have now been set up between contributors to the field of hypnosis thus facilitating the exchange of ideas. Hypnosis societies have established themselves among the reputable scientific organizations of the world and are making significant progress at reducing prejudice. Through these international associations men of good will who have been studying similar phenomena are able to interact and to stimulate in each other increased contributions which affect, both directly and indirectly, the physical and mental health, as well as the peace, of the world community.

INTERNATIONAL ADDRESSES

International Societies

The International Society for Clinical and Experimental Hypnosis (ISCEH)

    Executive Secretary: H. Clagett Harding, M.D.
                     2050 N. W. Lovejoy Street
                     Portland, Oregon, U.S.A.

Confederacion Latinoamericana de Hipnosis Clinica y Experimental (CLAHCE)

    President: Evarado Power, M.D.
                     America 111—Villa Ballester
                     Buenos Aires, Argentina

Federacion Latino-Americana de Hipnosis Clinica

    Director: Dr. Isaac Gubel
                     Calle Montevideo 945-Dto. 4
                     Buenos Aires, Argentina

Journals

English Language

The International Journal of Clinical and Experimental Hypnosis
    Editor: Martin Orne, M.D., Ph.D.
                                 74 Fernwood Road
                                 Boston, Massachusetts, U.S.A.

SCEH-ISCEH Newsletter (Published by SCEH but distributed internationally)
    Editor: Margaretta K. Bowers, M.D.
                                 4 Grove Street
                                 New York, New York

The British Journal of Medical Hypnotism
    Editor: Dr.S. J. van Pelt
                                 4 Victoria Terrace
                                 Kingsway, Hove 3
                                 Sussex, England

Spanish Language

Acta Hipnologica Latinoamericana
    Editor: Dr. Marcelo Lerner
                                 Araoz 2689 6. C.,
                                 Buenos Aires, Argentina

Revista Latino-Americana de Hipnosis Clinica
    Editor: Dr. Isaac Gubel
                                 Montevideo 945—Dto. 4
                                 Buenos Aires, Argentina

Hipnologia
    Editor: Dr. Angel Olives
                                 Avenida de Mayo 1229-40 A
                                 Buenos Aires, Argentina

Portuguese Language

Boletim da Divisao Nacional do Brasil da ISCEH (Separata of
    Revista de Psicologia Normal E Patologica)
        Editor: Enzo Azzi, M.D., Ph.D.
                                     Rua Monte Alegre 984-Perdizes
                                     São Paulo, Brazil

Japanese Language

The Japanese Journal of Hypnosis
        Editor: Gosaku Naruse, M.D., Ph.D.
                                     Department of Psychology,
                                         Faculty of Education
                                     Kyushu University
                                     Hakozaki, Fukuoka, Japan

HYPNOSIS IN BRAZIL

By

A. C. DE MORAES PASSOS, M.D.

Antonio Carlos de Moraes Passos; born 1921; M.D. School of Medecine of the State University of São Paulo; President (1962) of the I. S. C. E. H., Past-president Brazilian Division of the I. S. C. E. H.; Member, Medical Academy of São Paulo, Legal and Criminological Society of Medicine of São Paulo, Franco da Rocha Research Center, Pan-American Medical Association; Present Aspects of Hypnology, São Paulo, Linografica, 1961, (with Oscar Farina, M.D.); present position, Assistant Professor Paulista Medical School of the Ministry of Education, São Paulo, Brazil.

RECENT PAST

THE EVOLUTION of hypnosis in Brazil has had the same characteristics as those observed in other parts of the world towards magnetism; i.e., suspicion and curiosity during the first half and scientific interest in the last half of the nineteenth century. Since then there has been a loss of interest, with the almost complete disappearance of scientific hypnotism, at least for clinical purposes, and at the same time there has been an increasing emphasis on stage hypnotism. Scientific hypnosis reappeared and was extensively practiced for clinical purposes starting in 1956 and at the same time its use for purposes of entertainment was finally prohibited by a Federal Decree in July 1961.

The first scientific Brazilian text on hypnotism was probably F. Fajardo's *Hypnotismo* published in 1889. This was followed in 1896 by a second, enlarged edition with a broader title by the same author *Tratado de Hypnotismo (A Treatise on Hypnotism)*. The author was assistant professor of the Propaedeutic Clinic, Medical School of Rio de Janeiro (today the University of Brazil).

11

Fajardo reports in his second book that as early as 1832 the Sociedade de Medicina do Rio de Janeiro (Medical Society of Rio de Janeiro) had debated a monograph by Leopold Gamard, M. D. about animal magnetism. This work was reported by Cuissard, M.D. who said at that time: "I, therefore, declare myself a friend and foe of animal magnetism; friend, because I observed and recognized positive results in its use; foe, because I reject with all my strength the cheating the magnetizers employ and the mistakes they introduce in this art, in other words all the indiscreet applications they dare to chance . . ." After various considerations of the dangers of magnetism he said: "magnetism is still dormant in Brazil; beware! do not awake it." He concluded by requesting the Society to reject Gamard's paper.

In 1861, a group of doctors founded in Rio de Janeiro the Sociedade de Propaganda do Magnetismo (The Society for Propagation of Magnetism) and the Juri Magnético (The Magnetic Jury) whose statutes were approved by the Cabinet Council of the Imperial Government of Brazil. According to these statutes the members of the aforementioned society were given the right to study, propagate and practice magnetism and were duty bound to expose the charlatans who misused magnetism. The author has not found any record of how the society ended.

A new phase of the practice of hypnotism, says Akstein in a personal communication, was registered by Erico Coelho's report read at a session held at the Imperial Academy of Medicine (nowadays Brazilian Academy of Medicine) in 1889. This paper concerned the treatment of beriberi by hypnotic suggestion, and had repercussions in the Brazilian faculty. At that time the influence of French culture in Brazil was considerable, especially the influence of medical bibliography. Consequent to this the debates between the Paris and Nancy Schools were followed with great interest by Brazilian doctors who were predominantly in favour of Charcot. Many of them had been intimate friends of his at Salpetrière.

In 1919, Medeiros de Albuquerque published a book entitled *O Hypnotismo* (Hypnotism) which marked an epoch in the history of hypnosis in Brazil. The author, a member of the Academia Brasileira (Brazilian Academy), Academia de Ciências de Lisbôa

(Academy of Sciences of Lisbon, Portugal) and a member of the Société de Psychologie de Paris (Psychological Society of Paris) was neither a physician nor a psychologist, but simply a diligent intellectual (who counted among his friends many prominent doctors) dedicated to the study and practice of hypnosis. In order to write his book Medeiros de Albuquerque carefully consulted all the works listed in the *Quarterly Cumulative Index to Current Medical Literature* which he obtained and studied. He went to France several times to gather reference material for his work. He performed so meticulously that even today, there are only a few texts that can compare with his in scientific precision. Two prominent Brazilian physicians Professor Miguel Couto Filho of the Medical School of Rio de Janeiro and Juliano Moreira, president of the then Society of Neurology, Psychiatry and Legal Medicine of Rio de Janeiro, wrote the preface to his book. This book was recently reprinted in its sixth edition (1958), and even today is indispensable to those interested in hypnology.

In this phase of its evolution scientific research in hypnosis was conducted almost exclusively in Rio de Janeiro. This is understandable since the Faculdade de Medicina da Universidade de São Paulo (Medical School of the University of the State of São Paulo) was founded in 1914; while the Escola Paulista de Medicina (Paulista School of Medicine of the Ministry of Education) and the Instituto de Psicologia da Universidade Catolica de São Paulo (Institute of Psychology of the Catholic University of São Paulo) were founded in 1934 and 1952 respectively. Other medical schools were older than the Medical School of Rio de Janeiro but were not centers for research in hypnosis.

Outstanding in São Paulo, at this time, among others, was Domingo Jaguaribe, M.D. He devoted himself specifically to the treatment of alcoholism by group hypnosis. The results of his many years of work in this field were presented at the Sixth Brazilian Congress of Medicine and Surgery. Jaguaribe's reputation was so great that the street, in downtown São Paulo, where his office was located, today bears his name.

The practice of hypnosis in medicine disappeared in the twenties, except on rare occasions when it was discreetly used, inasmuch as doctors feared both their colleagues' opinions and public reaction. Some physicians were indifferent or skeptical while others strenuously opposed such practice.

In the Psychiatric Department of the University of the State of São Paulo's Medical School, Professor Pacheco e Silva continued to teach hypnosis as well as to use it in the treatment of alcoholics. These activities however were limited to this department.

PRESENT

Renewed interest in scientific hypnosis was brought about by its practice during World War II which directed the attention of Brazilian doctors to its use, and by the well known report on hypnosis published by the British Medical Association in 1955.

Toward the end of 1954, David Akstein attempted to indicate to his colleagues in Rio de Janeiro the advantages of hypnosis. He attempted to do this by organizing meetings with his fellow doctors among whom was Professor Mauricio de Medeiros (a brother of the author of O Hypnotismo) who was at that time (1956-1959) Minister of Health in Brazil. These meetings, however, had only a small effect on the medical profession until the year 1956, when Akstein, learning about the successful results of José Torres Norry's courses in hypnosis in Argentina invited this Argentinean Psychiatrist to come to Brazil and teach. Norry taught the first course on hypnosis which was sponsored by Akstein's Clinic and presided over by the Minister of Health. (Torres Norry had taught courses for physicians and dentists in Rio de Janeiro.) Accepting an invitation by Alvaro Badra to teach in São Paulo, Norry organized the first group of workers in this city whose population was over four million in 1960. Torres was thoroughly Pavlovian, and consequently Brazilian hypnologists followed the reflex theory of hypnosis. These courses were however very welcome in São Paulo where dentists were unfortunately being taught hypnosis by laymen. In point of fact the same thing was happening in many countries in this particular phase of the development of hypnosis. The groups which had been formed in Rio de Janeiro and São Paulo grew rapidly.

In 1957, the Sociedade Brasileira de Hipnose Médica (Brazilian Society for Medical Hypnosis) had been founded in Rio de Janeiro, the old capital of the Republic. This group was presided over by David Akstein, and later by A. R. de Castro Monteiro who succeeded him in 1962. The Brazilian Society for Medical Hypnosis of Rio de Janeiro has made hypnosis known among physicians, has fought popular prejudice, and has helped to prevent the practice of hypnotism by laymen. Six additional courses on hypnosis sponsored by the Society after its founding were added to the initial seven introduced by Akstein.

In 1960, a group had split off from the Brazilian Society for Medical Hypnosis and founded the Brazilian Society of Reflexology (Sociedade Brasileira de Reflexologia) under the chairmanship of José Paiva Carneiro. This group had an exclusively Pavlovian orientation .

In 1957, the Institute of Psychology of the Pontifical Catholic University of São Paulo (Instituto de Psicologia da Pontifícia Universidade Católica de São Paulo), under the leadership of Professor Enzo Azzi, requested the present author to take the chairmanship of the section on hypnosis. The first course in medical hypnosis officially approved as a post-graduate course by the Catholic University of São Paulo was taught in that year. Other identical courses also taught by the present writer followed. In 1961 two courses were taught by the author and by Oscar Farina in the inland towns of Taubaté (sponsored by the regional section of the São Paulo Medical Association) and in the School of Medicine of Ribeirão Preto (sponsored by the Rocha Lima Fraternity).

In 1961, the first course on hypnosis was taught by this author in the Escola Paulista de Medicina (Paulista Medical School of the Ministry of Education) sponsored by the Department of Psychiatry and Psychosomatic Medicine. It had the official approval of the Executive Council. In 1958, the author had become a full member of the Academia de Medicina de São Paulo (Academy of Medicine of São Paulo) with a monograph entitled—*Algumas Considerações sôbre o Uso da Hipnose* (A study on some uses of hypnosis). He taught the first course on hypnosis sponsored by the Academy and in 1960 another course followed.

In 1958, when the I.S.C.E.H. was founded, the present writer was asked to serve on its Board of Directors and to organize the

Brazilian National Division. Soon after the opening Congress of the I.S.C.E.H., held in Chicago (1958), the Brazilian Division was organized with the collaboration of the hypnologists of the Brazilian Society for Medical Hypnosis. Among the Rio de Janeiro's hypnologists who became members was David Akstein who was elected its Vice-President. The Brazilian Division has its seat in the Catholic University of São Paulo where regular meetings are held and where reports on hypnosis are presented. Several of these articles as well as others written by the members of the I.S.C.E.H.'s Brazilian Division were edited in 1961 by the author in collaboration with Oscar Farina, M.D. *(Aspectos Atuais da Hipnologia)*. Forty-one doctors, one dentist, one veterinarian, two psychologists and two technicians collaborated in this book. Most contributors were faculty members of the University of the State of São Paulo, Paulista Medical School of the Ministry of Education, University of the State of Paraná, Mackenzie University, Catholic University of São Paulo, Catholic University of Campinas, etc.

Brazilians have actively participated in the International Congresses on hypnosis. In 1958, Carolino Novaes attended the first Congress of I.S.C.E.H. in Chicago, Illinois. In 1960, Oscar Farina attended the thirty-fifth Anniversary Congress of the Pan-American Medical Association in Mexico City, reporting his own work and that of several of his colleagues who were unable to attend. In 1961, the second Congress of the I.S.C.E.H. was held jointly with the first Pan-American and first Brazilian Congress on Hypnology in Rio de Janeiro. These Congresses were a great success, despite the fact that only a few English speaking hypnologists attended. Among those present were Ainslie Meares of Australia, Bernard Levinson of South Africa and Louis Kosminsky (president of the Section on Clinical Hypnosis of the Pan-American Medical Association) of the United States. Latin-American representatives were numerous.

ATTITUDES
Medical

The attitude of the medical profession towards hypnosis, in a country as large as Brazil, must necessarily be manifold and is in direct relation to the progress hypnosis has attained in different areas. Therefore, in the larger cities where advanced courses are being given, where well-known professionals are practicing hypnosis, and where scientific research is being conducted, its acceptance by the medical class is of the best. On the other hand, in areas where hypnosis is neither studied nor practiced by accredited doctors, prejudice prevails. In São Paulo, Rio de Janeiro, Belo Horizonte, Recife and Curitiba there are groups of hypnologists highly regarded by the medical class. Their activities have been especially important in Rio de Janeiro and São Paulo. In the 1961 Congresses (Pan-American, Brazilian, and I.S.C.E.H.) the opening session was presided over by the then Minister of Health, Dr. Catette Pinheiro, representing the President of the Republic. In São Paulo we have, as indicated, taught official courses in hypnosis at the São Paulo Medical Association, Academy of Medicine of São Paulo, Catholic University of São Paulo and Paulista School of Medicine of the Ministry of Education. Enrollment in such courses always has to be limited, because of the large number of candidates. Professor A. C. Pacheco e Silva, Director of the Department of Psychiatry, State University of São Paulo Medical School and former president of the World Federation for Mental Health (1960-1961) is the present chairman of the Committee of Hypnosis in Psychiatric Medicine of the I.S.C.E.H. Professor Fernando O. Bastos, a member of the same department, is on the Committee on Ethics of the I.S.C.E.H., while Dr. Edmundo Maia, member of the Brazilian Division of the I.S.C.E.H. is the present director of the National Department of Mental Diseases of the Ministry of Health. Recently in Recife, (Pernambuco State) Dr. Lamartine Hollanda Junior founded the Pernambuco Section, Brazilian Division of the I.S.C.E.H. which has its seat in the Catholic University of Pernambuco. Thus, hypnosis in Brazil is in general gaining ground.

Dental

It is paradoxical to consider that while there were no restrictions to the practice of hypnotism by laymen before Decree No. 51009 of 1961, (to be described) there were (and still are) legal restrictions to the practice of hypnotism by dentists.

The proper authorities felt that lay hypnotism as an entertainment was not prohibited by law (before the aforementioned decree) whereas the therapeutic uses of hypnosis were not within the field of competence which the law confers to dentists in Brazil. Consequently its use by them for clinical and therapeutic purposes was (and still is) illegal. Some authorities interpret the present Decree (51009) as precluding dentists from practicing hypnosis.

In 1956, the dentists scheduled a series of courses on hypnosis and started its clinical practice on a large scale. However, even at that time, elements of their own profession were dubious as to the legality of the practice of hypnosis by dentists in Brazil. Sampaio Dória, at the time Professor of legal odontology at the University of São Paulo, was one who opposed the use of hypnosis by dentists. Thus there developed in Brazil the rather unique situation in which dentists actively used hypnosis in their profession yet legal interpretation would prohibit them from doing so!

At the end of the first course on hypnosis at the Catholic University of São Paulo, the present writer invited Professor Flamínio Fávero, to deliver a lecture on the legal and ethical aspects of hypnosis. This lecture was of the greatest importance due to the fact that Professor Fávero was the president of the Council of Medicine in the State of São Paulo, which by law supervises the practice of medicine in this State. He made it quite clear that the present university curriculum for a surgeon-dentist in Brazil does not teach the required subjects to allow him to use hypnosis in his clinic, and that the present legislation does not allow him to practice it for therapeutic purposes. This opinion caused some controversy, but other authorities on the subject expressed the same opinion, e.g., Pacheco e Silva, Meira, and Arbenz.

Nevertheless the dentists continued to practice clinical hypnosis and to organize courses. Judicial authorities rendered no judgment on this situation and the authorities responsible for supervising professional practice ignored it.

However, when the Brazilian Division of the I.S.C.E.H. was founded, a group of doctors under the leadership of the present writer decided to attempt to resolve the situation confronting the dentists since membership in the I.S.C.E.H. was at stake. According to the statutes of the parent body, admission of Brazilian dentists should be dependent on whether or not they use hypnosis in their practice. On the other hand the Brazilian Division of I.S.C.E.H. cannot accept as members, professionals whose legal right to use hypnosis is in question. It was decided, at least at the outset, to admit only physicians to membership thus the membership requirements read as follows: "Only medical doctors who legally practice medicine in the country may become members of the Brazilian Division of the I.S.C.E.H. Membership of other professionals depends on their legal right to practice hypnosis in Brazil. Recently an official request by the I.S.C.E.H. was sent to the Board of Control for Professional Practice (Serviço de Fiscalização Exercicio Professional) reporting this problem and asking for their point of view.

In reply the acting-director wrote as follows: "According to the terms of Brazilian Legislation for the practice of Odontology doctors of dental surgery are only permitted to practice the specific specialties which are part of their curriculum. Since hypnosis is not a part of their odontological curriculum, no Brazilian dentist would qualify to be a member of the International Society according to its statutes. Therefore, they cannot practice hypnosis.

To change this situation it is advisable to suggest to the National Congress that it enact a law which will include a course of hypnology in the curriculum of the odontological schools."

The author regrets that after so many years the members of the odontological profession have not solved the problem by means of specific legislation or simply by adding the required subjects in the school curriculum required to practice hypnosis. This latter measure alone would suffice to eliminate any doubts that might remain.

"In Rio de Janeiro," says Akstein "doctors take no note whether dentists practice hypnosis or not. The legal aspects here have not even been discussed. I believe that in view of the situation in São Paulo, the best solution would also be to regulate by law the practice of hypnosis by dentists (as well as physicians). At the same time, attempts should be made to change the odontologic university curriculum to include psychology and psychopathology."

The situation in Brazil created by the question of the practice of hypnosis by dentists requires an immediate solution.

Clerical

In an eminently Christian country with a Catholic predominance there has been total acceptance of hypnotherapy on the part of the clergy. The clergy showed an interest in a wider knowledge of hypnosis, precisely at the resurging phase of hypnosis (1956), when Catholics wanted to know whether it was permissible or not to submit to hypnotic treatment. At that time the author delivered two series of lectures for monks and priests, one of them held at the Theological School (Seminário Central do Ipiranga) of the Catholic University of São Paulo, which graduates priests for the São Paulo's Archdiocese. Several Protestant ministers have sought to obtain a better knowledge of the present phase of hypnosis. As a matter of fact, Professor Flamínio Fávero, President of the Regional Council of Medicine who delivered the closing lecture at many of our courses, is a Protestant minister. Several Jewish doctors have attended our courses, and the present writer was recently invited (1962) to deliver a lecture on the "Present Status of Hypnosis" at the Associaço Brasileira A Hebraica, a Jewish cultural association.

Public

The attitude of the public towards hypnosis and hypnotherapy is directly conditioned by the attitude of doctors in the different areas, as well as by the frequency and type of stage hypnotism they had seen. This latter was so until 1961 when a Federal Decree prohibited lay hypnosis. In cities where stage demonstrations were frequent and where spectators were affected there still prevails the old concepts of "magic power," "eye power," "dependency on hypnotist," etc. Here the use of medical hypnosis encounters resistance. In centers where the practice of psychotherapy is widespread, and hypnotherapy is practiced by reputable professionals its use has found complete acceptance. In São Paulo, for example, hypnologists often take patients, recommended by other doctors (often psychotherapists), who have previously motivated such patients for hypnotherapeutic treatment.

It is worth noticing that many colleagues who follow the reflex school rather strictly do not tell their patients that they are going to be hypnotised. They generally do not even use the word "hypnosis," but rather tell them that they are going "to relax," "to release tension," etc., but never that they are "to be hypnotised." However, the majority of the hypnologists as a rule do tell their patients beforehand that they are going to be hypnotised. The less enlightened patients maintain the old belief of magic power inherent in hypnotic phenomena and become suspicious and afraid to yield to the hypnotist. This is not observed in more enlightened patients.

LAWS

Until 1961, there was, in Brazil, no specific legislation concerning the practice of hypnosis. There was complete freedom of demonstrations of stage hypnotism, and only in the State of São Paulo, were minors under 18 years of age prohibited from volunteering their services.

As early as 1957, at the conclusion of the first course of lectures on medical hypnosis taught by the author at the Institute of Psychology of the Catholic University of São Paulo, a need for legislation prohibiting lay hypnosis was felt among the participating university professors and physicians. After the closing lecture on Ethical and Legal Aspects of Hypnosis, delivered by Professor Flamínio Fávero, president of the State of São Paulo's Regional Council of Medicine, the participants decided to send a petition to the House of Representatives requesting specific legislation for the practice of hypnosis in Brazil. It was further decided to send another petition to São Paulo's Juvenile Court, since the latter could act immediately on the necessary restrictions regulating the participation of minors in lay demonstrations of hypnotism. The Juvenile Court took the necessary steps and within thirty days announced Regulation No. 292-57 November 29, 1957, which reads as follows:

Dr. Aldo de Assis Dias, by virtue of the power accorded him by law, states that:

Whereas

The Juvenile Court should protect and aid minors, shielding them from moral and physical danger and;

In accordance with paragraph four article 128 of the Juvenile Court, demonstration before minors (less than 18 years of age) which may have a harmful influence on their moral, intellectual or physical development, or dangerously excite their imagination, or awaken bad instincts, or corrupt by the force of its suggestions, are forbidden, and:

In accordance with a statement by the Director of the Institute de Psicologia Experimental da Pontificéa Universidade Catolíca de São Paulo and the Curators for Juveniles, that it is harmful for minors to participate in or attend stage shows or televised programs which deal with hypnotism, and inasmuch as children and highly suggestible adults run a risk, mainly psychological, on being hypnotised by simply attending hypnotic demonstrations when practiced by unqualified persons without scientific objective.

Prohibits:

1. Admission, attendance or participation by minors in theatre or premises, where performances of hypnotism take place.

2. The televising of any program involving hypnosis before 10 P. M. in accordance with item nine regulation No. 68 of December 13, 1956.

Any violation will be punished by the levying of a fine of $0.45 for each minor present, such a fine to be cumulative and to be doubled upon reoccurrence. Besides these fines, the premises will be closed for a period not to exceed six months in accordance with article 128 paragraph seven of the Juvenile Code.

The parents of minors who violate the present regulation or contribute to its violation are considered responsible, as well as the proprietors of establishments, managers, directors, sellers or distributors of tickets or doormen. There will be imposed on them the fines specifically meted out by the Juvenile Code.

In order that it be known by all interested parties the Regulation in question is to be published by the Official Press after it is duly recorded. This will be accomplished by sending copies of the Regulation in question to the Director of Public Entertainment, (Radio broadcasting and Television Divisions) and let it be known to the Lower Court Judges, Curators of Minors, Theatres and Cinema Committees of this Jurisdiction and to the Commissioners for proper action.*

After the Hypnology Congresses (I.S.C.E.H., Pan-American, and Brazilian) were held in Rio de Janeiro in 1961, the President of the Republic signed a decree (51009, July 22, 1961) prohibiting lay hypnotism which read as follows:

The President of the Republic, by virtue of the power invested in him by Article 87 item 1 of the Constitution states that:

Whereas

There has been observed that in the states where no prohibition exists there has been an increasing tendency towards the commercial exploitation of performances and exhibitions of lethargy and hypnosis and;

Such exhibitions or performances are made up of improvisations, which run counter to the constitutional text on prior censure of public performances and amusements, in addition to exposing the spectators to moral constraint and annoyance imposed by the hypnotist and;

Eminent Brazilian and foreign physicians, through statements, articles, conferences and congresses have publicly inveighed against the commercial exploitation of hypnotism as a public amusement by laymen or unskilled professionals in this field and;

In the recent Brazilian and Pan-American Congresses of Hypnology the exploitation of hypnotism on the stage was vehemently condemned on account of the inconveniences and dangers incurred by those taking part therein;

---

*Published in the Diario Oficial do Estado de Sao Paulo on December 3, 1957, page 8. This is the official newspaper.

Prohibits:

Performances of single or many acts of hypnotism, lethargy°
of any kind in clubs, on the radio, on stage, in auditoriums,
over television and enacts other provisions and

Decrees:

Article 1. The commercial exploitation, with or without a
view to profit, of performances involving many or single acts
of hypnotism or lethargy of any kind, type, or form, put on in
clubs of any nature, auditoriums, on the stage, over the radio,
in television studios, or in any public premise, with or without
an entrance fee, are hereby prohibited all over the National
Territory.

Article 2. Demonstrations of a purely scientific character,
without any direct or indirect view to profit, made by physicians who have taken a specialized course in the subject, are
excluded from the prohibition covered by this Decree.

The demonstrations referred to in this article are subject to
approval by the competent authority in each State of the Federation, Federal District or Territory where they are to take
place, except when carried out in schools for didactic purposes.

Article 3. The demonstrations referred to in the foregoing
Article and paragraph shall not be permitted on television,
except in closed circuit exclusively to the interested parties
and with a scientific end in view.

Article 4. The demonstrations mentioned in Article 2 of this
Decree shall not be permitted to be broadcasted over the radio
except in closed circuit, restricted to the auditorium in which
they are held.

Article 5. Minors up to and including 18 (eighteen) years
of age shall not be allowed to enter the premises where scientific demonstrations of hypnotism and lethargy are being conducted.

Article 6. This Decree shall come into force on the day of
its publication, revoking all provisions contrary thereto.

Brasilia, July 22, 1961; 140th year of Independence and
73rd year of the Republic."

---

*See: The Lethargy Affair page 25.

Violation of this statute implies the illegal practice of medicine under which one may be prosecuted and receive a fine and/or imprisonment (Article 282, Brazilian penal code).

Additional Considerations (a)—The "Lethargy" Affair

In Brazil a group of people (including a few doctors) led by laymen have publicized a procedure that they have called "Lethargy." They fanatically insist on stating that it is completely different from hypnosis. By means of touch they induce a series of psychophysiological phenomena and they call themselves followers of "Janred's Belgian School of Lethargy." These touches are accomplished by placing the hands or fingers on certain parts of the body which they identify with those points which the Chinese called acupuncture (counter-irritation points). According to this point of view it is not a morbid condition of drowsiness or a stupor or Charcot's first stage of hypnosis. In some respects this so-called lethargy may be compared to the phrenology of the "Phreno-Mesmerists."

Most of the phenomena they induce such as physical relaxation (which they call obnubilation), drowsiness, muscular and visceral changes, automatic writing, regression, etc., are not different from hypnotic phenomena except possibly in the method of induction. In point of fact its own leader wrote "the reason for creating the lethargy school was to regulate and simplify what had been studied up to now in hypnotism." However, as indicated they desperately tried to differentiate their phenomena from hypnosis, extolling the swiftness with which the induction of lethargy is achieved by means of touch. Its speed, they say may be likened to that of a jet airplane while the speed of hypnotic induction may be likened to the speed of a covered wagon. Another important aspect is that they include in lethargy, phenomena which are not found in hypnosis. These are usually defined as parapsychological, i.e., phenomena resulting from extra-sensory perception (precognition, clairvoyance, telepathy, etc.). They have sought to reproduce on the stage the work carried out by J. B. Rhine of Duke University, North Carolina, U.S.A.

Eighteen stages of lethargy are differentiated and hypnosis is said to be only one of these stages. The stages are as follows: (1)

obnubilation, (2) drowsiness, (3) superficial insensibility, (4) muscular rigidity or rigid catalepsy, (5) muscular relaxation or flaccid catalepsy, (6) deep insensibility, (7) presuggestion, (8) suggestion, (9) visceral insensibility, (10) hypnosis (which they define as "an aggregation of the aforementioned and following stages, stating that there may be in classical hypnosis; neglect, hallucination, ignorance of the degree of depth"), (11) regression in space and time, (12) presomnambulism, (13) somnambulism, (14) pre-trance, (15) trance, (16) "jittery" trance, (17) pre-prostration and, (18) prostration. The mere eliciting of the so-called lethargic phenomena, despite its debatable sequence, shows that it is not fundamentally different from hypnotic phenomena. Little attention would be paid to "lethargy" were it not for the fact that it had caught the public imagination by its pseudo-scientific nature. Even decree 51009, by the President of the Republic prohibiting lay hypnosis, refers separately to "lethargy" as though it were in fact different from hypnosis.

In a demonstration of "lethargy" that I attended a "diagnosis at a distance," utilizing the services of a somnambule, was made. A 72 year old man, who was peacefully watching the demonstration, was diagnosed as having angina pectoris. He was immediately seized by anxiety. The Brazilian Division of the I.S.C.E.H. protested all such practices and were fully supported in their position by the São Paulo Medical Association. Later they were joined in their protest by other State Branches of the Brazilian Medical Association and this resulted in the authorities taking action to prohibit stage demonstrations of "lethargy" which at the time were frequently being televised.

There still however remains something in "lethargy" that requires investigation. The present writer attended several of its demonstrations and concluded that the rapidity with which the "touch" procedure elicits trance states is not usually encountered in hypnosis, private or public, scientific or non-scientific.

Additional Considerations (b)—Free versus Private Clinics

The author has observed that whereas it is easy to induce hypnosis and treat an above average patient (intellectually and economically speaking) it is extremely difficult to treat patients in a free clinic or needy patients in the clinics of medical schools. This is true even in a large center like São Paulo where hypnosis is used everyday in all large and important medical centers (a fact which suggests that the use of hypnosis is highly regarded by the medical profession). A dermatologist who practices hypnosis in his clinic and who has had no difficulty in maintaining good rapport with his private patients, tried to hypnotise a number of patients in a free clinic who suffered from eczema. He, however, encountered difficulties he had never observed before which stemmed from the patients' deep sense of suspicion. One such patient however was promptly relieved of prurigo and for the first time in years felt fine especially at night. A few days later, this dermatologist was approached in his free clinic by a woman who drawing him aside asked him in undertones "Could you say those special prayers for my son? The ones you said for my cousin, she's so much better . . ."

Additional Considerations
(c) Other South American Countries

Query from editor: Would it be possible to indicate that the situation, regarding hypnosis, in other South American countries is: (a) similar to that in Brazil, (b) different from that in Brazil, (c) is unknown?

Answer from contributor: I am afraid that I will not be able to answer this question very satisfactorily since the Congress in Portland (1962) is drawing near and I do not have the time to gather the relevant data. However I can provide the following data.

In South America there are thirteen countries; Columbia, British Guiana, Surinam (Dutch Guiana), French Guiana, Peru, Ecuador, Bolivia, Paraguay, Uruguay, Brazil, Venezuela Argentine and Chile. The I.S.C.E.H. has divisions in the last four countries. In Argentine there is considerable activity, in the field of hypnosis, under the leadership of Marcelo Lerner, M.D.; in Chile leadership is provided by Professor Julio Dittborn, M.D. of Experimental Psychiatry of the University of Chile; in Venezuela, apart from the fact that Professor Dittborn taught there, I know little; while in Brazil I have described some facts in the above. I should also like to add the following details:

In Chile hypnology has developed in the experimental field and they have accomplished much in their universities. Clinical hypnosis is limited and almost nonexistent.

As indicated, I know little of the details of the activities of the Venezuelan Division of the I.S.C.E.H. nor of the accomplishments achieved by Professor Dittborn of Chile when he taught in Venezuela at the University of Carabobo in Valencia. However, I believe that he expounded the same orientation as he had in Chile, that is, that of restricting hypnosis to the experimental field.

Hypnosis is well developed in Argentina where three groups may be found. The first one, as has been indicated, is that of Dr. Marcelo Lerner's affiliated with the I.S.C.E.H. This group works predominantly in the field of hypnoanalysis. It is a relatively small group, and following the I.S.C.E.H. orientation, stresses quality in its membership. The second group is that of Dr. Isaac Gubel who is President of the Argentine Society for Hypnotherapy. This is a large and active group under an eclectic orientation. It reputedly has 700 members in Buenos Aires alone. The third group, extremely limited in number, is under the direction of Torres Norry. It is the Pavlovian School whose orientation is strictly and exclusively Pavlovian. Both Drs. Gubel and Lerner, separately, decided to organize the several hypnotic societies of the Latin countries from the extreme south of South America up to and including Mexico. Each one founded his own group and presided over it. They are Dr. Gubel's "Federacion Latino Americana de Hipnose Clinica" and Dr. Lerner's "Confederacion Latino Americana de Hipnose Clinica e Experimental." We (Brazilians) have not taken an active part in either of these groups, although the Brazilian division supports Dr. Lerner as President of the Argentine Division of the I.S.C.E.H. Each publishes their own review of hypnosis: *Revista Latino-Americana de Hipnosis Clinica* (Dr. Gubel) and *Acta Hipnologica Latinoamericana* (Dr. Lerner).

In Uruguay the wife and husband team of Galina Solovey and Anatol Milechnin have been working actively in the field of hypnosis and have published several papers and two books.

I have heard reference made to the activities of Columbian hypnologists and some of them have attended congresses on hypnosis. I am unfortunately unable to be more specific.

FUTURE

In São Paulo we have endeavoured to have physicians from different medical subjects attend our courses and today we have hypnologists in most specialties—these are university people working in their several medical schools. We have in the past accomplished important clinical and experimental research and this should expand still further. For example the use of hypnosis in orthoptics (training for defective visual habits) is being studied by Belfort de Mattos and Lichtesteinluz, the uses of hypnosis in pedagogy and pediatrics by Oscar Farina, the use of hypnosis in obstetrics by Ciari Junior, Sampaio Goís while Baptista, Belliboni, Belda and others have been concerned with hypnosis in dermatology. This year we have scheduled a series of experiments to start in the Institute of Psychology, Catholic University of São Paulo, and the Escola Paulistade Medicina. In like fashion, Professor Pacheco e Silva will direct research on the electroencephalogram in hypnosis. All these studies will furnish a better scientific basis for the application of hypnosis.

The present literature about hypnosis in Brazil is in English, Spanish, French, and of course our own Portuguese language. Several foreign language books on hypnosis have been translated into Portuguese, for example, *Clinical Applications of Suggestion* by William T. Heron, and *Hypnotism* by George H. Estabrooks. A book encompassing the whole of hypnotic methodology and based on Norry's courses was published in 1958 by Osmar Andrade Faria—*Manual de Hipnose Médica e Odontológica*. This book is presently in its third edition. In 1961 the present writer, with Oscar Farina, edited a book entitled *Aspectos Atuais da Hipnologia*. This as previously mentioned was a collection of the leading hypnotic work performed in Brazil. Since 1958 the *Bo-*

letim of the Brazilian Division of the I.S.C.E.H. has been published as an integral part of the *Revista de Psicologia Normal e Patologica* of the Catholic University of São Paulo. From this publication offprints have been distributed *gratis* to all members of the I.S.C.E.H. in Brazil and to some abroad.

As to texts in English, while there is no difficulty in obtaining them, they are very expensive. With the possible exception of the city of São Paulo, there is a tendency to look for Spanish translations of medical literature. Acceptance of the reflex theory of hypnosis predominates in Brazil. This is because of the courses held by Torres Norry who had had translated into Spanish all the Palovian literature, and also because books printed in Argentina are sold in Brazil at reduced prices. Thus, not only is there the fact that the Spanish language resembles Portuguese, but also the fact that the prices of these books are lower than those books written in the English language. In similar manner, books in other foreign languages are translated into Portuguese or Spanish and this finds much acceptance for the reasons, as indicated, of language or price. The Hungarian F. Volgyesi's books and Platonov's book *La Palabra Como Factor Fiscologicoy Terapeutico*, while edited in Moscow, have been translated into Spanish. As a result of this, such books cost only about one quarter (¼) of the price of English books on the same topic. The same is true of many German texts which have been translated into Spanish, e.g., *Tecnica de la Hypnosis* by J. H. Schultz, etc. Books written in French also find wide acceptance, and there are bookshops specializing in scientific subjects which more than satisfy the purchasing public. One such example of a French text is Nora and Sapir's *La Cure de Sommeil*. French reviews about hypnosis are also read by hypnologists.

The last few years have been dedicated to making scientific hypnosis still better known in such large centers as São Paulo and Rio de Janeiro. In these two major centers of research it is now possible to carry out scientific investigation, however, pioneering work still remains to be done in other areas of Brazil.

The historical evolution of hypnosis in Brazil does not differ significantly from that which occurred in other countries. It followed the same sequence of events observed in the countries of

Europe during the last century. First there was the popular suspicion of animal magnetism and later keen interest was shown, as witnessed by the dispute between the Paris and Nancy Schools. Then in the 20's of this century clinical hypnosis, as such, dropped out of use and stage hypnosis predominated. After World War II, and especially after 1955, hypnosis reappeared with renewed vigor in such centers as São Paulo and Rio de Janeiro. Unfortunately in the more remote parts of Brazil the suspicion of yesteryears still prevails. In the large centers, mentioned above, where training courses in hypnosis are routinely given in the universities it is possible to plan and carry out long range research. This time hypnosis is here to stay.

IMPORTANT REFERENCES

Arbens, G. O.: Da utilização da hipnose pelos cirurgiões-dentistas, in *Aspectos atuais da hipnologia.* Moraes Passos & O. Farina (Eds.) São Paulo: Linografica Editôra Limitada, 1961.

Fajardo, F.: *Tratado de hypnotismo.* Rio de Janiero: Laemmert Editôres, 1896.

Fávero, F.: Aspectos legais e moraes da hipnose. *Rev. Psicol. Norm. e Patol.,* 3: 556-569, 1957.

Meira, A. F.: A hipnose em odontologia, in *Aspectos atuais da hipnologia.* Moraes Passos & O. Faria (Eds.) São Paulo: Linografica Editôra Limitada, 1961.

Pacheco e Silva, A. C.: Aspectos médico-legais da hipnose. *Revista Psicol. Norm. e Patol.,* 5:255-263, 1959.

HYPNOSIS IN CANADA

By

BERNARD B. RAGINSKY, M.D.

Bernard B. Raginsky; born 1902; M.D. (psychiatry, internal medicine) McGill University, Montreal; Gold medal in hypnosis, prizes for research in anesthesia, hypnosis, conditioned reflexes and pharmacology, Past president and Fellow I. S. C. E. H., Academy for Psychosomatic Medicine, I.S.C.E.H., Pan-American Medical Association (Clinical Hypnosis section), Fellow: International College Anesthetists, American College Cardiology, International College Angiology, American Association for the Advancement of Science, American Medical Writers Association; chapters in eight textbooks and 62 papers on physiology, pharmacology, cardiology, anesthesia and hypnosis; present position, associate physician Montreal Jewish General Hospital, private practice, Montreal, Canada.

RECENT PAST

DURING the first quarter of the twentieth century, hypnosis in Canada was seldom heard of. Following the First World War, an occasional physician or psychologist was known to be interested in its use but no record of it appeared in the scientific literature. As elsewhere, it was neglected or relegated to stage performers or quacks.

The earliest scientific publication by a Canadian (B. Raginsky) appeared in 1938. It was not until some time after World War II that interest in hypnosis in Canada took on a more vigorous aspect. The emergence and the acceptance of the psychosomatic viewpoint in medicine allowed more explorations of the hypnological aspects of the psychosomatic approach to medical problems. Occasional lectures on hypnosis at Canadian Medical Schools were given at the request of students but these were only tolerated by the faculty, not sponsored by it. Only now is the occasional excellent article on hypnosis appearing in Canadian Medical Journals.

By 1950, the importance of hypnosis in anesthesiology was beginning to be recognized. This author was asked to give one lecture (a whole evening! being devoted to it) every two years to the McGill University Diploma Course in Anesthesiology. This has been continued up to the present time. This must not be interpreted, however, as reflecting a true interest in hypnosis but only the acknowledgment of the fact that hypnosis can be a useful instrument in anesthesiology. No effort has been made to go into the matter more deeply. In spite of this there have been several requests from anesthesiologists in Canada for more complete courses in this subject in connection with their specialty.

PRESENT

The impetus given to scientific hypnosis in 1953 by the publication of the Journal of Clinical and Experimental Hypnosis, spread to several workers throughout Canada. A research project in hypnosis carried out at one of Canada's largest psychiatric centres was published in 1954 (Malmo, Boag, and Raginsky) and republished in two university textbooks. As in other countries in this hemisphere, the approval of hypnosis as a useful medical tool by the American Medical Association in 1958, allowed workers in this field to come out "in the open." More reports in the newspapers and television programs on hypnosis began to appear.

As a result, physicians, dentists and psychologists in Canada began to explore the use of hypnosis in the sphere of their interest. There were no formal courses open to them on the subject. They were trained in most instances by travelling groups of lecturers consisting of a physician, a dentist and a psychologist as the skeleton of the teaching staff. These were commercial ventures and the students were charged $150 on the average for a two to three day course. These courses were held in hotels. Naturally, this arrangement was not conducive to recruiting the best of the various professions involved. A different type of postgraduate student might have enrolled if the courses were given under the auspices of a University or Hospital and given in a clinical setting for a more prolonged period of time. As it was, the courses given, dealt mainly with induction procedures which often resulted in the "graduates" of these courses reflecting the attitude of "Look, Mom, no hands!" Very little of the basic psychiatric principles and psychodynamics were taught. The emphasis was placed on the control of the hypnotic patient or in these instances —the subject.

ATTITUDES

Medical

The interest shown by some members of the medical profession, the wild claims made for it by some misguided individuals and the increasing number of inquiries both by professionals and non-professional people, were some of the reasons which prompted the Canadian Medical Association to form the Special Committee on Hypnosis to investigate the whole question of hypnosis in Canada and to report its findings to the Association. This Committee has been at work on the problem since 1960 and their report is expected shortly. The Committee is made up as follows:

B. B. Raginsky, M.D., Chairman, Montreal, Psychiatrist and Internist; H. E. Lehmann, M.D., Montreal, Associate Professor of Psychiatry, McGill University, Clinical Director of the Verdun Protestant Hospital, and representative of the Canadian Psychiatric Association; J. B. Michaud M.D., Drummondville, Quebec, Generalist, representative of the Canadian College of General Practice; W. L. Esdale, M.D., Vancouver, B.C., Anesthesiologist, representative of the Canadian Anesthetists' Society; and R. J. Weil, M.D., Halifax, N.S., Assistant Professor of Psychiatry, University of Dalhousie, Corresponding Member from his district.

The report of this Committee is expected to play an important part in guiding not only the medical profession in Canada but the lay public as well. There appears to be an urgent need for a centre for authoritative information in this country to supply material on the subject for serious science writers, national magazines, local newspapers, radio and television producers. We are impressed with the seriousness of purpose and the great amount of research work done by these groups in an attempt to give their audience a true picture of the situation. It would seem that they have a better grasp of the total situation at this time than many professional people in teaching positions at the Universities.

Except for what has been mentioned, at the present time there is no formal training courses being given in Canadian Medical Schools. In the majority of the schools the subject is touched on in either the Department of Psychiatry (or Psychology) but it is not treated as a special subject. Hypnosis has been employed by graduate students at some of these institutions in connection with research projects. At one of the Medical Schools it is illustrated at the undergraduate level and employed at the graduate level in apprenticeship fashion as suitable cases for application arise. A group of enquiry into research aspects of hypnosis has been set up in one school. Several medical schools are ready to initiate a course of study in hypnosis if given some guidance by those in a position to do so. It has been reported that in several of these schools, students have shown an eagerness to receive instruction in hypnosis.

The attitude towards hypnosis by the various colleges of physicians and surgeons throughout the country may be summarized as follows:

The Department of Public Health and the College of Physicians and Surgeons in Alberta feel a concern about the possible abuse of hypnosis and note with concern the number of occasions on which some United States citizens come to Alberta and advertize short courses for teaching hypnosis. Several enquiries have been directed to the College of Physicians and Surgeons in Manitoba by those who have been attracted by claims made for hypnosis by several non-medical persons. Unsuccessful action was taken through the courts against a woman who insisted that she simply taught methods of self-hypnosis. Some members of the profession have been assigned the task of drawing up some regulations to govern the practice of hypnosis in this province. The Ontario College of Physicians and Surgeons has received complaints from misguided individuals who have sought treatment at the hands of unqualified hypnotherapists. In all instances it had been impossible to establish satisfactorily that the hypnotist had been practicing medicine. It is hoped that the Hypnosis Act of

1960-61 will help correct this situation. In the considered opinion of this writer it will be most difficult to convict anyone under this Act since all the hypnotist has to do to avoid prosecution is to use the word "relax" instead of "sleep." In this way it appears that he can circumvent the law. This difficulty occurs under most laws in existence mainly because it is so difficult to define the word "hypnosis." Colleges of Physicians and Surgeons in the other seven provinces do not appear to have had any experience, good or bad, with the use of hypnosis within their jurisdiction.

Because of lack of specific guidance by those in authority in hospitals, trouble may arise with the use of hypnosis. For example, a woman was delivered painlessly under hypnosis in a large general hospital in a Canadian city. The hypnosis had been induced by a lay person in the labour room of the hospital at the request of the patient and her physician but without the knowledge or consent of the hospital authorities. What concerned the hospital was the fact that a patient in the hospital was attended by someone whose qualifications were not approved by the Board of the hospital. Hospital officials considered disciplinary action against the doctor and members of the staff who assisted at the birth. A spokesman for the hospital stated that "medical authorities are looking into the merits of hypnosis but it is not yet an approved procedure in this hospital."

As elsewhere, the question of clinical psychologists using hypnosis for therapy has not been fully resolved. Dr. Tyhurst's Canadian Mental Health Association, Mental Health Services Committee has been working on this problem for the past six years as only one aspect of the total problem of mental health. The report of this Committee should be available in the very near future. In general, the feeling is that psychologists and other non-medical health professionals should not do psychotherapy without what is called "collaboration" with a psychiatrist. Supervision by a general practitioner does not appear to be adequate. It would seem that the supervisor should be a psychiatrist and that it should be continuous supervision so that the psychologist doing psychotherapy, or in this instance hypnotherapy, would not overlook physical complications which were the original cause for the psychological symptoms or may have developed during the course of psychotherapy. This is a knotty problem since, in our opinion, the psychiatrist himself frequently cannot assess adequately the physical components of the illness.

The question of referral of a patient for hypnotherapy also poses difficulties. It would seem inadvisable for a physician to simply refer his patient for hypnotic therapy to a licensed medical practitioner who is skilled in this particular technique, in a manner similar to that in which a patient might be referred for physiotherapy or radiation treatment. Whenever hypnosis is used, the therapist should first seek to obtain as thorough a knowledge as possible of the patient's psychodynamics, and, furthermore, he will have to develop a constructive relationship with the patient. Under these circumstances, it could hardly be expected that a patient could continue psychotherapy with another physican as though the hypnotic therapy had been an indifferent superimposed procedure.

Dental

The dental group became interested in hypnosis for anesthesia and for allaying anxiety in their patients. At the present time, they are probably the largest professional group using hypnosis in Canada. Some of them are very proficient in rapid induction and use it either to do fillings or easy extractions. They use it also for producing analgesia of the gums prior to the injection of local anesthetics. Unfortunately, as some dentists become more proficient with its use, they tend to misuse it outside the sphere of their competence. Some dentists are using it for the treatment of obesity and for some psychiatric conditions.

The dental use of hypnosis led the general practitioner in medicine to become interested in it. He soon found that it could be most helpful to him in many ways and allowed the careful generalist to study human behaviour more carefully and more intimately. But here, too, with more experience with hypnosis the generalist tended to use it in areas in which he was not competent. At first, psychiatrists looked askance at the whole procedure but in the past two years they have shown considerable interest in it and some have been actively engaged in hypnotherapy and hypnoanalysis.

Legal

There is no Federal legislation in Canada respecting the use of hypnosis either by professional or lay people. There is a section of the Criminal Code, however, dealing with the practice of witchcraft, etc. Section 308 of the Code covers the subject in which the hypnotic state might be regarded as "enchantment" within the meaning of this section. This section might be said to touch upon hypnosis in a very general sense.

In the various provinces of Canada the following legislative situation exists:

The Province of Ontario has just passed The Hypnosis Act, 1960-61. This is "An Act to Protect the Public from the Use of Hypnosis by Unqualified Persons." Regulations under this Act came into force on the fifteenth day of November, 1961. It will be some time before this Act can be evaluated in terms of real effectiveness. At a recent meeting, the Alberta Legislative Assembly made a change in their Public Health Act, giving authority to the Provincial Board of Health with the approval of the Lieutenant Governor in Council to make regulations regarding the licensing of hypnotists and the regulation and prohibition of the use of hypnosis in advertising and entertainment, or for any purpose the Provincial Board considers detrimental to the public health. Saskatchewan has no legislation specifically applying to or referring to hypnosis. The only legislation applicable is the Medical Professional Act. It provides for any person practicing medicine while not registered under this Act as being guilty of an offence and liable to penalty. British Columbia appears to have an interest in the question but no legislation as yet. The other provinces have no legislation and apparently little interest in it at this time.

Psychological

Psychologists, both clinical and experimental have always shown interest in hypnotic phenomena since, in some way, it appeared to be the anatomy of personality structure and behaviour. Some Canadian psychologists are using hypnosis in the investigation of alcoholism and character disorders.

Clerical

Official communication with the Catholic Clergy about ten years ago showed that their attitude towards hypnosis was even more permissive than that of the medical and dental professions —providing that hypnotic procedures were carried out by adequately trained men. They were in favour of its use, not only for therapy but for research purposes as well. At the present time, many Catholic physicans, Catholic dentists, and Catholic psychologists are using it in their practice.

TEACHING AND RESEARCH

In the past four years members of these three professions (physicians, dentists, psychologists) in the larger cities throughout Canada have invited excellent teachers to conduct courses over prolonged periods of time. In Montreal, there is one teaching group which runs a class of approximately thirty students in one of the outlying French hospitals. This course consists of thirty hours of lectures, instruction and demonstrations extending over a period of fifteen weeks. The lectures are given in French only. An active group of recognized specialists and generalists, known as the Manitoba Society for Medical Hypnosis, have been active in this field in Winnipeg. Most large Canadian cities have one or two hypnosis societies which meet on the average of once a month and occasionally have an outside invited speaker to help with enlarging their knowledge and experience in hypnosis.

While this professional interest in hypnosis was on the increase, many non-professional people also became interested and schools in hypnosis began to spring up all over the country, mainly in the larger centres. These lay people formed "Schools of Hypnosis," "Institutes of Hypnosis," etc. Their advertisements appear in most newspapers and include all manner of claims for hypnosis.

Additional Considerations (a)—Sensory Hypnoplasty

"Sensory Hypnoplasty" a new dimension in both the concept and the use of hypnosis in psychiatry has been developed in Canada. This is a procedure in hypnoanalysis wherein the patient is allowed to give plastic expression to repressed and suppressed material by constantly modeling with clay under hypnosis. Various sensory stimuli are added to the clay in order to stimulate basic primitive memories, associations, sensations, feelings and conflicts in order to guide, non-verbally, the investigation and treatment of the whole patient. In this way the therapeutic process is initiated exceptionally quickly and intensified markedly. The deep emotional participation by the patient is reflected by the rapidity and the permanence of his recovery. During the entire session the therapist remains passive and silent. This technique does away with many specialized techniques in hypnosis such as visual and auditory hallucinations, automatic writing, dream visualization, deep stages of hypnosis, post-hypnotic suggestions, etc. It also does away with the need to dominate the patient or to implant suggestions. It has been used successfully in the treatment of character disorders, mild forms of alcoholism, anxiety states, anxiety hysteria, conversion hysteria, phobic reactions, obsessive-compulsive neuroses, depressive reactions, diverse neurotic symptom complaints, a wide variety of psychophysiologic reactions involving all systems of the body and some psychotic reactions of schizophrenia.

Additional Considerations (b)—Balanced Anesthesia

The concept of the use of hypnosis to produce a "balanced anesthesia" originated in Canada. Since its introduction it has been receiving increasingly wider acceptance by anesthesiologists throughout the world. In the past, balanced anesthesia consisted of a combination of anesthetic agents in combination or in sequence. This combination produced a more satisfactory anesthesia than could be obtained with any one single agent alone. We believe now that a balanced anesthesia in the broadest sense should include some form of hypnosis in combination with chemical anesthetic agents. Such combinations have proven to be very satisfactory. In almost all cases where this method had been carried out, the quantity of the anesthetic agent used was diminished by 25 per cent-85 per cent.

The administration of an anesthetic is an example of psychic and somatic liaison. The prime purpose of the anesthesiologist is to attack the psychic factor of consciousness with its concomitant perception, apperception and memory, and substitute for them a temporary oblivion. Anesthesiology and psychiatry are the only specialties in medicine whose sole objective is psychic change. Anesthesia, however, can in some instances end in failure or disaster either in the somatic or psychic spheres or both. With the use of balanced anesthesia one can now envision the end of the dichotomy existing in the use of anesthetics wherein the anesthesiologist uses only the anesthetic fraction of the agent while the psychiatrist uses only the disinhibiting fraction of the same agent.

Anesthesiologists have been active in seeking and remarkably successful in finding better and more efficient anesthetic agents for the relief of pain. Psychiatrists in their own field have been searching for shorter and more efficient methods for uncovering the psychodynamics of the neuroses and psychoses and for using shorter therapies for these conditions. Intravenous injections of sodium amytal and sodium pentothal have been found to be helpful in the evaluation and treatment of certain types of neuroses. The most prominent effects of such drugs have been shown to be exerted on the central nervous system. They are manifested chiefly by a change in the mental state of the patient characterized by drowsiness, euphoria, detachment and willingness to discuss intimately personal matters. Whatever salutary effects may follow the administration of sodium amytal in painful conditions, they do not stem from the blocking of pain perception. They must occur either because of alterations in the reaction of the patient to the painful experience or from the interruption of the mechanism responsible for the noxious stimulus. The similarities between the effects of chemoanesthesia under these conditions and psychoanesthesia become more apparent.

Hypnotically induced anesthesia can be accepted by the medical profession only if it is restricted to competent individuals. It appears to be well recognized that its use in major surgery is extremely restricted. It may be of occasional help in minor surgery in suitable individuals. Its greatest potential appears to lie in its use as an adjunct to chemoanesthesia as part of a balanced anesthesia.

FUTURE

The future of hypnosis in Canada appears to be moderately good. In such a conservative country one finds that medical procedures run on the conservative side. Consequently, progress in hypnosis is anticipated to be rather slow but solid. As more men learn to use this modality, not as an exceptional activity but just as another medical technique, hypnosis will find more general use. Hypnosis societies are springing up in almost all the large cities across the country. The Canadian Division of the I.S.C.E.H. established in 1959 was the first national hypnosis society in Canada with members from all parts of the country and from all disciplines. A purely Canadian hypnosis society is in the process of formation. It is called the Canadian Society of Clinical Hypnosis with the British Columbia Division as the starting point.

IMPORTANT REFERENCES

Hanley, F. W.: The use of hypnosis in psychiatry. *Can. Psychiat. J.*, 6: 59-65, 1961.

Malmo, R. B., Boag, T. J., and Raginsky, B. B.: Electromyographic study of hypnotic deafness. *J. Clin. and Exp. Hypnosis*, 2: 305-317, 1954.

Raginsky, B. B.: Hypnotism and its relation to anesthesia. *J. Conn. State Med. Assoc.*, 2: 11-20, 1938.

Raginsky, B. B.: Psychosomatic medicine: Its history, development and teaching. *Am. J. Med.*, 5: 857-878, 1948.

Raginsky, B. B.: The use of hypnosis in anesthesiology (balanced anesthesia). *J. Pers.*, 1: 340-348, 1951.

Raginsky, B. B.: The sensory use of plasticine in hypnoanalysis (sensory hypnoplasty). *Int. J. Clin. and Exp. Hypnosis*, 9: 233-247, 1961.

HYPNOSIS IN CZECHOSLOVAKIA

By

J. HOSKOVEC, PH.D.

Jiří Hoskovec; born 1933; Palacký University, Comenius University, Ph.D. Charles University (The possibilities of hypnosis and suggestion as a research method in psychology, Českosl. Psychol., 1958, 2, 147-154), studied hypnosis under E. Wolf, L. Pekárek, V. Zikmund, R. Konečný, and J. Špelda; Corresponding Editor of the Amer. J. clin. Hypnosis, Executive Secretary of the Journal of Czechoslovakian Psychology, International Editor of the Revista Latino-Americana de Hipnosis Clínica; Member, Czechoslovakian Psychological Society, Czechoslovakian Psychiatric Society, Czechoslovakian Physiological Society, Czechoslovakian Society for the Study of Higher Nervous Activity; Schultz's autogenic training, Českosl. Psychol. 1962, 6, 103-109; present position, Curator Archives Diagnostic Material, Institute Psychology, Charles University, Prague Czechoslovakia.

IN CZECHOSLOVAKIA as in many other countries after the second world war a growth of interest in the clinical application and experimental study of hypnosis is evident. This chapter concerns the uses of hypnosis in Czechoslovakia, especially during the last ten years, 1950-1960, which may be called a beginning of the renaissance period of hypnosis in this country.

RECENT PAST

Czechoslovakian doctors have been concerned with the problems of hypnosis from the nineteenth century onwards. The most well-known names were J. E. Purkyně, J. N. Czermak, R. Krejčí, J. Thomayer, J. Hraše, F. Mareš, and B. Hellich. In the first half of the twentieth century the most important papers concerned with hypnosis and suggestion were published by J. Charvát, J.

Stuchlík, N. Osipov, and V. Vondráček. Apart from these specialized papers—prior to the second world war—there appeared many popular pamphlets and publications of which a great majority, written by non-specialists, discredited hypnosis in the eyes of doctors and research workers. Only since 1945 has the distrust of hypnosis been slowly receding. In the period after the session of the Academy of Medical Science of USSR in 1950 concerned with Pavlov's work, (a report which was very influential in Czechoslovakia) the attitude of Czechoslovakian medical and psychological circles became more positive. This Pavlovian Session pointed out the great theoretical and practical importance of hypnosis. Since then the specialized interest in both the application of hypnosis in medicine and in the study of hypnosis in research has increased.

PRESENT

Only physicians and clinical psychologists use hypnosis. It is considered a method only to be applied by personnel properly qualified in psychopathology. Professors at universities emphasize to their medical students or to psychologists in training the possible dangers in misusing this method. Clinical psychologists usually cooperate with physicians in the investigation of hypnotic behavior and in hypnotherapy. Stage hypnosis is not practiced.

According to popular conception among non-scientific personnel hypnosis is a state similar to sleep. During the last decade pamphlets dealing with hypnosis were written under the influence of the Pavlovian theory. The general public has been influenced along these same lines by radio and television lectures.

ATTITUDES

Medical

Czechoslovakian physicians use hypnosis, for psychotherapy, for producing anaesthesia, as a method of active training, as a method of evoking therapeutic sleep, and as a differential diagnostic method. Of methods related to hypnosis, Schultz's autogenic training is chiefly used. This procedure is recommended in cases of neuroses (E. Bena, S. Kratochvíl, J. Špelda), for the alleviation of pain in gynaecological practice (J. Čepelák) and for rehabilitation of the nervously ill (K. Obrda and J. Karpíšek).

Local physicians accept the fact that the hypnotic state enhances suggestibility and because of this makes a differentiated and therapeutically effective word interference possible—a situation which is not met with very often in the waking state. Hypnosis should be regarded as a method which offers opportunities for a better use of other therapeutical measures for hypnosis is frequently used in combination with other therapeutic methods.

The chief object of hypnosuggestive therapy in psychiatry are the neuroses. The physiological mechanisms of suggestion and autosuggestion which in some cases cause the neurotic symptoms, may also be used to remove them. With a certain category of neurotic patients hypnosuggestive therapy is causal psychotherapy. Hypnosuggestion obtains excellent results especially with those pathological-reactive states in which the causes of the illness are known. Hypnosis is often used to remove specific neurotic symptoms. The effect in treating hysterias, phobias, and obsessions are usually short-term and unsatisfactory, if phantasies, wishes, and experiences expelled from consciousness (and which are the causes of the symptoms of illness) are not successfully revealed. J. Stuchlík and L. Pekárek recommend hypnosis in the therapy of stammering; hypnotherapy is selected for patients whose stammering is caused emotionally. L. Pekárek reports that in cases of enuretics, awakening upon pressure in the bladder was effected by means of hypnotic sleep and hypnosuggestion. Suggestion in the waking state prior to falling asleep is also recommended in enuresis nocturna. Hypnotherapy holds an important position in the therapy of chronic alcoholics. According to R. Konečný, group hypnotherapy is successful in many cases of alcoholism; V. Zikmund also reports good results. Recommended is a combination of hypnosuggestive or suggestive therapy with other methods of therapy for alcoholism.

In neurology hypnosis is of assistance in therapy and also in differential diagnosis. B. Rudlová and L. Rudlová are aided in making differential diagnoses by the fact that pains and difficulties in motor functions are easier to treat than those resulting from organic disturbances. Hypnosis may serve to supplement an anamnesis by its helping to recollect facts that the patient is not able to tell us when awake. Hypnosis also helps in the therapy of sensory and motor disturbances. By means of hypnosis, physicians can bring on protracted sleep and remove sleeplessness in patients who have been unable to sleep even after large doses of barbiturates. Hypnosis is also a means of removing negative emotions and lessening the instability of moods even in serious cases of organic illness.

In internal medicine hypnosis is used first of all as a palliative method, facilitating the struggle of the organism against injurious factors. By means of hypnosis; the emotional and reactive neurotic state of the patient may be balanced, physical suffering may be diminished, pain may be removed, mood may be improved, and sleep, appetite, and the functions of the digestive tract may be renewed. V. Zikmund and M. Ondrejčák studied the relation between the emotional stimuli and Raynaud's disease. In the hypnotherapy of this disease, they succeeded in influencing to a certain degree the spasms of the blood vessels.

B. Janoušek and J. Vlárský discussed the techniques of hypnosis in dermatological conditions which involved the cooperation of the patient. By means of hypnotherapy they found it possible to influence favourably not only dermatoses, in whose development mental trauma played a part, but also other dermatoses, especially the itching type. The therapeutic results they achieved by hypnosis were more satisfactory, they concluded, than those they previously obtained by pharmacological sleep.

Hypnosis in gynaecology and obstetrics is successfully applied chiefly as sleep therapy in cases of abortus habitualis and in cases of neurotic women suffering from dysfunctional bleeding. The method of hypnorelaxation is often used to relax and calm exhausted and affectively excited patients. In obstetrics and gynaecology, verbal suggestion in hypnosis is most extensively used especially in hyperemesis gravidarum. Hypnosis is not used in actual child-birth.

It is well known that the success of an operation depends to a considerable degree on pre-operational preparation and post-operational treatment of the patient. E. Žalman recommends, therefore, applying the hypnosuggestive method before and after the operation. He considers that it is better to hypnotize the patient elsewhere than in the operating theatre, so that negative emotions which could influence the prognosis would be, as far as possible, eliminated. According to the general opinion of Czechoslovakian physicians, hypnosis does not have much practical significance in major operations. Suggestion in the waking state, is recommended in removing pre-operative excitement and post-operative sleeplessness.

Dental

Czechoslovak stomatology has as yet made very limited use of hypnosis and suggestion. The prevalent opinion of dental surgeons is that its application in stomatological practice at the polyclinics is too time-consuming and thus not economical. Even J. Ležovič, who successfully used hypnotic anaesthesia with post-hypnotic suggestions of painlessness, considers the application of hypnosis in stomatology limited because deeper hypnosis is necessary but cannot be induced in many patients in a short time.

Legal

Since the Czechoslovak legal code does not contain any specific provision regarding the use of hypnosis in therapy or otherwise, the author of this chapter turned for professional advice to a member of the Czechoslovak Lawyers' Association, barrister JUDr. Jan Štěphán of Hradec Králové, the acknowledged legal authority on Czechoslovak health care. According to his information one can draw the following conclusion from the existing legal regulations:

(a) Only a highly qualified specialist ought to use hypnosis as a therapeutic method or in experiments, such as a psychiatrist, clinical psychologist, doctor, or psychologist in another branch of medicine or psychology, providing he has the required psychopathological education and experience.

(b) Any person, who intentionally causes a criminal act to be committed by means of hypnosis, would according to Czechoslovakian law be as guilty of the criminal offence as would the so-called indirect malefactor, that is, as if he the hypnotist had committed the crime himself.

(c) If by the use of hypnosis a person's health is impaired due to negligence, the person who caused it is guilty provided he could have and should have foreseen the difficulty.

(d) Negligence in the use of hypnosis is punishable by the payment of compensation for the damages incurred. This principle applies both to impairment of a patient's health, or to other injurious effects suffered by him, or caused to others by him due to hypnosis. In the event of injuries resulting from the negligence of a doctor or another employee of the National Health Service in the course of his duties, the state will pay compensation and exact a certain part of it from the employee whose negligence caused the injuries. Hypnosis carried out by improperly qualified personnel may also be considered as negligence.

(e) The use of hypnosis to extort evidence from the accused is excluded without exception according to the Czechoslovakian code of penal prodecure; under paragraph 91 the accused may not be compelled in any way to give evidence.

Psychological

The attitude of the universities is positive. Among the research tasks of the Medical Faculty of Charles University, Prague, supported by State plan, is research on suggestibility, directed by MUDr. I. Horvai. A study of relaxation techniques related to the hypnotic methods is being conducted by Associate Professor M. Machač, Ph.D., Assistant Dean of the Faculty of Philosophy. M. Machač lectures and gives practical demonstrations to students on hypnosis.

Clerical

The attitude of the clergy is not decisive in Czechoslovakia.

Public

The public is very interested in hypnosis and suggestion. Popular scientific publications and the daily press request specialists to clarify problems in this field. At present the public considers hypnosis as a therapeutic method. The old ideas which regarded hypnosis as "occultism" are gradually disappearing, due to the influence of the press which publishes mainly professional statements of psychiatrists or psychologists.

TEACHING AND RESEARCH

Lectures accompanied by practical demonstrations of hypnosis are usually given within the sphere of psychiatry to students of medicine within the frame of psychotherapy. Students of clinical psychology for the most part are as yet concerned with more fundamental aspects of hypnosis. If a student wishes to acquire further knowledge in this field, individual consultations with specialists are available. Research in this sphere is concentrated in Prague and Bratislava. At the Psychiatric Clinic in Prague, problems of hypnotic age regression and hypnotic hallucination are studied under the guidance of I. Horvai. The Institute of Experimental Medicine in Bratislava carries out research concerned with the clinical applications of hypnosis (V. Zikmund) and with animal hypnosis (D. Svorad).

The interested student either undergoes individual training from an experienced specialist in hypnosis, or applies to a larger medical center which arranges for his schooling and training. Currency regulations limit the quantity of hypnotic literature obtained from certain countries. Consequently students and specialists have to request such material from central libraries where it is generally available. All journals on hypnosis are at present received in Czechoslovakia, and some are reviewed in the chief Czechoslovakian psychological journal along with many books on hypnosis.

MISCONCEPTIONS

In the last ten years the study of hypnosis was conducted from Pavlov's point of view, and produced good results in this respect. However, the omission of other theoretical sources and methods failed to develop varied approaches to research and applications of hypnosis. Recently, however, psychological aspects are increasingly being taken into consideration in the theoretical, experimental, and clinical study of hypnosis.

Additional Considerations
(a)—Human Hypnosis and Suggestion

After the second world war hypnosis and suggestion as dealt with in Czechoslovakia were predominantly under the influence of the theory of I. P. Pavlov. Most authors conceive this theory as a theoretical framework describing the physiological basis of hypnosis. They underline the need for further detailed investigation of many actual problems in hypnosis. These scholars agree that the difference between natural sleep and hypnotic sleep, in accordance with Pavlov's opinion, consists of varying degrees of extensity and intensity of cerebral inhibition. The presence of various phase states, particularly the paradoxical phase, is regarded by them as a characteristic phenomenon of hypnotic sleep. In addition the dissociation of brain functions, in the sense of a subdivision of the cerebral hemispheres into sleeping and waking parts, as well as the existence of guardian zones (which represent the physiological foundation of hypnotic rapport) are held to be characteristic of hypnosis.

In Horvai's opinion it may be presumed that the inhibition in many during hypnosis is concentrated mainly in the cortex, i.e., in the highest cerebral structures. Human hypnosis, in a narrow sense of the word, has its origin predominantly in the mechanism of conditioned reflexes.

Some experimental work of recent date leads us to the conclusion that hypnosis does not have to be always related to a change in the level of vigilance towards sleep. Of importance in this connection are electroencephalographic findings. Krákora showed that no differences from the waking pattern appeared in the electroencephalogram while the hypnotist spoke with the subject or while some manipulation was taking place under hypnosis. After a given time interval from the last suggestion, however, the typical sleep pattern sets in. If the electroencephalogram showed a sleep pattern, then the subject was not observed to follow a given suggestion in that period. Krákora concluded, therefore, that the subject loses contact and goes into a state of deep inhibition which has the character of normal sleep with a marked "guardian point" in the Pavlovian sense. From this state the subject returns to contact when the hypnotist resumes talking. According to Diamant *et al.*, electroencephalographic data do not support the concept that the nature of hypnosis and sleep is qualitatively the same. Electroencephalographic signs of decreased wakefulness in hypnosis can be demonstrated in some patients, but these were also present without hypnosis. This latter effect appears to be subclinical sleep activity which is frequently seen in the neuroses. Reactivity to external stimuli under hypnosis was also, in most cases, equivalent to reactions in the waking state.

On the basis of experimental data it is possible to say that there exist two continua: (a) from the waking state to sleep, or to so-called sleep hypnosis, (b) from the waking state to so-called waking hypnosis. Hypnosis is considered a phenomenon which has not only its physiological, but also its psychological components. Complete explanation of this phenomenon is therefore to be neither expected solely on a physiological basis, nor solely on a psychological basis. The ideal solution will be perhaps a multidimensional theoretical approach. But before a satisfactory multidimensional theory can be formulated, it will be necessary to assemble much experimental data.

Apart from the study of hypnosis *per se,* attention is paid in Czechoslovakia to the application of hypnosis and suggestion as a means of research in studying the human psyche. Hypnosis, which by means of suggestion makes possible the elimination, isolation, dissociation, and sensitization of certain brain functions, is according to M. Móravek, M. Schürer and others a suitable research method for the study of higher nervous activity. Cases of spontaneous hypnotic states which occurred while driving long distances on straight highways have also been investigated.

Additional Considerations (b)—Animal Hypnosis

In Czechoslovakia the physiological mechanism of animal hypnosis was carefully analysed by D. Svorad. He carried out thousands of experiments on frogs, lizards, hens, rabbits, rats, and cats. Animal hypnosis (or "paroxysmal inhibition" in Svorad's terminology) is an inhibitory "seizure" process in the central nervous system, elicited by a supramaximal stimulus, which has its origin and termination in the subcortical regions and has all the characteristic properties of an inhibitory process. Animal hypnosis is considered to be a reaction which in lower evolutionary forms is a normal, more or less adaptive function of the animal to its environment. In higher evolutionary forms this same reaction loses this significance and is a pathological reaction. Phylogenetically animal hypnosis is an old mechanism, which in higher evolutionary forms represents atavistic regressive behavior, when the relation of the organism and its environment is not "realized" by the cerebral cortex, but by subcortical reflex centres. Animal hypnosis is considered a suitable experimental model for the study in man of the physiology and pathophysiology of sleep, the catatonic syndrome, hysterical and catatonic stupor, hypnotic semiconscious states, narcolepsy and cataplexy.

FUTURE

It is the desire of Czechoslovakian specialists interested in clinical or experimental hypnosis to have closer relations with their colleagues abroad. As concerns their internal organization there is a plan to form a section devoted to hypnosis within the Society for the Study of Higher Nervous Activity. It may be said that both the study and the use of hypnosis have good prospects.

IMPORTANT REFERENCES

Diamant, J. et al.: An electroencephalographic study of the waking state and hypnosis with particular reference to subclinical manifestations of sleep activity. Int. J. Clin. Exp. Hypnosis, 8: 199-212, 1960.

Horvai, I.: Hypnosa v lékařství, (Hypnosis in Medicine). Praha: Státní zdravotnické nakladatelství, 1959.

Krákora B.: Elektroencephalogram při usínání, spánku a hypnose, (The electroencephalogram during drowsiness, sleep and hypnosis). Neurol. Psychiat. Českosl., 16: 141-154, 1955.

Roth, B.: Narkolepsie a hypersomnie z hlediska fyziologie spánku, (Narcolepsy and hypersomnia from the aspect of the physiology of sleep.) Praha: Státní zdravotnické nakladatelství, 1957.

Svorad, D.: Paroxymálny útlm — Experimentálna analýza hypnózy zvierat, (Paroxysmal inhibition—An experimental analysis of animal hypnosis). Bratislava: Slovenská Akadémia Vied, 1956.

Svorad, D., and Hoskovec, J.: Experimental and clinical study of hypnosis in the Soviet Union and the European Socialist Countries. (Bibliography) Amer. J. Clin. Hypnosis, 4: 1, 36-46, 1961.

HYPNOSIS IN DENMARK

By

Paul J. Reiter, M.D.

Paul J. Reiter; born 1895; M.D. (psychiatry) University of Copenhagen; Fellow, I.S.C.E.H., Past-president of the Danish Division of the I.S.C.E.H., Honorary Member of Danish Psychoanalytic Society, Corresponding Member of the American Psychiatric Association, of the Royal Medico-Psychological Association, of the Wiener Verein für Psychiatrie und Neurologie, of the Schweizerische Gesellschaft für Neurologie und Psychiatrie, Executive Board Member of the World Federation for Mental Health (1952-56), Member of the Common Danish Medical Union, of the Danish Medical Society, of the Danish Psychiatric Society, of the Scandinavian Psychopharmacological Society, Past-president of the Danish League for Mental Hygiene; Korrfattet Vejledning Psykoterapentisk Teknik (Text, with a section on Hypnosis), Westermann, Copenhagen 1951, Anti-social or Criminal Acts and Hypnosis, Munksgaard, Copenhagen 1958 (monograph); present position, director (retired) psychiatric clinic, private practice (psychiatry), Copenhagen, Denmark.

PAST

In a rather curious way Denmark has been a pioneering country in the field of hypnotherapy. Even before the first vague attempts to organize the treatment of mentally sick persons, before the foundation of the first Mental Hospital in Denmark and more than a century before any systematic psychotherapy was attempted in our country, a prominent Danish physician, Joachim Dietrich Brandis, introduced hypnotherapy in the clinical treatment of patients. Brandis was born in Hildesheim, Germany, in 1762. After finishing his medical studies and training he enjoyed a brilliant career. In 1803, he became a professor of medicine at the University of Kiel in Holstein; in 1810 he was called to Copenhagen to be physician for the Danish queen, and until his death in 1845, lived as a highly skilled practitioner, highly esteemed by both his colleagues and clientele. He was interested in all fields of therapy, and after he became acquainted with Mesmer and his methods, began to apply hypnosis in his treatment, especially with patients who had various hysterical manifestations. In 1818, he published his views and experiences in a treatise. He did not, however, teach about hypnosis, and apart from a certain amount of curiosity, he did not arouse much serious interest in his colleagues, and with his death interest in hypnosis completely faded for a long time.

In the last part of the nineteenth century the Danish Professor of Psychology, Alfred Lehmann, a many-sided personality, partook in the general interest in hypnosis, which emanated from the groups around Bernheim and Charcot. In 1890, he published the first Danish textbook on hypnosis.

In the beginning of the twentieth century, little by little a few Danish psychiatrists became aware of the potential value of hypnosis as a useful technique. In 1924, Frode Krarup published two forensic cases of criminal acts committed in the hysterical twilight state. These states were described as leaving complete amnesia for the happenings when they were perpetrated. The first case concerned anonymous letters of an indecent nature written by a male, while case number two concerned a male, who had committed a theft. During hypnosis the amnesia disappeared, and memory for every detail of the events that transpired was clear. (In a third case, murder in an epileptic twilight state, the hypnosis failed to remove the amnesia.)

Around 1927, the psychiatrist Dr. Einar Geert-Joergensen, M.D., and the author, independently of each other, began to apply hypnosis in the psychotherapy of mental disorders, especially for neurotic symptoms, psychosomatic disorders, impotence and the like. They have both continued using hypnotherapy as well as other types of psychotherapy, especially psychoanalytic procedures. The author had in this early period successfully and with lasting effect treated a case of a twenty-four year old female patient, who suffered from kleptomania. This was an especially sensitive case, as she was the adopted daughter of a chief-constable.

Geert-Joergensen together with a colleague published experimental work concerned with the attempt to produce hyperglycemia by suggestions in hypnosis. The result was negative.

About 1930, the late Icelandic professor of psychiatry, Dr. Helgi Tomasson, M.D., at that time assistant psychiatrist in Denmark, performed various experimental works in the field of hypnosis. Along with others he aroused interest in academic circles especially by his successful use of hypnoanesthesia in a cholecystectomy, in which the use of chemical anesthesia had been contraindicated. After his return to Iceland a few years later—as far as I know—he did not continue with his use of hypnosis. At the end of the thirties the psychiatrist Dr. Herman Reistrup took up hypnotherapy. He published a paper on hypnosis and is continuing as a skillful hypnotherapist.

In the period in which the author was the director of the psychiatric clinic at the Municipal Hospital at Copenhagen (1941-1960), he lectured at the Copenhagen University on neuroses, psychosomatic disorders, and psychotherapy. Under the latter heading, he lectured on clinical hypnosis and hypnotherapy, their indications and contraindications—with case material obtained from the clinic and private practice. Furthermore, as a consultant in Forensic Psychiatry to the Danish Ministry of Justice, he investigated three cases in which crime and hypnosis played a role. Of special interest was one case which was concerned with the question of serious criminal acts perpetrated under the influence of hypnosis. This has been separately published as a monograph in 1958, and will be described later.

PRESENT

In the spring of 1959, the Danish Society for Clinical and Experimental Hypnosis was founded. The author was its first president and after his term in office he was succeeded by Dr. Fr. Wagner who is its present president. At present the society has eleven members, most of them are psychiatrists and only one a psychologist.

ATTITUDES

Medical

In Denmark there are at present 6,700 physicians. In general I think it may be stated that Danish physicians are mainly oriented toward the following aspects of a disease: its normal and pathological physiology, its biochemistry, its hormonal and enzymatic functions, its physical, dietetical and surgical treatment, and its pharmacology. Psychiatry as a speciality has developed enormously since World War II especially with respect to forensic and administrative psychiatry, psychopharmacological treatment, psychopathology, psychotherapy, etc. There are excellent state mental hospitals, and at several of the larger units there are first-class clinics. There is an increasing understanding of the importance of an adequate doctor-patient relationship, of the psychosomatic background of many diseases and of the important role of psychotherapy and psychiatry in general. But true psychiatric methods of examination and treatment have until now, only slightly penetrated the medical profession in Denmark. While the reasons for this vary, and it would not be worthwhile to go into detail, developments despite this are still promising. From our two centers for medical training (at the Universities of Copenhagen and Aarhus) and from the Danish Psychiatric Society there have been strong efforts for the last fifteen years to improve the training facilities in psychiatry, medical psychology, etc. Within the next decade a satisfactory result in both undergraduate and graduate training may be hoped for.

In psychotherapy, interest and activity within the inner circle of psychiatrists has been growing rapidly. Despite the fact that the first attempts to introduce psychotherapy in modern Danish medicine were concerned with the clinical application of hypnosis, the attitude of the physicians, including many psychiatrists, has been indifferent or rather ambivalent and without deep interest in the phenomena of any of the psychological aspects of hypnosis. In general it may be said that the attitude of the physicians is not much different from that of the lay public. Many of them do not believe in hypnosis at all, others—and partly the same people—regard it still as a form of magic or charlatanry and not as a matter for the medical profession. In the forties when I lectured on different psychotherapeutic techniques for medical students, the auditorium became crowded, when I got to the section on hypnosis. Unfortunately only a very few showed a durable and real interest and continued with practical work in this field. The rest obviously regarded hypnotic demonstrations as a kind of stage presentation. Furthermore, in the late forties when Dr. Reistrup read a paper and presented a film on the topic of experiments concerning crime in hypnosis, he encountered criticism from one of his older colleagues who remarked that a late and highly revered Danish professor (one who introduced Kraepelinian views into Danish psychiatry) would turn over in his grave, if he knew what was transpiring. A further example is present in the case of a thorax surgeon in Copenhagen, who some ten years previously had to perform a small operative intervention in which chemical anesthesia was contraindicated and he therefore wished to apply hypnoanesthesia. He did not, however, call one of the psychiatrists who was known to be skillful in this technique, but instead, he called a lay hypnotist. It may be added that the person in question was not successful.

I think that contributing to the lack of real interest in hypnotherapy among psychiatrists is the fact that only a few years later psychoanalysis was introduced into Danish psychiatry and Danish psychotherapy. Psychoanalytic training was sponsored by the Swedish Psychoanalytical Society in 1949 and in 1957 an independent Danish Psychoanalytical Society was certified by the International Psychoanalytic Association. This group has had a considerable influence on the development of Danish psychiatric thinking and practice since that time. While the two principles (hypnosis and psychoanalysis) do not in any way exclude each other and while, in my opinion, psychoanalytic theory is a desirable preamble for the proper use of hypnosis, I think that the ordinary types of psychoanalytically oriented techniques have, at least provisionally, stolen the picture from hypnotherapy. With the founding of the Danish Society for Clinical and Experimental Hypnosis it is likely that hypnotic techniques gradually will gain their proper place in the therapeutic armamentarium.

At present hypnosis is applied as a treatment-technique in suitable cases by about ten psychiatrists, mainly members of the Danish Society for Hypnosis. Furthermore it is used in dubious fashion by a few ordinary medical practitioners who do not possess the necessary psychological qualifications.

Elsewhere hypnotherapy in Denmark has until recently been mainly in the hands of mere quacks who, at best, have a very dubious background. One of them for example was an old paralytic who began his hypnotic activities after successful malaria treatment. Another had been sentenced for murder and started hypnotic work after his term of punishment had expired, and still another was known as a heavy drinker, and so on. Many of them have obtained their clientele by simultaneously doing stage hypnosis. They give themselves a mysterious aura by changing their regular family names to unusual sounding professional titles which have an Indian or Occult sound. One of the more serious and honest of these individuals was, by profession, a fitter in a machine shop!

Dental

Danish dentists in general may be said to be still less interested than physicians in hypnosis as well as applied psychology in general. Danish dentistry has a high standard, not only in surgical dentistry and manual techniques, but also in the physiological field. Dental treatment is well organized with access for everyone through an obligatory public health insurance system for necessary dental care. In addition much work is done in the field of prophylaxis and oral hygiene in childhood by a system of school dental clinics. Only the psychological aspects of dentistry have been neglected. A few dentists apply waking suggestion and train their patients in systematic relaxation, but even this is rather unusual. No Danish dentist, as far as I know, applies hypnosis *per se* in the treatment of patients.

I have been invited a few times to read a paper at the annual meeting of the National Association of Dentists. I utilized this opportunity to advance the proposition that the curriculum of the Odontological School should embrace a course of medico-odontological psychology and hypnodentistry. The discussants afterwards evinced a keen interest in the subject but it did not result in any action as the key individuals of the School were indifferent or biased against such study.

Legal

Only a very few people in the legal profession are interested in hypnosis and their knowledge, ideas, prejudices, and misconceptions do not differ essentially from those of lay people. That a university professor attended a few sessions of deep trance hypnosis and was very interested in the resulting behaviour is rather exceptional. Their general lack of interest and knowledge, concerning the age-old problem of the possibility of using hypnosis for criminal purposes is rather curious. Their view concerning this problem is of a purely speculative nature, tending either toward absolute confirmation or absolute rejection. Concerning the latter most modern authors maintain that it is impossible to get a person in the somnambulistic trance or by posthypnotic suggestion to commit antisocial or criminal acts which are contrary to their habitual moral code. It is postulated that in such cases they will either wake up, react violently against the hypnotist, or will at least refuse to obey his command. Proof, no matter how careful the experiment, is not acceptable if the only reason given is that the subject carried out the required act because he trusted the hypnotist and was convinced that he would not endanger him in any way. The only real proof that would be acceptable would be a criminal act perpetrated by an individual under the influence of the hypnotist when the latter had serious criminal intentions. Even then there is a tendency to react hypercritically, and to attempt to explain (away?) the obvious. In the history of crime, pertinent cases are very rare but this would not excuse the error of dogmatism. Theoretically a crime may be committed by a normal individual having no criminal record who is susceptible to deep hypnosis. This is especially true in unusual situations (I would refer here to the excellent exposition on this topic by P. C. Young, Hypnotism, *Psychol. Bull.*, 38: 92-104, 1941). While Young's critics may often be right a rule without exceptions such as they are suggesting, may be likened to a dogma. I shall illustrate the point with case material.

In my own experience, as a consultant to the Danish Ministry of Justice in Forensic Psychiatry, I examined some 700 cases, in the years 1941-1960. In three of these cases hypnosis played a part.

> Case I concerned a forty-four year old male Yoga instructor. He was charged with the sexual abuse of a patient (female) whom he was treating for rheumatic pains by the use of hypnosis. There was little doubt that he had had sex relations with her when she was under hypnosis. However the extent to which she had voluntarily consented (as a result of the transference which neither of them realized), or, the desire on her part for "committing sin without guilt" may be debated. Despite such possibilities the Yoga instructor was found guilty by the court and sentenced to prison.

While the use of hypnosis for sexual purposes is a more frequent possibility, case II concerning Mr. H. is both interesting and very rare. This case, much more complicated and rather unique in criminal history, as previously indicated, was published as a separate monograph in 1958. I shall present only a summary of the case here.

> Case II. In August 1950 a robbery happened in a suburban bank in a neighbourhood of Copenhagen. A young masked man, with a revolver, made the cashier give him about $3000 in cash. He escaped, and during the following months the police were unable to solve the robbery. Scarcely half a year later, another attempt at robbery took place shortly before noon in a Copenhagen bank. It happened in a crowded street at rush time. Again a young masked man armed with a revolver entered the bank, this time filled with people, fired a warning shot at the ceiling and demanded that the cashier give him money. As he hesitated he was shot as was also the bank manager who had attempted to press the alarm bell. Without getting the money the criminal, Mr. H., retreated and tried to hide in a neighbouring house. Here he was trapped by the police, with the gun still in his possession. After his arrest his behaviour was obviously abnormal and he was, as

a result, examined by the police psychiatrist. The examination was unusually difficult and lasted about nine months. The delinquent suffered from delusions and hallucinations and behaved in a paranoid way. He had in the meantime been charged not only with the murder and robbery involved in this attempt, but also with the successful robbery of a little more than half a year before. He denied these charges and denied that he had had an accomplice. He said that he had performed the crime at the command of a patron-ghost and for the benefit of a secret illegal political organization, directed against the communists. His attitude was one of superiority in accord with his megalomanic delusional system. Apart from what he told of his delusions, he revealed little. The case presented many unusual characteristics and made the psychiatrist, even during the examination, suspect that the psychosis was an artifact. He finally, however, delivered a carefully worded statement in which he concluded that the delinquent (Mr. H) suffered from paranoid schizophrenia and that he had acted under the compulsion of his delusions.

Scarcely three weeks later the psychosis disappeared leaving Mr. H. in a relatively normal although still very tense state of mind. In the meantime he had written down a full confession, not only concerning the latter crime but also the previous hitherto unresolved robbery. There then unfolded a fantastic story in which Mr. H. said that he had acted under the hypnotic influence of one of his past fellow-prisoners, and that his psychosis was also due to this. The said fellow prisoner was then arrested, and the perpetrator, i.e., the person who had actually held up the banks was handed over to me for still further examination. The case presented severe difficulties, and in the first few months it was absolutely impossible to bring him into a hypnotic trance. His behaviour made me suspect that this state of affairs might be due to suggestions that he could not be hypnotized by anyone else given to him by the preceding hypnotist. I was aware of all the tricky difficulties which might thus be involved. Then all of a sudden in the beginning of July 1952, approximately two years after the first successful crime, I succeeded in breaking down the barrier. From that time onward he was a typical trance subject, and was able on command (verbal, written, or by telephone) to enter a deep somnambulistic trance with spontaneous posthypnotic amnesia. After many hypnotic sessions the whole course of relevant events were redramatized, and the details were written down on posthypnotic suggestion. From this procedure it was revealed that both crimes as well as his psychosis had come about as a result of an unusual prolonged and careful hypnotic training by a Mr. N., who had been his fellow prisoner for years and had been assigned, by the warden, to the same cell.

Mr. H. had originally had no criminal record. Born in 1924, he had, during his adolescence been induced to join the Danish Nazi Party and because of his youthful conviction had shown considerable activity which had benefited the Germans during their occupation of Denmark in 1940-45. He had finally, for a few months, been promoted to the hated Nazi-supported auxiliary police corps ("Hipo"). Immediately after the capitulation by Germany he was arrested and sentenced to the severe punishment of fourteen years imprisonment. Mr. N. ten years older was a habitual psychopathic criminal with a long preceding record. At the time of H's imprisonment he was serving a long term prison sentence for robbery. Previously he had studied Yoga and hypnosis and had been a member of an occult circle.

The two (H and N) met in prison. H. had at that time developed a psychogenic depression. He had heard of N., who was known for his boasting, and had had from the beginning ambivalent feelings towards him. Very soon, however, N. had H. so completely under his influence that H. blindly obeyed all N's commands and wishes. Very soon H. developed a latent homosexual dependency which was utilized by N. in a cunning way. N. saw to it that they were alone not only in their cell but also in the work shop. This had happened day and night for about two years, during this time N. induced a permanent hypnotic trance, in which he gradually modified H's superego and trained him systematically for criminal purposes. Obviously N. elaborated fantastic plans in order to commit the "perfect crime." In doing this he had used H. as a tool. After three years imprisonment for his activities on behalf of the Nazis, H. was pardoned. N. had been pardoned six months earlier. With the aid of posthypnotic suggestion, N., immediately after H's discharge from prison, again got him under his influence and the training continued. N. was successful until the time that the whole system broke down during the last robbery, inasmuch as events did not transpire in the way that N. had anticipated. The particular suggestion, however, concerning the crime that N. had given to H. had actually remained active for nine months. During this period H. had denied having any companion in crime, and, thus had sheltered N.

In July 1954 the jury returned the verdict that H. was guilty, but insane at the time of committing the crime, and was therefore exempt from punishment. He was incarcerated in the institute for criminal psychopaths. N. was found guilty not only as the instigator but as the essential perpetrator by having effected the crimes by influencing H. in different ways, amongst others by hypnosis. He was sentenced to life in prison.

Both sentences were appealed to the Supreme Court, later on the Danish Court of Appeal and finally before the UN-Commission on Human Rights in Strassbourg. In the meantime a large number of medico-forensic statements were delivered about H. and N. by different psychiatric experts, most of whom had never had personal experience with hypnosis, excepting knowledge which they had gained in the case. Most of them differed in their theories about H. Some of them were cautiously neutral, and a few,—especially those defending N. —opposed my conclusions. Meanwhile N. succeeded in smuggling out the manuscript of a sentimental autobiography written in prison and in getting it published. As a result of a favorable press, public opinion sided with N. At the Court of Appeals the many diverging opinions of the psychiatrists (and the doubt resulting thereof) was skillfully utilized by the defence so that the complete problem of the role played by hypnosis was excluded from consideration. The sentence was however upheld and review of the case denied on the grounds that the remaining evidence constituted strong proof of N's guilt.

I have reported the case in some detail because it well illustrates, with perhaps a few exceptions, the attitude of the legal profession in Denmark. This attitude is highly imbued with prejudice and misconception, and is not one which regards hypnosis in a scientific or objective fashion. Rather it is one in which hypnosis is to a great extent confused with magic. In the trial report, occultistic ideas and witch trials were frequently mentioned. My conclusions were explained (away?) as brainwashing. While scientific proof in such cases may be possible, legal proof, at least in Denmark, is out of the question.

> Case III involved a forty year old male who had killed his wife in a fit of jealousy. Afterwards he had complete and genuine amnesia for his crime. A single hypnotic trance sufficed to return his memory to him in full detail.

Psychological

The two Danish Universities (Aahus and Copenhagen) have been described as being rather indifferent to hypnosis. At the time that I was director of the psychiatric clinic in Copenhagen, I gave private lectures in hypnosis to students of medicine and psychology. The listeners were interested but very few have pursued the topic. I further tried to get some clinical psychologists interested in doing experimental work in this area, but had no success. As indicated only one psychologist belongs to our Danish Society for Clinical and Experimental Hypnosis.

I think that what we lack in Denmark are well known clinical psychiatrists or psychologists studying hypnosis as a specialty, doing research, giving clinical demonstrations, as well as lecturing and training other professional persons.

In our society, at one of our meetings, I presented a program for systematic training in hypnosis. This would lead to certification by an appropriate committee, and such training would correspond to the requirements indicated by the I.S.C.E.H. Those attending, however, did not feel that the time was as yet propitious.

Clerical

Denmark is a Protestant country, and in general the attitude of the clergy is one of complete neutrality and indifference toward hypnosis. There are no prejudices existent in these circles.

Public

In the mind of the average Dane—likewise I imagine as in other countries in the civilized world—hypnotism stands for something unusual and mysterious. It is thought of as being on the same level as occultism and spiritualism, and it is not by accident that a non-scientific association with a boastful name (The Society for Psychical Research, mainly devoted to spiritualistic experiments) also has hypnosis on its program. Most people associate hypnosis with what they have seen or heard of in stage presentation and therefore think of it in conjunction with conjuring tricks and magic. Everything related to hypnosis arouses curiosity and is good sensationalistic material for the newspapers, especially when the central figure is a stage hypnotist or a quack. Less is generally publicized when it concerns a professional man. This is due in part to the fact that many psychiatrists and psychologists shun publicity of this kind which is only sensationalistic and supports misconceptions.

Such ideas, as above, are widespread and exist even among educated people. They are very deep-rooted and presumably tied up with magical expectations, persisting unconsciously from early infancy, expectations which every physician is acquainted with from his clientele. In this context it is usual to look at the reasons people advance for the desire to be hypnotized. Very often, in my own practice, relatives of individuals with schizophrenia have asked me to treat the latter with hypnosis even though they (the patients) have been resistant to ordinary types of therapy. They believe strongly that hypnosis will help, even though all other procedures have failed. Similarly for example obsessional neurotics have called on me to rid them of their compulsions by hypnosis, and when other more appropriate types of psychotherapy are proposed, they feel frustrated and fail to understand. Paranoiacs with persecutional delusions of being under hypnotic influence by some distant persons who influences all their thoughts and actions by telepathic means also come in order to be dehypnotized by an honest hypnotherapist.

In my opinion such ideas will continue to persist and will not be eradicated by sober common-sense information, because they have a strong irrational background in infantile dynamisms. Besides it is questionable how far one should go in eliminating symptoms, in this case misconceptions. In the interest of honest and scientifically founded hypnotherapy it is naturally important to eliminate superstitious ideas that arouse anxiety, for example the idea that hypnosis may mean continuous dependency on the hypnotist or the idea that they will be deprived of "free will" or abandoned to a state of uncontrollable submission to a stranger, etc. The skillful, responsible and properly trained hypnotherapist actually utilizes in a careful manner some of these infantile dynamisms in the techniques he uses.

LAWS

No actual legislation concerning hypnosis exists in Denmark. The only regulation is a government circular of January 19, 1945 which states:

> By request the Ministry of Justice shall enjoin, the holding of public hypnotic, spiritualistic or antispiritualistic presentations. Permission for presentations under the heading of thought-reading, suggestion, autosuggestion and the like may only be given on condition that no persons among the audience cooperates, by displaying behaviours identical with the presentations mentioned in the first section. Permission will not be granted, unless the medical officer of health certifies in each case that the demonstrations are not similar to hypnotic presentations.
>
> The above-mentioned decisions are to be applied to all public presentations and demonstrations in question, even if the admission is free of charge. The prohibition includes presentations in a circus, a vaudeville theatre or the like.

It appears from the governmental regulations that only public stage presentations are prohibited, although these may take place in clubs, associations and the like. Persons, ordinary physicians, with any background, or those with none whatsoever (quacks), may treat patients with hypnosis. All of them, however, are responsible in the eyes of the law for any unfortunate consequences that may result from their demonstrations or treatment.

While the criminal case referred to above was still going on, I tried to draw attention to the legal question involved. In a lecture I pointed out the danger implied in such a case by the fact that a criminal, only recently released from prison, without any other training than the mere reading of a popular book on hypnosis, could establish himself as a hypnotist-healer. I also indicated the possible pernicious aspects of this situation in war time. While I proposed further steps to limit the public exercise of hypnosis by people with insufficient psychological training, nothing was done.

Additional Considerations—Hypnotherapy

With regard to clinical indications and contraindications for hypnotherapy, I would merely refer to the many modern textbooks on this topic. I think that, at least in the Western World, there is general agreement concerning this problem. Hypnosis is not regarded as the only psychotherapeutic technique nor even as a generally preferable procedure, but rather as a useful technique in addition to others which in some cases may be the method of choice. I should like, however, to add a few remarks based on my own experience and the principles I follow in the selection of cases, where the question of indications and contraindications for the use of hypnotherapy arises.

As a general rule I find it necessary before induction of hypnosis to start with a series of interviews based on psychoanalytic principles in order to formulate a reasonably tenable hypothesis of the type, structure and dynamics of the personality before me. In some cases, but not all, in which the subject enters a deep hypnotic state, this may be omitted. In other cases it may be limited to a relatively short series of interviews. As a general rule, however, it is advisable to have such partially therapeutic interviews in order to discover the more or less complicated etiological mosaic. It is important not to start hypnosis before the etiological situation is clear and is sufficiently analyzed so that therapeutic work with hypnosis may begin. The use of hypnosis should be regarded as a decisive step, as it may cause a fundamental change in the transference situation. The border between cases which should be continued with analytically oriented therapy, or those cases in which hypnosis may be safely used to effect a cure is not always obvious.

Another matter, always to be kept in mind is that hypnosis does not mean "therapia magna" (radical cure) for it has only a limited scope, i.e., the removal of a symptom or a not too complicated syndrome. In practice, however, this may, though not always, mean a permanent restoration to health and normalcy. In my experience the addition of hypnosis may add to the effectiveness of a therapeutic result. One should remember at all times that by the use of hypnosis one does not solve the basic problems, or resolve conflicting elements within the individual. Instead of attempting pure symptom removal one should aim at substitution of an obviously morbid and eventually incapacitating symptom with one that is socially harmless, i.e., one should attempt to procure another type of cathexis. A few brief illustrative cases will later be shown.

It should be mentioned that, in addition to hypnoanesthesia in major surgery, hypnosis may be of use in: minor surgery, dentistry, gynecology, and obstetrics. It also is a very useful tool often for the preparation of patients for serious major surgical operations. Its use may contribute to the successful outcome of the latter.

An indication for the use of hypnotherapy may also be found in the treatment of what we may term limited situational crises. An example of this which deserves special mention is anxiety which is present before an examination. In my own experience I have treated more than sixty cases of this type—without a single failure. In nearly all these cases, students, about to take an examination, were involved. They had on previous occasions failed the test two or three times and now, by special permission of the university faculty, were faced with their final chance. Naturally, in such cases, it is necessary by psychological testing to determine the reason for their previous failures and it is hardly necessary to add that these failures were due not to intellectual inferiority but to severe neurotic disturbances. While question may be raised as to what such successful hypnotic treatment will mean to their future career, it has, in the meantime, by overcoming this hurdle, resulted in a decisive improvement in their life situation and made a better adjustment possible.

Finally I should like to bring out the specific effect of hypnotherapy in the traumatic neuroses due, for example, to acute war experiences, detention in concentration camps or catastrophic-like accidents. Such cases are marked by blocked affect, which is often manifested by repetitive night-mares in which the traumatic event is relived. The time elapsed between the trauma and the treatment is unimportant. In one of my cases the interval was twelve years, and during this time the patient did not present other mental disorders of any kind other than a severe chronic and completely incapacitating depression. After treatment he was completely cured and able to reassume his functions as a shipmaster. He is still symptom-free after six years. (I have reported a series of such war neuroses at a congress of Scandinavian psychiatrists. *Acta Psychiatrica et Neurologica Scandinavia,* Supplementum, 1946, Pp. 653-67.) The technique involves psychocatharsis through revivification of the pathogenic situation by regression.

Concerning the treatment of such limited syndromes as writer's cramp, stammering (with a rather doubtful prognosis), enuresis, constipation, and especially impotence and frigidity (without organic etiology), hypnotic treatment may be very profitable and require only a few therapeutic sessions, or in other cases because of extraordinarily varied etiology treatment may be protracted and complicated.

A special field of indication for hypnotherapy is "Erwartungsneurose" (Kraepelin) or the neurotic superstructure of neurological disease. In a series of mild to averagely severe cases of disseminated sclerosis and spasticity it has been possible to improve and utilize the remaining functions considerably. A young sclerotic woman (aged 26), who for about a year had felt unable to walk without help recovered so far as to learn dancing.

Details concerning hypnotherapeutic removal of hysterical and psychosomatic symptoms may be read in any modern textbook. I would only emphasize the importance of symptom-transformation or symptom-substitution in such cases by reference to an interesting case treated from December 1953 to December 1954. Sessions at the beginning were held once a week, and from May on every second week. Post-treatment sessions were held once a month during the first six months of 1955.

The patient, a thirty-nine year old married male, who was manager of a public social office in a provincial town, suffered from an atypical respiratory disorder of non asthmatic type. Symptoms were air-hunger, tachypnoea, habitual compensatory hyperventilation, choking sensation and associated with this last symptom the fear of death. In addition he was sexually impotent. The beginning of his disorder could be traced back to when he started school at the age of seven. At first his difficulties were only periodic and not too troublesome, but after his marriage rapidly became more and more incapacitating until finally in the last three months before treatment he had been completely unable to work. From his anamnesis and his dreams (he was an excellent dream-reporter) it was evident that behind his syndrome was a strong oral-aggressive fixation. He had been born in 1914 in North Slesvig, which was at that time part of Germany, just before the beginning of World War I. He had never known his father who had been called to service in 1914 and killed in 1918, when the boy was only four years old. During the absence of the father, conditions at home—especially those concerned with nutrition—were very poor.

During treatment his respiratory disorder as well as his impotence completely disappeared and not only was he fully able to return to his work and to married life but even more significantly he was decidedly more competent. His incapacitating symptom of air hunger was replaced by an enormous appetite and subsequently he gained forty-four pounds. This overweight not only did not affect his respiration, but in his symptom-language was interpreted by him as reflecting the fact that he now "carried more weight" (in the Rembrandt-burgomaster style) and in this way he felt much more competent as a leader.

I shall conclude by a brief summary of an extraordinary case illustrating the difficulty concerning so-called appropriate therapy.

Theoretically as well as practically hypnotherapy is of no use, if not actually contraindicated, in the treatment of obsessional neuroses. I think that the majority of experienced psychotherapists agree that if the patient is at all tractable the therapy of choice in such cases is psychoanalysis or at least psychoanalytically oriented psychotherapy. Furthermore, as is well known, obsessional neuroses presents severe difficulties and even psychoanalytic treatment by a very skillful and experienced analyst, is in general a very prolonged procedure. In my own experience I have seen the treatment of a few obsessional neurotics in whom an improvement was gained through successful psychoanalysis supplemented by brief hypnotherapy. This combination succeeded in eliminating all symptoms. But some cases may be so severe that they normally are regarded as completely beyond the reach of psychotherapy and only fit for lobotomy.

I had such a case referred to me for treatment in a private clinic. The patient was a thirty-six year old unmarried woman living in a provincial town in West Denmark. She had originally worked in an office, but for the last fifteen years had been a total invalid because of her disease.

Since her twentieth year she had suffered from a rapidly progressing mysophobia with a washing compulsion. Her fear was particularly of tuberculosis, but later on included all kinds of contagion and filth, and even cancer. Her precautions were universal. She particularly feared contagion through the mouth of others or even through her own mouth. She developed a complicated washing ritual, and several times each day she had to brush her hands and teeth—seven times seventy— and when she did not feel sure of having counted correctly, which she usually did not, she had to start the whole counting and washing procedure anew. She washed the door-handles, the garden gate, the furniture, even the newspaper and compelled her whole family to follow her example, which they did with grumbling protest. In her room, which was carefully locked, she kept a whole cache of trimmed finger nail ends, combed-off hair, as well as other waste material in sealed containers, etc. She had for many years been a total invalid and a despair to herself and to her family and several times she

had been on the brink of suicide. She had been treated repeatedly in psychiatric clinics, with convulsive therapy without
beneficial effect.

At the time of admission to the clinic her status was very
poor. She was pale and underweight, her posture was very
tense and stiff, her manners polite and formal, her capacity
for contact and communication with others extremely restricted, and her voice monotonous, low and forced. She did
not, however, present the picture of a melancholic. She was
smiling and could speak fluently of her symptoms, and case
history. She was, however, inhibited and shy on matters
touching her inner life, especially her sexual development and
experiences, with the exception that she said that at the age of
twenty she had been engaged for about a year, but had broken
off the relation because of her illness. The case seemed completely beyond therapy. Psychoanalysis especially appeared to
be absolutely impracticable and I only gave in because of
intense pressure from the patient and her family and promised
to try to do my best. After an initial subcomatose insulin
treatment (it was before the era of psychopharmacology) she
became a little more communicative, and in order to obtain
still more material for further analysis I asked her to report
her dreams. This she did with true obsessional meticulous-
ness, and, as indicated, she proved to be an excellent reporter
of dreams. Daily she narrated the dreams of the night before
in great detail and precision. The dreams were astoundingly
full of phantasy, varied in material, but easy to interpret and
revealed a bulk of oral and anal-agressive traits which had
been extensively elaborated. With the help of free association
she learned by degrees to interpret the material for herself,
and during her first stay at the clinic she obtained the beginning of insight into some of the mechanisms of her illness, this
was however of small value.

At the same time I had started to teach her how to relax,
according to the autosuggestive method of J. H. Schultz, and
this was learned quite adequately. Then, despite my own experience, that obsessional neurotics are usually difficult to hypnotize, I attempted supplementary hypnotherapy. She responded to the hypnotic suggestions. At first it took her about
an hour to go into a light trance, but there was no doubt about

its authenticity. By repetition, the hypnotic induction was lowered to ten to fifteen minutes, and simultaneously the trance became much deeper. After having given her detailed suggestions to transgress one of her strongest taboos (to walk alone in the streets of her town, an act which hitherto had filled her with an unescapable panic), I sent her home for a few days in order to let her test her powers and then to return and report her experiences. This she did, and to her own great surprise she was successful, and from that moment on her secondary mysophobia (fear of contagion to which she might be exposed) completely disappeared as well, never to return. The ice was broken. Her first stay in the clinic had been of four months duration.

During the following seven years she returned to the clinic two to four times annually, staying at first for a month, then later on for only two weeks, and after this she stayed only for three days. Then no further treatment was necessary.

In her longer sojourns during the first years I continued with the psychoanalytically oriented therapy and worked through her dream-material. Daily hypnotherapy of one to two hours duration was also utilized. At the end of each stay she was allowed to test the result, as described for her monophobia. A second suggestion to her was to unlock the door of her room, let her sisters clean-up and throw away her various caches. Afterwards she was to invite them and other visitors of the family to have tea with her.

At each return there had been small relapses and naturally new problems appeared and had to be worked through. In this way I continued with surprising success, gradually and steadily her whole condition improved. She broadened her social contacts and her complicated protective obsessional ritual no longer predominated. More rational precautions (for example instead of washing her hands, she would now rub them with a cosmetic cream—without counting) were substituted. She made new social contacts, outside the family, and on her own initiative became a member of a female club. Subsequently she began to work to support herself.

As a spontaneous substitution for her obsessive disorder she now developed certain psychosomatic manifestations (obesity and a relatively harmless duodenal ulcer), which did not, however, affect her social adaptability.

It is obvious that the patient has achieved a significant and durable remission without remaining dependent on her therapist despite the gradual development on her part of a therapeutically favourable transference.

Naturally there is no question of a radical cure in the strict sense, but practically she is *socially* much improved. Her personality has to a certain degree become restructured to function better, and her remaining regressive tendencies have found more harmless outlets.

The above case is unusual and may not serve as a model. It may be objected that the treatment had been unnecessarily protracted and therefore expensive. But this cannot equal for example "endless psychoanalysis." For practical reasons it had to have long interruptions which resulted in a fractionated type of treatment. The total sum of therapeutic hours hardly surpasses those needed in normal psychoanalytic treatment for much less severe cases of this type, consequently it has not been more expensive. It required enormous patience, from both patient and therapist, but the driving force which made this possible was the honest and strong desire for therapy as well as the good transference situation.

Theoretically it is an interesting case. Space, however, allows only this brief summary. It has presented many interesting theoretical problems that might have deserved a separate monograph.

FUTURE

As to the future of hypnotherapy and research in the field of hypnosis in Denmark, it is difficult to prognosticate. Interest in hypnosis has moved along an undulating curve. With intervals of about twenty years it has come to the fore for a while and then faded. This same phenomenon, i.e., of waxing and waning of interest, is also apparent in a number of our psychotherapists. Some of them have been very active in a given period but later on were more occupied by other fields of psychiatry and psychotherapy. As a result, they became less interested in hypnosis. One of the reasons for this is, in my opinion, similar to that which held true for psychoanalysis. It took a long time before psychoanalysis gained a foothold in this country because of prejudice among professional people due to the many "wild analysts" which we had (and still have) and similarly we have at present many "wild hypnotists."

Another reason at present is that psychoanalysis had been organized among psychiatrists and psychologists, who had been co-operating with the universities, to their mutual gain. Psychoanalysis now monopolized their interest. This was not, however, an obvious disadvantage to hypnotherapy, because it was realized by our people that there is no contradiction between the two fields, that they rest on different principles and that they supplement each other.

A number of the members of our society, although all of them have had practical experience in hypnotherapy and some in research, spent most of their time with psychoanalysis and at present do not practice hypnotherapy to any great extent.

Personally I believe it advantageous to have had psychoanalytical training, knowledge of psychoanalytical theory, and experience with other types of psychotherapy in order to be a competent hypnotherapist. It is, however, difficult for some people to change from the doctor-patient relationship of psychoanalysis to that involved in hypnotherapy. This brings us to a third reason for the slow progress of scientific hypnosis.

It is generally admitted that the technique of hypnosis can be taught and learned by most people. But to handle this instrument skillfully is another matter. It cannot after all be denied that it requires a special talent which some people have and others do not. A number of stage hypnotists are undoubtedly talented in this way, but their skill is usually accompanied by a lack of self-criticism, a belief in their being endowed with extraordinary or even supernatural gifts, and by the absence of any vestige of scientific background. The combination of rigorous scientific training, sober objectivity, criticism (including self-criticism), perfect honesty, and a "born" talent for hypnosis, all in one per-

son is a rather rare occurrence. The reason for example that
Freud defected from hypnosis and developed his own epoch-
making method was just that he felt he did not belong to this
type. The presence here of a few such personalities would considerably further the development of hypnosis and be the best
prerequisite in forming a school and organizing training and research in this area.

Our Danish Society, still a modest body, must build a sturdy
and reliable basis for hypnotherapy and for research made possible by the exchange of experiences with members of the International Society for Clinical and Experimental Hypnosis.

IMPORTANT REFERENCES

Brandeis, J. D.: *Magnetismus*. Copenhagen, 1818.

Geert-Joergensen, Einar: *Ugeskrift for Laeger*. (Danish) 1928, 100,
    749-751.

Geert-Joergensen, Einar: *Medicinsk Forum*. (Danish) 1957, 10,
    Fascic. 2.

Krarup, Frode: *Zeitschrift fur die gesmte neurologie und psychiatrie*.
    90: 638-645, 1924.

Lehmann, Alfred: *Hypnosen*. (Danish) Monograph, 1890.

Reistrup, Herman: *Ugeskrift for Laeger*. (Danish Medical Weekly)
    100: 29-36, 1938.

Wagner, Frederik: *Acta psychiatrica und neurologica Scandinavica*.
    26: 91-94, 1951.

HYPNOSIS IN FINLAND

By

C. CEDERCREUTZ, M.D.

Claës Henrik Laurentius Cedercreutz; born 1917; M.D. (surgery); President of Finnish division of the I.S.C.E.H., Fellow I.S.C.E.H.; Member, Finska, Läkaresällskapet (Finnish Medical Society), Finlands Kirurgförening (Surgeons' Society in Finland), Finlands Ortopedförening (Orthopaedists' Society in Finland), L'Association Française de Chirurgie; Hypnotic treatment of phantom pain in 100 amputees, Acta chir. Scand. 1954, 107, 158, Hypnotic treatment of 70 enuretics, Ann. paediatr. Fenn. 1956, 2, 56, etc.; present position, Head of the Hamina Municipal Hospital, Finland.

RECENT PAST

As FAR AS IS KNOWN, the first medical practitioner in Finland to take an interest in hypnosis was the Medical Officer of Health for the city of Turku, Berndt Gustaf Hahl (1825-1912). He is described by his contemporaries as a remarkable and versatile man. Hahl's interest in hypnotherapy is mentioned in the annals of the Turku Medical Association, but it is not known when and where he acquired his skill, nor to what extent he practised it.

In 1887, Dr. Karl Eberhard Lindén (1847-1927) gave a lecture on hypnosis at a meeting of the Finnish Medical Society. At the time, a touring Danish professional hypnotist, by name of Hansen, who had acquired fame through his demonstrations and miracle cures, was active in Finland. A young man, hypnotised by Hansen, was found, on awakening, to suffer from muscular weakness, fatigue, and headache. The symptoms remained for months. From Lindén's detailed account, it can be concluded that Hansen had been guilty of incomplete de-suggestion and had subsequently failed to re-hypnotise and de-suggest. Lindén warns those, who do not completely master the science of hypnotherapy, against practising this form of treatment.

In 1890, two well-informed articles on hypnosis by the eminent neurologist Axel Fredrik Holmberg (1844-1912) appeared in the periodical *Finsk Tidskrift*. Holmberg throws light on pertinent phenomena, which he illustrates with examples from literature on the subject and from his own experience. He predicts a future for this form of therapy and writes: "Hypnosis has worked its way back from the oblivion into which it had sunk, and, although slowly, is yearly gaining more and more recognition in medical practice."

Emil Reinhold Teodor Eriksson (1861-1930) studied hypnosis in Paris and Nancy. In 1892 he gave a lecture on hypnosis to the Finnish Medical Society.

Severin Wandalin Gustaf Tigerstedt (1882-1954) served as a lieutenant in the Russo-Japanese War. Once when inspecting the troops' quarters, he was the witness of a violent fight. A giant-like soldier had run amok, striking four of the men unconscious, and when Tigerstedt entered the barracks, the soldier vented his fury on him. Tigerstedt, who had studied hypnosis, realized that the only way to master the raving man was by surprise tactics. He raised his hands, looked the man straight in the eye, and said calmly and firmly: "Your arms and legs are paralyzed, you cannot move a step, you feel drowsy, you are falling asleep." The soldier stopped, surprised. He was unable to move from the spot, and fell asleep.

When, later on, Tigerstedt changed his profession and qualified as a dentist, he performed many tooth extractions, during the First World War, under hypnotic anesthesia.

At the Women's Clinic in Marburg, the Principal of which was Professor Zangemeister, Dr. Julius Frans Christian Meyer, learned to hypnotise. When Meyer was appointed assistant at the Womens' Clinic in Helsinki, he was able to try out his methods. Severe cases of hyperemesis gravidarum (excessive vomiting) were treated hypnotherapeutically. The results were mediocre. Good results, were on the other hand, obtained by Meyer when treating phobias. The Principal of the Women's Clinic, Professor Seth Edvin Wichman (1885-1939) occasionally treated patients by the hypnotic method. In 1930, he performed an oophorectomy (surgical removal of an ovary or ovaries) under hypnotic anaesthesia.

Hypnotherapy has also found followers among neurologists. For instance, Sven Evert Donner (1890-   ) and Martti Eero Kaila (1900-   ), both Professors at the University of Helsinki, and Kaarlo Ilmari Kalpa (1912-   ), member of the Medical Board, all to this day practise this form of therapy at times. While hypnosis is not taught at the University, it has been touched on in lectures. Donner states that he has had good results, especially when treating obsessions and phobias.

Paul Somny (1904-   ), a student of theology and psychology, practised the art of hypnosis, guided by assiduous study of available literature. He was helped in this by his brother, Dr. Kurt Erich Saravuo (1901-   ), and a few other medical students. Subsequently as a clergyman, he gave up hypnosis, as his congregation looked askance at such activities. Dr. Saravuo continued with hypnotherapy, and as senior obstetrician at the Maternity Hospital at Joensuu, gained great reputation as a hypnotist. The following episode is told: A photographer had displayed a picture of Saravuo in his window. A patient saw the picture, and promptly fell into a deep hypnotic sleep!

Between 1930 and 1940, there appears to have been little interest in hypnosis. Around 1945, a layman, Leo Hildén (1919-   ), a film director by profession, started to study hypnotherapy, with very successful results. More and more patients are being sent to him, such was the confidence he inspired in psychiatrists and other medical practitioners. Hildén has given numerous lectures on hypnosis.

In 1946, Uno Remitz (1921-   ) came over from Sweden and settled in Finland. He has lectured on hypnosis and given demonstrations at the Institute of Psychology attached to the University of Helsinki. In 1948 he made a feature film about hypnotic phenomena, which attracted much attention. With Kai von Fieandt, Professor of Psychology (1909-   ) he made a second scientific film—a myographic examination of muscular response under hypnosis. The film was shown at the international Psychology Congress in Brussels in 1957. Dr. Remitz's many articles and lectures have helped to spread knowledge of hypnotherapy.

At a dental meeting in Turku in 1952, a dentist, Mauri Kinnunen, (1910-   ) performed a successful extraction under hypnotic anaesthesia. This was the first demonstration of its kind in Finland. Another dentist, Hannu Siirilä (1928-   ) has for several years anaesthetised by hypnosis, both for extractions and other treatment. In his capacity as lecturer at the Dental Clinic in Helsinki, he has demonstrated his methods to students. His articles in medical publications have helped to dispel prevalent misconceptions of hypnosis.

Finally, mention must be made of the psychiatrist, Dr. Martti Kaarlo Hjalmar Paloheimo (1913-   ). He has made excellent contributions to the development of hypnotherapy in Finland. It is thanks to his organizing abilities, his energy and interest that the Society for Scientific Hypnosis was established.

PRESENT

The Society for Scientific Hypnosis was founded in Helsinki in 1959 by Mr. Hildén, Dr. Paloheimo, Dr. Remitz, Mr. Siirilä and the writer. The object of the Society is to further knowledge about hypnosis and how it is applied in practice, and also to prevent abuse and the spreading of misconceptions. To realize its object, the Society arranges two courses of instruction each year. In the short time the Society has existed, three courses have been held: a general one for medical practitioners, dentists and psychologists, and two special courses—one for gynaecologists and one for surgeons. These courses have resulted in two doctors at the Maternity Hospital in Helsinki anaesthetising by hypnosis for childbirth cases, and—even if only on a limited scale—the practice of hypnotherapy, for the elimination of pain sensations, at our two leading orthopaedic hospitals in Helsinki, Invalidstiftelsen (the Institution for Disabled Persons) and Universitetets Ortopediska Klinik (the University Orthopaedic Clinic). There has recently been a favourable change in the attitude of the Board of Professors, so much so that two of them have joined the Society.

They have also invited members of the Finnish Society for Scientific Hypnosis to give lectures to the staff and pupils of the hospitals. The famous professor K. E. Kallio, head of the University Orthopaedic Hospital has taken up hypnosis himself with considerable success and in the spring he delivered a lecture on hypnosis to the Association of Surgeons in Finland. The change of attitude may possibly have been influenced by the fact that two Swedish gynaecologists came to Finland last year to learn hypnosis and the Finnish professors feel that there would be nothing to lose by trying out methods which have interested other Scandinavian doctors.

As far as I know there has not been a single case where a member of the clergy has opposed the use of hypnosis and in fact both in Sweden and in Finland there are two doctors practising hypnosis who are also priests. There has also been a discussion on the radio between a priest and a doctor in which the priest expressed an opinion that if a sick person could be cured by hypnosis there would be no objection on religious grounds.

In my knowledge public opinion is in favour of hypnosis and from comments in the press I have not noticed any criticism although a considerable amount has been written. People in general believe that there is some strange secret in the ability to hypnotize, even if you explain to them what hypnosis is, there is never complete belief on their part because they love to think that there is a secret. This of course is understandable as there has as yet been no book published in Finnish explaining to the general public what hypnosis is. While stage demonstrations are forbidden by law in Finland, amateurs may give demonstrations combined with lectures.

About fifteen doctors practice symptomatic hypnotherapy, besides which a few doctors perform hypnoanalyses as an adjunct to traditional analysis. There is little interest in hypnosis among psychiatrists, and no lectures on hypnosis have been held at the University, in spite of requests from medical students.

For the past five years Dr. Remitz has lectured on hypnosis at the Psychological Institute attached to the University, and has also performed a series of scientific experiments.

Additional Considerations—"Phantom Pain"

When an extremity has been amputated, the patient usually has the sensation of the amputated part still being there. The illusory limb is known as "phantom" and the accompanying sensations as "phantom sensations." A feeling of pain in the phantom is called "phantom pain" to distinguish it from the stump pain which is located in the stump. According to Lunn (1948) 57 per cent of amputees suffer from phantom pain.

A great many operations of different kinds have been tried in order to remove phantom pain but none have given satisfactory results. Good effects have mostly been transitory and permanent recovery is the exception. In 1926 S. Betleheim was the first to succeed in influencing phantom sensations through hypnosis.

I have treated 100 amputees, ninety-two men and eight women with hypnosis. Complete relief from symptoms (elimination of both pain and phantom) occurred in twenty-two cases. Pain elimination, although the phantom did not vanish entirely, occurred in five cases, while an appreciable easing of pain and permanent change in the shape of the phantom occurred in eight cases. Thus, favorable results were achieved in 35 per cent of the cases (permanent change in the shape of the phantom as well as temporary alleviation of pain was produced in ten other cases).

In all cases where post-hypnotic anaesthesia can be achieved it may be predicted that treatment will be successful. If the phantom reacts quickly under treatment and vanishes after two to three hypnotic sessions, long-lasting effects are generally achieved, even if posthypnotic anesthesia cannot be produced. Regressive changes often occur during treatment, which means that the phantom is shortened. This shortening of the phantom does not signify, and still less guarantees, that treatment will be successful. On the contrary it shows that the patient is incapable of entirely following the suggestion of freedom from symptoms that has been given. The frequency of relapses among these patients is also considerably higher than among those whose phantoms have immediately vanished. If more than seven hypnotic sessions are required for elimination, the frequency of relapses is high, (however, relapses can always be eliminated through new hypnotic sessions). Several of these patients are still free from symptoms five years after completion of treatment.

FUTURE

There is a growing interest among dentists, thanks to Mr. Siirilä, lecturer at the Dental Clinic in Helsinki, who gives practical instruction in hypnosis to interested students. It is only a question of time before hypnosis will be included in the curriculum of the Medical Faculty.

IMPORTANT REFERENCES

Betlheim, S.: *Zur Lehre vom Phantom.* Dutsche Ztschr. F. Nervenheilk. *90:* 271, 1926.

Holmberg, A. F.: Hypnotismen, *Finsk Tidskrift. 28:* 99, 1890.

Holmberg, A. F.: Hypnotismen, *Finsk Tidskrift. 28:* 176, 1890.

Lindén, K. E.: *Finska Läkaresällskapets Handlingar. 29:* 281, 1887.

Lunn, V.: *Om legemsbevidstheden.* Academic dissertation. Copenhagen, 1948.

HYPNOSIS IN GERMANY

By

J. H. SCHULTZ, M.D.

J. H. Schultz; born 1884; education in general medicine, psychoanalysis, psychiatry, neurology, at Lansanne, Gottingen, Breslau; President German division I.S.C.E.H.; Member German Medical Association; Basic questions in the study of neuroses, Stuttgart, Thieme, 1955, Autogenic Training (with W. Luthe M. D.) New York, Grune and Stratton, 1959; present position, private practice, neurology Berlin, Germany.

PAST

THE GERMAN doctor-Franz Anton Mesmer born near the Bodensee in South Germany had observed that a certain individual named Hell was able to heal by means of "passes" i.e., slow monotonous movements of both hands along the body of the sick person from head to lap. He believed this procedure elicited "magnetical forces" and under this treatment some patients showed a changed state of mind. With this "animal-magnetic sleeping" or kind of dreamy state came the discovery of hypnosis in Europe in the eighteenth century.

Under the name "animal magnetism" the method soon was applied in many parts of Germany. If the psychological aspect, as in the North of Germany, was stressed then more objective and more sober statements were made, otherwise they were more fanciful and romantic. The authors of the first kind of statement soon concluded that the effects of animal magnetism were in actual fact the action of imagination.

In the following decades the interest in hypnosis in Germany was restricted to small groups of "outsiders" with all the advantages and disadvantages inherent in such adherents.

In the years 1880-1885, there was an increase in the interest in hypnosis shown by German scholars. This can be attributed to

84

the sensationalistic stage demonstrations of a Scandinavian layman named Hensen. As a result many famous scholars in Germany studied the problems of hypnosis from a medical, physiological, psychological or legal viewpoint. The names of such persons can be found in every book concerned with the history of hypnosis, e.g., A. Moll (*Der Hypnotismus*, Fischer-Kronfeld, Berlin), L. Mayer (*Hypnosetechnik*, J. F. Lehmann, München), and especially the excellent reports of W. Hilger and the *Zeitschrift für Hypnotismus*.

Oskar Vogt, son of a clergyman in Schleswig-Holstein, North Germany, established a private institution toward the end of the last ten years of the nineteenth century. His German researches resulted in scientific and critical thinking in the field of hypnosis. His data and his observations were carefully obtained and his experimental procedure was meticulous in design. Since his works the problems of hypnosis in Germany were clearer and due to him many of its problems were solved.

PRESENT

ATTITUDES

Medical

Until the first war the attitude of the medical profession was generally very reserved vis-à-vis hypnosis. The majority of doctors without any experience whatsoever thought that hypnosis was a foolish procedure good only for hysterical women, and had no real importance. The most self-evident observations as well as the simplest facts and theories of hypnosis were not known, for there had been no discussion of these problems in either medical or psychological circles in the preceding years. Despite these difficulties a small group of doctors were interested in hypnosis and tried to show its importance. (O. Binswanger, Jena; O. Bunnemann, Braunlage; G. Flatau, Berlin; A. A. Friedlander, Frankfurt; W. Hilger, Magdeburg; L. Hirschlaff, Berlin; L. Loewenfeld, München; A. Moll, Berlin; J. H. Schultz, Frankfurt; E. Tromner, Hamburg.)

The failure of psychoanalysis in the treatment of hundreds of cases of neurotic tremor during the first war and the excellent results achieved by hypnosis for such cases brought on a new and serious interest in the field of hypnosis. There occurred so to speak both a revival and a sort of justification for those already engaged in hypnotic work, e.g., the writer had published in 1909 with E. Heller, M.D., a case involving stigmatisation which was very precisely controlled by hypnosis. Not only hypnosis but psychotherapy of every form became socially acceptable in medical circles. As a result of this trend many excellent younger individuals worked with hypnosis in Germany. (G. Hansen, Heidelberg; F. Glaser, Würzburg; E. Grafe, Heidelberg; G. R. Heyer, München; W. Kauffman, Halle; E. Kretschmer and his staff, Marburg and Tübingen; A. Kronfeld, Berlin; L. Mayer, Heidelberg; M. Levy-Suhl, Berlin; F. Mohr, Düsseldorf; K. Schmitz, München; V. v. Weizsäcker, Heidelberg; E. Wittkower, Berlin.)

The majority of university psychiatric clinics soon gave special courses of lectures about general psychotherapy and hypnosis. Since 1926, a general medical organization for psychotherapy (Allgemeine ärztliche Gesellschaft für Psychotherapie) was founded by R. Sommer who was its first president. Later on E. Kretschmer and C. G. Jung became its presidents.

Dental

In the dental profession in Germany the understanding of the role of psychotherapy in general and hypnosis in particular was as yet not understood. Recently, however, there have been small gains with regard to instruction.

Legal

In the legal field problems involved with hypnosis have been frequently and earnestly discussed. Mayer at Heidelberg has written a very interesting book about hypnosis and crime (*Das Verbrechen in Hypnose und seine Aufklärungsmethoden*, München, 1937), with a description of an outstanding case which presented unusual and novel ideas. The victim was for years under the influence of the criminal both in hypnosis and in her waking state. As a result of this particular case many authorities tried to have a law passed against such malpractice and against the stage-hypnosis by unreliable or immoral individuals. However, in Germany, prohibition against such practice is still only dependent on local option.

Dr. L. Mayer showed me all of his proofs, documents and observations in this particular case. For in this case the country court did not punish the hypnotist, who had been a criminal for a long time, because "hypnosis exists only in superstition." The facts were a minor official came to Dr. Mayer with his wife and reported that the latter had been treated some years before by a doctor who charged her a large sum of money despite the fact that the patient had become progressively worse. On examination the wife was found to be in an altered state of consciousness and Dr. Mayer soon gained the impression that hypnotic influence was active in her case. On hypnotising her, she immediately went into a deep trance state in which different hallucinations were very easily elicited and other phenomena of the deep trance state were also produced. All attempts however, to learn the name of the mysterious "doctor" were without success. She only said that the doctor was with her when she was on the trip to Heidelberg to see a physician. The hypnotist told her this time that he was a very successful doctor who healed all diseases by hypnotism. She believed in him, trusted him, and fell in love with him to such a degree that in a few days she was completely dependent upon him. He used her for criminal acts, for example, she twice tried to kill her husband by involving him in car accidents which only by chance did not succeed. She was also involved in concealing tools that were used for various crimes. In the process of doing this, she contracted some unusual diseases, for example, the fingers on her hand were so violently squeezed into the hollow of her hand that they penetrated the skin and no one was able to extricate them. Dr. Mayer, after several sessions, clearly recognized that every attempt to cast light as to who the "doctor" was had been accompanied by great anxiety. In the first weeks it was only possible to make her relate the license number of the "doctor's" car. The police reported that this was a license of a stolen car. To find out the name, Dr. Mayer placed an empty sheet of paper on the table and said to the patient "here is a letter from your 'doctor,' please copy it." As the writing of the name was not overly threatening and as she perceived no particular threat, she now wrote the name—Dr. Bergen. (Ver-bergen in German means to hide, an interesting symptomatic act). This name was well-known to the police as an alias used by a well-known criminal whom could now be arrested. In addition, Dr. Mayer also used the contradiction technique in order to learn more about the "doctor." In provoked hypnotic hallucinations he caused the patient to visualize certain scenes when they (the patient and the "doctor") had been together. Dr. Mayer then said, "oh yes! there he is, the fat old man with the black beard" and immediately the patient said "no that is not him, he is long, slender and blond with charming gold fillings in his teeth!" This kind of identification made the task of the police easy.

The victim had been so thoroughly trained in hypnosis that on a given word she would instantly go into a deep trance, during which she could be given to other men for money. By means of another word she would awake with complete amnesia. For eighteen months Dr. Mayer studied this patient and his book contains many very interesting details verified by police data. Despite his plentiful material, the country court pronounced the aforementioned astonishing disposition. Dr. Mayer came to see me in Berlin and asked if I would be willing to come to Karlsruhe and go to the Supreme Court of the country as an expert witness. He showed me the protocols of his eighteen months observation which was some 1,800 pages in length. As our "grand old man" Oskar Vogt lived nearby, I suggested to Dr. Mayer that he ask him. Some six months later the criminal "doctor" was sentenced to twelve years in jail. The so-called "doctor" was an infantile and moderately intelligent person with a dysplastic and therefore ugly constitution.

Psychological

The psychological institutes in the German universities generally are not interested in the problems of hypnosis where research in this area is concerned. Theoretically, however, in every course of lectures, the topic of hypnosis is taught and discussed. However, only professors Ach and Welleck have actually added to our knowledge by experiments and theory formulation.

Clerical

Clergymen in Germany rarely have adequate knowledge about hypnosis and frequently compare hypnosis with problems of mysticism, magic, and superstition. At times they are apprehensive that the God-given free will of the individual be in danger. However, the more scientifically instructed clergymen are free of such misconceptions, although, the doctor practicing hypnosis in Germany does not generally find much understanding or support from the clergymen.

Public

The attitude of the public in Germany depends in large measure on the particular group that one is describing. Instructed and intelligent circles are quite knowledgeable about the medical uses of hypnosis but the majority of the public still think of hypnosis with superstition. They liken it to dangerous magical exorcism or some may think of it as silly humbug. Therefore, it is often better to use the word relaxation or calming rather than hypnosis. In all therapy, instruction corresponding to the cultural level of the patient is as indispensable as a complete psychological and physical examination. By means of such procedure most difficulties and unsuccessful experiments can be avoided.

After the first war in Germany a rash of stage-hypnosis shows occurred, in which many of the "artists" ended as criminals. After the second world war the police were cognizant of this possibility and there were no repetitions of these kinds of shows. (In *Gesundheitsschäden nach Hypnose*, i.e., *Harm to Health by Hypnosis*, 1923, 1955, Marhold, Berlin, I reported a hundred such cases.)

TEACHING AND RESEARCH

Since the first war the medical faculties of the different universities have lectures about psychotherapy, however, they vary greatly in quality and only certain clinical institutes show a deep concern about this situation, e.g., E. Kretschmer, psychiatrist at Tübingen, F. Curtius, psychiatrist at Lübeck; Heilmeyer, internist at Freiburg; Kolle, psychiatrist at München; V. v. Gebsattel, psychiatrist at Würzburg; H. Kleinsorge, internist at Jena; and G. Störring, psychiatrist at Kiel.

Training in special types of psychotherapy, psychoanalysis, etc., in Germany even today is given by private institutions. In the majority of these institutions, hypnosis and other active methods of therapy are not discussed and are often passed over in favor of psychoanalysis, a situation which it is hoped will change. As a result of all this, private practical lessons, i.e., apprenticeships from doctor to doctor are very important in Germany. On the basis of forty years' experience, I would say that the practioners are very interested in such training.

MISCONCEPTIONS

Misconceptions are important in different ways. Some patients fear that the doctor will hear secrets that they the patients do not wish to divulge, others that they will not awaken and return to normality, others that their willpower will be diminished, and still others fear that in the state of hypnosis they are absolutely defenseless. Consequently it is not too difficult to see how superstition, sensationalistic moving pictures, and infantile complexes work together to produce some of these misconceptions. It is, as a consequence, important to fully and wisely instruct the patient regarding therapeutic procedure and to make him realize that at all times he is in full control of the hypnotic state. The real question is whether or not one can establish a satisfactory depth.

Additional Consideration

If patients come themselves, i.e., are not referred by an appropriate person, and desire hypnosis, they may be suffering from a severe neurosis or even a psychosis and they actually do not really wish to be cured. Very often patients visit a hypnotist when their resistance to their analyst is high. Then the question arises as to whether or not the analyst realizes that sometimes hypnotizing of the patient by another doctor may remove resistance. It may even be that the "loved-hated" analyst to whom the resistance is directed should not be the therapist. Or from the opposite point of view one might wonder whether the hypnotist was sufficiently versed in medical psychology and psychopathology to decide whether a case should be treated by psychoanalysis, hypnosis or some other form of therapy. In any and all cases it is wise to make contact with the analyst. In actual practise a strong active conscious wish to be hypnotized is an impediment to hypnotic therapy, for an over-anxious, over-desirous and highly expectant state of mind, all reflect attitudes which absolutely contraindicate the possibility of being hypnotized.

Certain studies about hypnosis in Germany seem to be of great importance, e.g., those by F. Curtius concerning colitis ulcerosa; A. W. von Eiff concerning physiological changes of the organism during hypnosis (especially those concerned with regulation of temperature); V. E. von Gebsattel concerned with hypnocatharsis; H. Hengstmann concerned with hypnotical lobotomy; H. Kleinsorge and G. Klumbies concerned with ablation-hypnosis (this means continuation of the hypnotic influence by means of discs or other technical tools); E. Kretschmer concerned with gradual active hypnosis (derived from autogenic training); H. Marchand concerned with prolonged hypnosis in the therapy of tbc and finally the work of P. Polzien also concerned with the physiological changes of the organism during hypnosis. This latter individual was especially interested in evidence that in every true hypnotic state there was a hyperthermy externally and hypothermy internally especially in the rectum.

In Germany interest and understanding in hypnosis was increased with the development of autogenic training and in 1920 psychological experiments showed that every hypnotic state is characterized by feelings of heaviness and warmth, i.e., relaxation of the muscles and the blood vessels. The question then arose as to whether it would be possible by self-exercise to create an autohypnotic state. By the year 1926 research indicated that this was possible and at present we have many thousands of trained people, according to the calculations of the American translator W. Luthe. Today in Germany this method not only is appreciated but frequently used. It gives the effect of medical hypnosis without the danger that is involved when the patient is too desirous of help because of infantile dependency strivings. Autogenic training suggests that there be a cooperative effort with the doctor. The general plan of the autogenic method is somewhat as follows: The patient is trained in six sessions under the supervision of the doctor. This latter individual teaches the patient any special technique that may be required. At the end of this training the general clinical effects of hypnosis may be obtained. People supervising such training may cooperate with any psychologically oriented doctor who happens to be utilizing specialized psychotherapeutic methods.

FUTURE

In 1960, Germany joined the I.S.C.E.H., and the writer had the honor to be elected its president. The German group is as yet small but we hope it will grow.

IMPORTANT REFERENCES

Kleinsorge, H., and Klumbies, G.: *Psychotherapie in klinik und praxis.* Munchen, Urban, Schwarzenberg, 1959.

Mayer, L.: *Technik der hypnose.* Munchen, Lehmann, 1951.

Schultz, J. H.: *Seelische kranken behandlung.* VII. Stuttgart, Fischer, 1959.

Schultz, J. H.: *Das autogene training.* Stuttgart, Thieme, 1960.

Schultz, J. H., and Luthe, W.: *Autogenic training* (English Edition). New York, London, Grune & Stratton, 1959.

Stokvis, B.: *Hypnose in der arztlichen praxis.* Basel, Karger, 1955.

HYPNOSIS IN GREAT BRITAIN

By

W. D. FURNEAUX, A.I.P., M.Sc.

W. D. Furneaux; born 1919; M.Sc. University of London (physics, psychology); Diploma (experimental) American Board of Examiners in Professional Hypnosis, American Division. I.S.C.E.H.; Member, British Division I.S.C.E.H., Advisory Committee British Section U.N.E.S.C.O. for International study of university admission; The Chosen Few, Oxford, University Press, 1961, Hypnotic susceptibility as a function of waking suggestibility, ch. 5 in Experimental Hypnosis *(Ed. L. LeCron), N.Y., MacMillan, 1952, The application of personality theory and drive concepts to the study of suggestibility, p. 3-14 in* The Nature of Hypnosis *(Ed. M. V. Kline), Baltimore, Waverly Press, 1962; present position, Psychologist-in-charge, Nuffield Project and Honorary Lecturer, Psychology Department, Institute of Psychiatry, Maudsley Hospital, London, England.*

PAST

WITHIN THE EARLY Celtic population of Wales, Scotland, and Ireland, was a class of seers, sorcerers, and philosophers known as the Druids. They claimed occult and prophetic powers, and there is evidence that they were using techniques akin to hypnotism as long ago as the first century B.C. Trance was induced by an appropriate chant, and it appears that the verbal content of this was as important as its rythmic nature. After a "magic sleep" had been produced, direct verbal suggestion was employed for such purposes as producing amnesia (in order to assuage grief), or for the detection of lying. The raising of blotches on the face, and similar psychosomatic effects, are also mentioned in the relevant records.

In more recent times, another Celt, a Scotsman by the name of Maxwell, postulated the existence of a *spiritus vitalis* having much the same properties as were later attributed to the universal magnetic fluid by Mesmer. In about 1600 he was describing techniques for transferring human disease and pain to plants and animals, with consequent cure of the sufferer.

After the publication of Mesmer's own first circular in 1775, over sixty years elapsed before the phenomena to which he directed attention received really serious study in Britain. In 1837, John Elliotson (1791-1868) who was regarded as the foremost physician of his day, witnessed some mesmeric experiments, and soon began to demonstrate and use the technique at University College Hospital, in London. He understandably accepted the explanations of mesmeric phenomena which were current in his time, and his reputation was greatly damaged when, in 1838, Thomas Wakeley (the first Editor of the *Lancet*, the well known medical journal) was able to disprove his claim that certain metals had greater powers, as concentrators of the magnetic fluid, than had others. The Dean of the hospital urged him to give up his mesmeric work, and when he refused the Hospital Committee was instructed to take steps to prevent the practice of mesmerism within the institution. Elliotson thereupon resigned his appointments, and established a mesmeric hospital in Fitzroy Square. Later, in 1843, he started the *Zoist*, a journal dealing with cerebral physiology and mesmerism. This ceased publication in 1855, but its influence led to the opening of many institutions where mesmerism was used for purposes of anaesthesia and treatment. At a single one of these, in Exeter, the surgeon Parker mesmerised one thousand two hundred people over a period of years and performed some two hundred painless surgical operations.

Elliotson's pioneer work was at first followed up quite intensively, and it is curious that the most important work in this field, so far as Great Britain was concerned, was carried out by three more natives of Scotland. Two of these, James Braid and James Esdaile, carried out their first experiments soon after Elliotson had resigned from University College Hospital. Strictly speaking, Esdaile (1808-1859) should not be included in the present survey, since all his important work was carried out in India. His results were so remarkable, however, that they must receive at least some brief mention. Working from reports of Elliotson's techniques, he first used mesmeric passes to induce anaesthesia for an operation on a Hindu convict in 1845. Within a few months he had performed over one hundred similar operations, and a committee appointed by the Deputy-Governor of Bengal, to investigate his claims, reported so favourably that he was placed in charge of a hospital in Calcutta for a period of one year. During this time he continued to obtain excellent results, and the continued support of the Deputy-Governor later secured for him a further official appointment, which he retained up to the time that he left India in 1851. In his hands, using mesmeric anaesthesia, the mortality associated with operations for the enormous scrotal tumours, which made up a large proportion of his cases was only about five per cent, as compared with something like fifty per cent when conventional methods were used. It seems likely, of course, that the use of *any* anaesthesia would have produced at least some improvement, by allowing time for a more careful operation.

After returning to Scotland, Esdaile settled in Perth in 1852, and reported that the Scots were no less susceptible than inhabitants of India. Under his guidance, the surgeon at the Perth Infirmary started using mesmeric techniques, but was prevented from continuing by his colleagues, who threatened to resign their appointments if he continued with his work.

The most important figure in the early development of hypnotism in the British Isles was undoubtedly James Braid (1795-1860), whose original notebooks are still preserved in the library of the University of Manchester. Although initially skeptical, he became convinced of the reality of mesmeric phenomena in 1841. After a series of experiments he rejected theories involving animal magnetism, and found that he could induce a trance-like state by techniques involving prolonged visual fixation. He was at first inclined to believe that most mesmeric phenomena resulted from physiological changes in the brain which could be attributed to the effects of the restriction of attention to a single limited field. As his work developed, however, he was increasingly impressed by the importance of purely subjective determinants. Since he rejected mesmeric theories, although admitting the reality of many of the phenomena, he proposed that the term neurohypnotism, or nervous sleep, should be substituted for that of

mesmerism. His views did not easily prevail. Both Elliotson and
Esdaile regarded him as an opponent, and continued to prefer
mesmeric theories. He continued to publish work on hypnosis
until shortly before his death in 1860.

For a period of some twenty years the status of the subject
then declined, and there was little systematic investigation until
after the Society for Psychical Research was founded in 1882.
One of the objectives of this organization was the careful study of
hypnotic phenomena, and under its auspices E. Gurney and F. W.
H. Myers were soon making useful contributions. Both were men
of outstanding ability and reputation, and the development by
Myers of his theory of hypnosis as a co-conscious state was of particular importance in re-establishing the subject as a proper one
for serious study. By the end of the nineteenth century highly
respected members of the medical profession were again actively
investigating, and using, hypnotic techniques, the work of Tuckey,
Felkin, Vincent, and Bramwell, exciting special interest. The latter in particular, was a most careful and competent investigator,
whose work still repays careful study. A Medical Society for the
Study of Suggestive Therapeutics, was formed in 1906, and in
less than four years achieved an active membership of nearly one
hundred, although it does not appear to have survived for very
long. During the 1914-18 war many thousands of cases of "shell-
shock" were treated by using abreaction under hypnosis, in particular by William Brown, and by J. A. Hadfield who personally
treated over six hundred cases. By the end of the war, however,
a reaction against purely symptomatic forms of treatment had set
in, and this was soon strengthened by the gradual spread of
Freudian concepts. From about 1920 onwards, hypnosis then fell
increasingly into disuse as a therapeutic tool, even among psychiatrists. The 1939 war produced some revival of interest, and Hadfield treated cases of "war neurosis" by using a combination of
catharsis and re-education, under hypnosis, for which technique
he coined the term "hypno-analysis." In general, however, the majority of British psychiatrists preferred to use drugs for the various
forms of abreactive therapy which were extensively used.

PRESENT

ATTITUDES

Medical

At the present time the tendency is increasingly to regard the study of hypnotism as a branch of normal psychology, and it is to theories of learning, role-playing, conditioning, habituation, motivation, and the like, that the worker in this field must frequently turn for his basic concepts. In Mesmer's time, however, psychology did not exist as a separate discipline, and it was mainly within the medical profession that the systematic study of human behaviour was attempted. It was to doctors, therefore, that people naturally turned for an authoritative evaluation of the claims of the mesmerists. The medical profession's concern with the subject was greatly increased when the early theories of hypnosis were evolved, for the most influential of these classed the phenomena firmly with those of psycho-pathology. This early concern has persisted, albeit sporadically;—mainly as a matter of policy on the part of the Profession's governing bodies rather than as a reflection of any real interest in the subject on the part of the majority of doctors and psychiatrists.

It is hardly surprising that attempts to introduce techniques savouring so strongly of the magical, and linked so closely with astrological and mystical traditions, encountered much initial opposition from medical men. Numerous experiments, from the time of Elliotson onwards, showed quite clearly that the theoretical background to mesmerism was unacceptable, and many influential investigators therefore concluded that the phenomena themselves were the product of trickery, and that those who claimed to produce them were quacks. It must also be remembered that mesmerism was commonly used for the production of anesthesia, and that the desirability of relieving pain, during surgery and childbirth, was itself a matter for vigorous debate. At a meeting of the Royal Medical and Chirurgical Society in 1842, the surgeon Copland proposed that no record of a paper on mesmeric anaesthesia, which had been read by Ward, should be entered in the minutes of the Society. "Pain is a wise provision of nature," he asserted, "and patients ought to suffer pain while their surgeons operate; they are all the better for it, and recover better." In the same year Braid himself was refused permission to read a paper on hypnotism before the Medical Section of the British Association for the Advancement of Science.

By the time Braid died in 1860, however, the early hostility had to some degree abated, being replaced in general by a cautious skepticism. In 1880, the British Medical Association (B.M.A.) invited the German physiologist, Prior, to address them on the subject, and at the Birmingham meeting of this association in 1890, a committee was established to test hypnotism "psychologically, physiologically, and therapeutically." When this committee presented its report in 1892, the reality of the phenomena was recognized, and hypnotic techniques were warmly recommended for purposes of therapy, particularly for the treatment of insomnia, pain, functional disorders, and dipsomania. A further important step forward followed in 1898, when the same Association invited F. W. H. Myers to address them on the subject at their annual general meeting in Edinburgh; for Myers, although a scholar of considerable repute, was not medically qualified.

The findings of the 1890 committee had little practical result. The theory and practice of hypnosis received only passing mention within the curriculae of medical schools, although from time to time, isolated individuals with interest in the subject would arrange special lectures and demonstrations for their own students. As recently as October of 1953, Doctor Gordon Ambrose, writing to the British Medical Journal, complained that ". . . students can find no facilities for acquiring the art of hypnosis. Doctors mastering the technique . . . sooner or later come up against ignorance and prejudice from fellow practitioners." The majority of doctors qualifying in 1962 have had only one lecture on the subject in the course of their training, and have never seen an officially sponsored demonstration of the phenomena. A few medical students carry out private experiments, but they are precluded from systematic study by their lack of any adequate background in normal psychology.

Nevertheless, there have been a number of very important developments in more recent years. In the world of psychiatry, some re-awakening of interest resulted after World War II from the appearance of reports of the successful hypnotic treatment of cases of "War Neurosis." The tenets of Freudian psychology never received in Britain the universal endorsement which they won in many of the countries of continental Europe, and in the United States. The outlook of many leading psychiatrists remained essentially eclectic, and although few of them used hypnosis, or indeed knew very much about it, there were many who were perfectly willing to investigate its possible value. An important step forward was taken when Hadfield in England, and Brenman and Gill in the U.S., showed how hypnotic and analytic techniques could be synthesized in the various forms of hypnotherapy, for this demonstration relieved the anxieties of many who would have felt uneasy about adopting any form of purely symptomatic treatment.

It is possible that the development of the National Health Service also had some influence. Before its inception, most of the less crippling forms of neurotic disorder received only palliative treatment in the hands of a general practitioner, since psychoanalysis was too expensive to be practicable for most patients. With the abolition of all fees for medical treatment, the general practitioner, for the first time, felt free to recommend for such cases any form of specialized consultation which seemed to be appropriate. In consequence, the resources of the Mental-Health Services were seriously strained, and techniques such as hypno-analysis, which promised to be less time-consuming than those in current use, seemed to merit investigation.

A further stimulus resulted from the publicity given to demonstrations of hypnosis arranged as a form of entertainment in theatres, which were quite popular in the years around 1950. A number of prominent medical men, including the president of the British Society of Medical Hypnotists (Dr. J. van Pelt) campaigned for the introduction of legislation to ban such demonstrations, and to restrict the use of hypnosis to those with medical qualifications. Their case was greatly strengthened by reports of harm suffered by some of those who acted as subjects. The resulting controversy, both inside and outside the profession, did much to re-awaken interest in the less disreputable uses of the technique.

An early development, in April of 1951, was the circulation of a formal statement of the views of the BMA, in the form of a letter from the Secretary, to all Divisions and Branches. It expressed the opinion that lay hypnotists should not give demonstrations at Division meetings, and that it was unnecessary to go outside the medical profession when seeking suitable lecturers to explain the use of hypnosis or to demonstrate the procedure. By May of 1952 the Psychological Medicine Group Committee of the BMA had issued a further statement, to the effect that hypnosis should be induced only for therapeutic purposes. Its value was held to be extremely limited, since results were indefinite, and relief did not appear to be permanent. It was held that the procedure tended to increase the subject's suggestibility, and that for this reason its use had been largely given up by the medical profession. In any case, the statement concluded, it should be induced only by a medical practitioner, *or under his direction and in his presence.* The words in italics were later deleted at the suggestion of the Central Ethical Committee of the Association. In spite of such official discouragement, however, a group of fifteen doctors submitted a petition to the Council of the BMA in July of the same year, asking that a Medical Hypnotists group be set up within the Association. This was presumably considered, but no action resulted. In January of 1953, as a result of the great interest which had been aroused by the passage through Parliament of the Bill designed to control stage demonstrations of hypnotism, the Psychological Medicine Group organized a discussion on the uses, limitations, and dangers of the technique. During this meeting, Professor Alexander Kennedy expressed the view that hypnosis could not rank as a speciality, and that it could never be a very high-grade occupation. He considered that hypnosis in psychiatric treatment should be used against the general background of psychiatry, and that its users should be specialists in psychiatry rather than in hypnosis. Although this meeting forwarded no formal resolutions or recommendations, it was clear from the report of its proceedings that Professor Kennedy's views were endorsed by the majority of those present.

In November of 1953, a most important development occurred. The Psychological Medicine Group appointed a sub-committee under Professor Ferguson Rodger, whose task was, in effect, to repeat the work of the 1890 committee. The formal terms of reference were: "to consider the uses of hypnotism, its relation to medical practice in the present day, the advisability of giving encouragement to research into its nature and application, and the lines upon which such research might be organized."

The sub-committee considered a mass of evidence, and consulted American as well as British authorities. Its report may be seen in the *Supplement to the British Medical Journal* of April 23, 1955. In brief, this stated that the sub-committee was satisfied that hypnosis could be of value, and that it might be the treatment of choice in some cases of so-called psychosomatic disorder, and psychoneurosis. It could also be used for revealing unrecognized motives and conflicts, for the production of anaesthesia or analgesia, for surgical and dental operations, and in suitable subjects, for relieving pain in childbirth. The sub-committee therefore regarded hypnosis as a proper subject for inquiry by the tried methods of medical research.

The report stressed the fact that hypnosis has its indications and contraindications, and that considerable knowledge and expert judgment are required to decide when it is likely to help the patient. It should therefore not be regarded as a speciality independent of psychological medicine. Although its dangers were exaggerated in some quarters, the sub-committee believed that they did exist, and that harm could be done by using hypnosis on unsuitable subjects. The use of hypnotism in the treatment of physical and psychological disorders should be confined to persons subscribing to the recognized ethical code governing the relation of doctor and patient. However, they considered that this would not preclude its use by a suitably trained psychologist, or medical auxiliary, who would carry out, under medical direction, the treatment of patients selected by a physician. They recommended that information about hypnotism should be given to medical undergraduates during their psychiatric course. Instruction in its clinical use should be given to all medical postgraduates training as specialists in psychological medicine, and pos-

sibly to trainee anaesthetists and obstetricians. The report concluded by stating that research in hypnosis might best be organized through university departments and research foundations.

It must be remembered that the sub-committee was set up at a
time when there were powerful elements within the Profession
who favoured a strong assertion that only those with medical
qualifications should be allowed to induce hypnosis. An equally
strong faction would have welcomed a statement discouraging
any use of a technique which they regarded in much the same
light as sympathetic magic, or juju (tribal magic). Moreover, for
nearly two years, the national press had carried frequent accounts
of the alleged misdemeanours of stage hypnotists. Against this
background, the meticulous objectivity of the report exerted a
profound influence. Almost overnight, hypnotism ceased to be
regarded as a rather dubious activity on the part of a few eccen-
trics, and was accorded official status as an acceptable field for
specialist study. The Council of the BMA welcomed the report,
and took immediate steps to bring it to the notice of suitable
research organizations. In consequence, although it would hardly be true to say that those who wished to pursue research in this
field found their path miraculously smoothed, yet nevertheless,
their difficulties were greatly reduced.

At the present time, hypnotism is employed by only a tiny minority of physicians and surgeons. A rapidly increasing number
of psychiatrists are coming to regard it as a standard technique
for use in suitable cases, just as they might use electroconvulsive
therapy, or group therapy. A rather small number specialize in
hypnotic treatment, a very few seem to regard it almost as a universal panacea. It is still extremely difficult to obtain adequate
training, except by joining one of the specialized societies which
organize courses for their members. The major change, during the
last two decades, has in fact been one of attitude, rather than
practice, and its full effects have yet to be seen.

Dental

Dentists normally use hypnosis to control apprehension and to
produce analgesia or anaesthesia. They do not have to concern
themselves very much with most of the more controversial as-

pects of the technique, such as the desirability of giving purely symptomatic treatment, the problem of resolving transference in hypno-analysis, and so on. They seem, therefore, to have developed a much more matter-of-fact attitude to its use than have their medical colleagues. There was little in the *British Dental Journal* to reflect the peaks of interest which were very apparent in the *British Medical Journal* in 1952 and 1955.

Individual dentists have experimented with the use of hypnosis for several decades. No statistics are available, but it seems reasonably certain that the number of these increased from about 1949 onwards, partly because of the stimulus resulting from reports of American work, and partly as a consequence of developments which have already been described in the previous section. In 1953 the British Society of Dental Hypnotists was formed (see under Additional Considerations (a)—Societies) and in 1954 two members of this group gave demonstrations of extractions under hypnosis at the Annual General Meeting of the British Dental Association. In 1955, a correspondent in the *British Dental Journal* raised some questions as to the advisability of dentists using hypnosis, but his points were concerned with expediency rather than principle. In 1957, the *Journal* allotted a great deal of space in one of its numbers to a paper describing the uses of hypnosis in dental surgery. This provoked a certain amount of correspondence in the issues which followed, but again, the matters raised were mainly concerned with technique. Towards the end of 1961, however, a correspondent did comment unfavourably on an article which had described the use of hypnosis with children, questioning whether this was either ethical or desirable. The *Journal* itself has for many years given prominence to reports of the activities of the British Society of Dental Hypnotists, and of the other organizations which later developed from this.

As far as it has been possible to ascertain, dentists training for their degree or licentiate do not receive training in the use of hypnosis, at any British university. Those who have qualified can obtain courses of instruction through the specialized societies.

It is unlikely that the total number of dentists using hypnosis exceeds one or two hundred. There is little evidence of any very rapid increase in this number, but there is at the moment a fairly steady increase of interest in the possibilities of the technique.

Legal

This section is concerned with some legal aspects of hypnotism, as they apply in England and Wales. Not all the statements made are necessarily true of Scotland and Northern Ireland, although in most respects the legal codes of all the countries within the United Kingdom are very similar.

The only laws framed specifically to take account of the existence of hypnotic states are those relevant to the Hypnotism Act of 1952 (to be described). There are no enactments specially framed to take account of the possibility that a crime might be committed under hypnotic influence, for example. In such standard works as *The Nature of Responsibility*, etc., (Ginsberg, M., 1953) and *Criminal Law* (Williams, G. L., 1961) the word hypnotism does not appear in the index, and even in such a specialized work as *Mental Abnormality and Crime* (Radzinowicz and Turner, 1944) hypnosis is mentioned only in connection with treatment. In *Psychological Disorder and Crime*, however, Neustatter (1953, page 86) does imply, by classing the hypnotic state with hysterical amnesia and fugues, that the hypnotized subject will only do something anti-social if fundamentally he wants to do it. An assertion of this kind from an acknowledged authority might receive considerable weight if advanced as expert opinion in a court of law. Most British lawyers would probably start their search for references to hypnosis in Archbold's *Criminal Pleading* (Archbold, J. F., 1960,) but here again they would be disappointed.

In the absence of expert guidance, all that can be attempted here is to quote some rulings and opinions which, although not directly concerned with hypnotism, are clearly relevant to it.

(a) It is stated in Archbold that every person of the age of discretion is, unless the contrary is proven, presumed by law to be sane, and to be accountable for his actions. But if there is an incapacity, or *defect of the understanding*, as there can be no consent of the will, the act is not punishable as a crime.

To establish a defence on the ground of insanity, it must be clearly proved that at the time of the act the party was labouring under such a defect of reasoning, from disease of the mind, as not to know the nature and quality of the act, or if he did know it, that he did not know that it was wrong. By 1957, it had been established that the intent of the words "from disease of the mind" was primarily to limit the effects of the words "defect of reason," so as to exclude defects caused simply by brutish stupidity. "Brutish stupidity" can itself be a defence on other grounds, but these have no relevance in the present context.

It appears that a person claiming that he committed a crime while under hypnotic influence, might therefore succeed in his defence if he could prove that he was hypnotized, and that being hypnotized produced a suitable incapacity or defect of the understanding. It should be noted that in Britain the onus of proof is normally with the prosecution, but it is transferred to the defence when the plea is "unsound mind." In the present state of our knowledge of the nature of the hypnotic state, the prosecution would undoubtedly be able to produce experts of standing who would deny that a hypnotized person must necessarily suffer a defect of the understanding. It would then be for the jury to decide the issue, and in his summing up the judge would attempt to clarify for them the conflicting points of view advanced by the expert witnesses.

Such a defence would seem to lean primarily on the nature of the hypnotic state, rather than on any specific instructions given by the hypnotist.

(b) It is stated in Archbold that a person not in other respects insane, but labouring at the time of a crime under an *insane delusion* in respect of one or more subjects or persons, so that for example he did the act complained of in order to redress some imagined grievance or injury, or to produce some public benefit, might not be held accountable. He would, however, be held responsible if he knew when committing the crime that he was acting contrary to law. If he were to commit a crime under such an insane delusion as to existing facts, then he would be in the same situation, as to responsibility, as he would be if the imagined facts were real. Thus, if he were to kill a man because of a delusion that this man was attempting to take his life, he would be exempt from punishment on the grounds of self-defence. However, if he killed in revenge for an imagined insult, then he would nevertheless be liable for punishment.

It appears that "insane delusion" might provide a promising line of defence in the case of a crime alleged to have been committed while a person was under the influence of a hypnotist. The defendant would presumably have to prove that he had been hypnotized, and that in consequence of this (whether the crime itself was committed under hypnosis or not) he was deluded in respect of certain subjects or persons, and that his act would not in fact have been criminal if these delusions had been true. In seeking to establish such a defence, the exact nature of the hypnotist's suggestions might become a point of crucial importance. For example, it is not a defence to prove that though a person knew a particular act to be against the law, he believed that in his own view or in the view of some other persons, the act might be justified.

(c) In some recent cases the assertion that the defendant committed a crime without being conscious of his actions, i.e., in a state of *automatism,* has formed the basis of a successful defence. As with other variants of "unsound mind," the defence must produce evidence from which the jury can reasonably infer that the accused acted in a state of automatism.

The precedents recently established have been concerned with disorders of consciousness such as those which are known to occur, for example, when a person is concussed. They would probably be of little use to one claiming to have committed a crime without being conscious of it, because of the effects of hypnosis. In the light of all the evidence, it would be difficult to maintain that a hypnotized person is unconscious, since even when there is amnesia for the events of the trance, this can normally be removed. A defence of this kind might thus be very difficult to establish.

(d) The defence of *uncontrollable impulse* did not exist at all under English law. The position is now rather similar in principle to that applying to states of alleged automatism. If this defence were attempted in a case involving hypnotism, then even if the fact of the hypnosis were proved, the prosecution would certainly be able to produce expert witnesses to assert that a hypnotized subject will only do something anti-social if fundamentally he wants to do it.

(e) It might be thought that some of the difficulties which have been indicated could be avoided by asserting that a person committing a crime when hypnotized is, in effect, *compelled* or coerced by the hypnotist. Unfortunately this is a very poor defence in British law. In cases of murder, only direct physical compulsion, as by A forcing B's hand to push a knife into C, is recognized as a valid defence. If A were to assault B, to the peril of B's life, to compel him to commit a crime, this would be no excuse in a case of murder, although it might serve for lesser crimes.

It thus appears that in cases of murder, this defence would be of no value. In other cases, it would presumably be necessary to show that a hypnotist had produced in the defendant a conviction that his life was in imminent danger at the hands of the hypnotist, and that he could only escape this danger by agreeing to commit some criminal act, which the hypnotist would himself have to specify.

(f) Under some circumstances it may be a valid defence that a person was under the influence of *alcohol or drugs*, etc., at the time a crime was committed. A successful defence on the grounds of hypnotic influence might be facilitated if it could be shown that hypnosis might have effects similar to those produced by alcohol or drugs.

In general, a defence based on the influence of such agencies could not succeed unless the degree of effect could be shown to be such as to make the person incapable of forming a criminal intent, or incapable of knowing that what he was doing was dangerous. However, the mere fact that the defendant was drunk, or under the influence of drugs, would itself usually constitute a valid defence, if the state resulted from the action of some other person, and particularly if the defendant had resisted this action.

In all cases of British law, a great deal depends on the total context within which rulings have to be applied. In assessing the

likely outcome of any case in which "hypnotic influence" might
be raised as a defence, it would be worth bearing in mind an
assertion of the late Viscount Haldane, when he was Lord Chan-
cellor, and which is quoted in *Medical Aspects of Crime*, by W. N.
East:—

> "I have never heard of the rules (governing the legal defi-
> nitions of criminal responsibility) embarassing any judge who
> really had a case before him in which justice required an
> acquittal . . . for instance, where the impulse was so dominant
> as to deprive a person of freedom, or of any realisation of
> what he was doing."

(g) As in the case of crimes committed under the influence of
a hypnotist, there are no special enactments to deal with *hypnotists who commit crimes* against their subjects while they are
hypnotized. Possible examples would arise should a hypnotist
seek to influence his subjects to give him money, or attempt a
sexual assault. Legal sanctions can easily be applied in such cases,
but the law is concerned with the offence, and not with whatever
special techniques might have been employed in its commission.

(h) There are no special enactments defining the *legal obli-
gations of the hypnotist*, but he is bound by the law as it normally
relates to contract and tort. It is under the latter heading that
most of the points of interest arise.

The hypnotist shares in the general duty to observe care
toward others, and if harm is caused by an act or omission, even
if no harm was intended, then an action for negligence can usually succeed. The standard of care demanded, is however that
which would normally be expected in similar circumstances. For
example, a doctor using hypnosis would be expected to exercise a
much higher standard of care and responsibility than would a
stage hypnotist. In the Slater trial, to be described, the judge
took care to make it clear to the jury that they were required to
decide whether he had been negligent as a stage hypnotist. If a
subject specifically agrees to accept a particular risk involved in
the use of hypnosis, then no action can succeed in respect of that
risk. However, in the absence of a specific agreement to accept

a risk, mere knowledge that it exists does not amount to consent.

If a hypnotist, without his subject's consent, performs any act which menaces or touches the subject's body, or produces a "nervous shock," then subject to certain conditions, he can be charged with assault. If there is any direct application of force, however slight, whether intentional or negligent, then he can be charged with battery.

A hypnotherapist might be sued under the law of contract if he had promised specific benefits from his treatment, if the patient had accepted treatment as a result of the promise, and if it was not fulfilled. He would be running a considerable risk if he falsely claimed to possess any qualification, particularly of such a kind as would usually be taken to imply a certain skill as a hypnotherapist. Advertising worthless or meaningless qualifications might be of little significance, save in so far as this might be adduced as evidence in support of a more widely based assertion that there was an intention to deceive.

The mere fact of claiming to be a hypnotherapist, or acting as one, gives rise to the danger of an action under the law of tort if the therapist behaves in a way which is unseemly, dangerous, or incompetent, or in a way which involves an assault or battery. Accepting the role of therapist, particularly if the acceptance is explicit, imposes the obligation to act in conformity with the standards normally expected of a person accepting such a role. As an example, the case of Dyke vs. Vinmar, in 1960, may be adduced. Mrs. Dyke had accepted treatment for a "nervous disorder" from a lay hypnotherapist working under the name of Victor Vinmar. She alleged that Vinmar had assaulted her, and tried to persuade her to remove her clothes, while she was hypnotized. The action came to trial twice, and the result of the re-trial was that the hypnotist was ordered to return the fee of fifty-three pounds which had been paid to him. The judge ruled that most of the allegations against him had not been proved, but that it was clear that he had not conducted himself in the proper and seemly manner which the plaintiff was entitled to expect.

(i) There appear to be no records of statements made by a hypnotized subject having been put forward as *evidence* in a

British court of law. It would probably be possible to have such evidence admitted, subject to certain safeguards, but it would almost certainly be difficult to persuade the court to give it much weight. It would first have to be established that the subject had agreed to be hypnotized, after the consequences had been explained to him. Any statements he might make while hypnotized would have to be shown to him, and he would have to agree that they could be produced in evidence. Expert witnesses would have to be produced, willing to assert that statements obtained in such a fashion could have evidential value, and the opposing side would almost certainly seek to counter this opinion. In at least some cases formidable difficulties might arise, because a witness must be prepared to swear that he remembers the facts which are included in his depositions.

In general, confessions and statements made under compulsion are not acceptable, nor are those resulting from hope or fear excited by persons in authority. No promise or favour, or any menace or undue terror, must be made use of in order to obtain a confession. Statements made under hypnosis could certainly not be accepted as evidence if there were any reason to believe that obtaining them had involved breaking any of these rules.

Psychological

As has already been mentioned, most of the initial experimental work in Britain was regarded as a branch of medical science. Only after the formation of the Society for Psychical Research did the early representatives of the still embryonic discipline of psychology begin to make their contribution. Within the Society for Psychical Research, however, serious study tended from the start to be rather specialized and unrepresentative, much of it being concerned with such problems as telepathic induction, and the possibility of using hypnosis for investigations of travelling clairvoyance, and the like. F. W. H. Myers was nevertheless concerned with some extremely interesting work, and reference has already been made to his theory of hypnosis as a co-conscious state.

Although William McDougall (1871-1939) was medically qualified, he seems never to have had any intention of practicing, and his work was certainly that of a psychologist. While lecturer in experimental psychology at University College, London, he became interested in hypnosis, and conducted a number of experiments. This work continued after he had been appointed Wilde Reader in Mental Philosophy at Oxford University. He was probably the first British experimental psychologist to investigate hypnotic phenomena systematically, and to explore the relationships between susceptibility and other aspects of personality. His views are clearly set out in his famous *Outline of Abnormal Psychology*.

After McDougall left England to go to Harvard, work at Oxford was continued by William Brown, who was at one time director of the Institute of Experimental Psychology there. Brown can reasonably be classified both as psychologist and psychiatrist, and he held advanced degrees in arts, science, and medicine. Like McDougall, he was interested in the relationships between personality characteristics and susceptibility to various forms of suggestion. His approach was comparative rather than experimental, and much of his later work was concerned with the use of hypnosis in therapy.

The surge of interest in suggestibility and hypnosis which took place after the 1914-1918 war is clearly reflected in the pages of the *British Journal of Medical Psychology* (to which both McDougall and Brown contributed) and to a smaller degree in the *British Journal of Psychology*. This interest did not, however, continue beyond about 1927, after which date neither of these journals carried any further reports of British work until 1939. In that year H. J. Eysenck published the result of some experiments on the reality of improvements of mental and physical functions in the hypnotic state. This proved to be the first of a whole series of investigations, with various collaborators, the results of many of which were eventually collected together in a chapter of *Dimensions of Personality* (Eysenck, 1947). True to the tradition established by McDougall and Brown, much of this work was concerned with the correlates of hypnotic susceptibility, but it was also profoundly influenced by the pioneer work of Clark L. Hull, in the U.S. In addition, extensive use was made of techniques of statistical analysis which were still, at that time, novel.

After the publication of *Dimensions*, psychologists in Britain made few further contributions for some years. The work of Eysenck and Furneaux for example, on primary and secondary suggestibility, was not followed up at all, although it stimulated work in other countries. The next important development occurred in 1957, when the Nuffield Foundation accepted a research proposal from Professor Eysenck, and agreed to finance work on hypnosis in the department of psychology at the Institute of Psychiatry (University of London). In offering this support, the Foundation was greatly influenced by the 1955 report of the BMA sub-committee. The fact that this grant was offered to a non-medical university department inevitably excited a great deal of comment among some of those psychiatrists who felt that work in this field should be confined to those with medical qualifications. The Foundation had foreseen this development, however, and discussed the whole matter at some length with the BMA before making the grant available.

Most of the universities in Great Britain now include a department of psychology, and the syllabus for a first degree in all such departments calls for some knowledge of hypnosis. It is taken for granted that work involving hypnotism, if carried out under competent supervision, is a legitimate undergraduate activity. In general, however, there is little special interest in this field, and the majority of students complete their courses with their knowledge in this area at least ten, or even twenty years out of date, and with no personal experience of hypnotic phenomena.

For the most part, British psychologists are interested in the nature of hypnosis, in the relationships between hypnotic susceptibility and various cognitive and orectic (desire) attributes, and in the study of the modifications of human performance which may be produced by the technique (but not, however, with special reference to the possibilities of therapy). They cannot be said to have any coherent "attitude" to hypnotism, in the same sense that the medical profession has. It is taken for granted that the field is worthy of study, and that the welfare of subjects used for experiments and demonstrations must be safeguarded, as in any other field.

Most of the lay hypno-therapists in Britain are not university trained psychologists, and few of the latter would be prepared to undertake therapy, except with medical collaboration. It will be remembered that the possibility of such collaboration was mentioned in the BMA's 1955 report on hypnotism. One problem is to define "therapy" in this context. Many qualified psychologists would be prepared to use hypnotism, without medical collaboration, for such purposes as improving study habits, and their professional organizations would probably consider this a legitimate activity. Few would undertake a hypno-analysis, however. Attitudes to such therapy, both inside and outside the profession, are still developing, and will probably not become very clear for some time to come.

Clerical

The Church of England has no special official attitude to hypnotism. Dignitaries of the Church, speaking in an official capacity, would almost certainly advise Church members to be guided by medical opinion, if the question of hypnotic treatment should arise. Individual clergymen undoubtedly hold as wide a range of opinions as do educated laymen, and their advice to parishioners naturally reflects their private views. The writer has the impression, from personal contacts, that Church of England clergy with high-church leanings are more likely to believe that submission to a hypnotist involves spiritual dangers, than are those of low-church persuasion.

This shading of opinion within the Church of England can probably be extrapolated. The caution of the high-church group seems to appear with stronger emphasis among the Roman Catholic clergy. The more favourable attitude of the low-church group is fairly characteristic of that most frequently encountered in Non-Conformists, and those of similar denominations.

Even where there is the greatest caution, however, it would be unusual for any clergyman to seek to influence someone to disregard medical advice. Within the low-church groups are to be found a number of ministers who believe that clergymen should combine the practice of psychotherapy with their spiritual ministrations. Many of these would argue that hypnotism can appropriately be used by a minister of religion who has received appropriate training. The well-known Methodist minister, Leslie D. Weatherhead, holds this view, and has in fact used hypnosis fairly extensively (Weatherhead, 1938). In the high-church groups, if there is interest in psychotherapy, it seems usually to be associated with the acceptance of Jung's psychology, and there is then a lack of interest in hypnotic forms of therapy.

Public

Until about 1947, members of the general public were poorly informed about hypnotism. Within the less educated sections of the community it was either "believed in," but classified with occult phenomena, or else it was held to be mainly a form of trickery or conjuring. These views were also prevalent among those with a good education, but opinion in these circles was also influenced by books giving popular explanations of the subject, which sold in large numbers. Although some of these were admirable, the average reader would receive from the majority the impression that hypnosis was concerned with a mysterious influence of one person on another, that induction was mainly a battle of wills, that submission to a hypnotist resulted in enfeeblement of the will (and that continued submission would result in insanity) and that the subject was mainly of concern to students of psychopathology.

The first result of the epidemic of stage hypnotism after the 1939 war, was to stimulate interest without providing enlightenment. There followed a phase when newspapers and magazines published articles on the subject. Some of these were the work of uncritical enthusiasts, but the majority were of reasonable quality. At about the same time, the British Broadcasting Company (BBC) considered a suggestion that demonstration of the phenomena should be televised. Trials were made on closed circuit, with the result that a substantial proportion of those who viewed the induction, including control-room staff, became as deeply hypnotized as did the subject. No demonstrations were therefore broadcast. In 1955, the BBC television service did devote a programme to hypnotism, and this was produced with the advice and participation of experts. The induction itself was not shown, but a previously conditioned subject was used to demonstrate the phenomena. Since that time, occasional programmes of a similar nature have been transmitted by both the BBC, and the Independent Networks. In one of these, in 1961, a previously conditioned subject was shown entering a state of trance on receiving a pre-arranged signal from the hypnotist. A report subsequently appeared that a thirty-nine year old man, who had had hypnotic treatment in an attempt to give up smoking, went into a trance when the signal was given and later awoke when the subject was aroused. There appear to have been no other reports of untoward experiences. All the programs have been handled with a sense of responsibility, and have clearly been of educational value.

Any book on the subject is obtainable without restriction through the extensive network of free public libraries. Skilled advice as to the selection of books of this kind is not usually available, however. An authoritative volume by Marcuse, designed for the reasonably well educated layman, and produced cheaply as a paperback, has had a considerable influence.

There are no legal restrictions preventing people without special qualifications from practicing hypnotism, except those set out in the Hypnotism Act of 1952 (to be described) which are intended to regulate public performances for the purpose of entertainment.

The number of amateur hypnotists in Britain is unknown. Books describing induction techniques in detail are freely available, but the general impression gained by talking to people is that very very few have ever attempted hypnosis, and that among those who have, an unsuccessful first attempt has resulted in loss of interest in a substantial proportion of cases.

Provided he does not claim to be medically qualified, any person may advertise as a hypno-therapist, and accept fee-paying patients. Such people cannot of course operate within the National Health Service, and the majority of reputable publications will not accept their advertisements. The BMA does not permit registered practitioners to collaborate with unqualified therapists of this kind.

There is still much ignorance, and many misconceptions, and doctors and dentists using hypnosis still find that patients usually need a certain amount of explanation and reassurance, before they will accept the method.

RESEARCH

In this section it will not be possible to provide a comprehensive survey of all the work which is being carried out in Britain at the present time. All that can be attempted is to provide the reader with information which may help him to obtain further details, either by suggesting contacts, or by quoting key references. *The Nuffield Investigation at the Institute of Psychiatry:* This investigation has so far been concerned with three main areas of study. These are:—

> The personality correlates of susceptibility, and the relevance of drive-concepts to the explanation of differences in susceptibility (W. D. Furneaux).
>
> Suggestibility in children, including the study of response sets. Preferred methods of concept formation, intolerance of ambiguity, and credulity; as determinants of hypnotic susceptibility in adults (H. B. Gibson).
>
> Verbal conditioning, suggestibility, and hypnotic susceptibility (L. Lindahl).

In practice all these fields have been found to overlap, and some work outside these areas is also in progress.

The Nuffield investigation itself is primarily concerned with the nature of the hypnotic state. In addition, the Unit makes available advice on such questions as experimental design, statistical analysis, and psychological theory, to doctors who wish to conduct investigations involving hypnosis, but who lack the necessary training in research techniques. In one such collaborative investigation a general practitioner carried out a controlled study of emotional disturbance in dyslexia, and showed that hypnotic treatment could be of value for the treatment of this condition. The value of hypnotic analgesia, during childbirth, has also been investigated with the Unit's help.

Hypnosis in Obstetrics and Gynaecology: This appears to be one of the most popular and fruitful fields of study. The work is usually concerned with the value of hypnotic analgesia in labour, but dysmenorrhoea, hyperemesis, infertility, incompetence, etc., have also received attention. A useful introduction to British work of this type can be obtained by reading the *Proceedings of the Royal Society of Medicine* for June of 1960.

Surgery under Hypnosis: The use of hypnosis for anaesthesia in major surgery has received comparatively little study, but a certain amount of work has been done, and at least one such operation has been filmed. The best contact for this area of study is probably Dr. A. A. Mason, M.B., B.S., who should be approached in the first instance through the secretary to the Society for Medical and Dental Hypnosis (see under Additional Considerations (a)—Societies).

Eczema, Ichthyosis, and Related Conditions: Interest in the use of hypnosis for conditions of these kinds was greatly stimulated when Dr. A. A. Mason published his celebrated report of the application of the technique in a case of congenital ichthyosiform erythrodermia of Brocq *(Brit. Med. J.,* August 23, 1952). There appear to have been no reports of this kind of study during the last few years, however.

Asthma: The value of hypnotic therapy for the symptomatic relief of some forms of asthma now appears to have been established to the satisfaction of most British investigators (Mather-Loughman *et al.;* A controlled trial of hypnosis in the symptomatic treatment of asthma, *Brit. Med. J.,* August 11, 1962).

Alcoholism: Dr. Griffith Edwards is conducting a controlled trial of hypnotic aversion therapy, at the Institute of Psychiatry, Maudsley Hospital, London, S. E. 5.

Sexual Abnormality (Behavioural): The value of hypnosis for the control of some forms of transvestism is being investigated at the Institute of Psychiatry. Further information can be obtained from Dr. F. Morgenstern.

Dangers of Hypnosis: In the *British Medical Journal* of February 13, 1960, there appeared a letter from Dr. A. A. Mason, asking doctors who had evidence from their own practice of patients

suffering harm, following hypnotic treatment by unqualified practitioners, to communicate the details to him at 24, Avenue Road,
Regents Park, London, N. W. 8.

LAWS

Stage demonstrations of hypnotism, designed primarily as entertainment, were by no means unknown in Britain before the
1939 war, but for the most part they excited only local interest.
After the war, the activities of two unusually accomplished show-
men brought this type of demonstration to the notice of a much
wider public.

One of these was Peter Casson. Although lacking either medical or psychological qualifications, he developed a serious interest in the subject while on active service, and became a most
accomplished operator, with a good theoretical background. His
abilities were recognized by some army psychiatrists, who appear
to have enlisted his assistance on a number of occasions in connection with the emergency treatment of cases of "battle neurosis." Immediately after the war he established a clinic for hypnotic treatment, working, at first, in close collaboration with a
London psychiatrist. The latter soon found it necessary to with-
draw from the arrangement, as statements issued by officers of
the BMA made it clear that associations of such a kind would be
regarded as unethical. He also offered his services freely to both
psychiatrists and psychologists who might wish to study hypnotic phenomena.

Casson also toured the British Isles giving demonstrations of
hypnotism on the stage. These were designed for purposes of
entertainment rather than instruction. He achieved a great deal
of publicity by arranging for complicated demonstrations of post-
hypnotic phenomena. Subjects who responded satisfactorily to
induction during a stage performance were given a post-hypnotic
suggestion to the effect that they would assemble together in
some public place the next day and there behave in some way
designed to invite attention. Most of these demonstrations were
highly successful, and many were widely reported.

The other major figure was Ralph Slater, a stateless alien of
Russian birth. Like Casson, he campaigned vigorously for a

greater use of hypnotism for purposes of therapy, while at the same time building up a career on the stage. By 1951, he was playing to packed audiences in the London Coliseum, where it was not unusual for nearly two thousand people to witness his demonstrations each night, while as many as forty volunteers made their way to the stage every time he appealed for subjects.

During the course of one of his demonstrations in 1950 an incident occurred whose delayed effects probably helped to ensure the passage into law of the "Hypnotism Act" of 1952. Diana Rains-Bath, aged twenty-three, having been hypnotized with a number of other subjects as part of a stage demonstration, showed signs of emerging from her trance prematurely. Slater performed some manipulation which involved pushing her head forward on to her chest, while at the same time commanding her to remain "asleep." It seems possible that he was performing the rather dangerous 'carotid' manipulation which is sometimes used when an abbreviated induction is required. This suggestion, however, is entirely a guess on the part of the present writer, and no clear evidence is available which could support the assertion. He then suggested that she would feel like a baby, becoming frightened and crying for her mother, presumably to demonstrate that she was still hypnotized. These suggestions were accepted. Some ten days after taking part in this demonstration the subject began having periods of severe depression, during which she also felt frightened. She was compelled to seek treatment from Dr. van Pelt under whose care she remained for a period of some five months. As a result of this experience she sued Slater in the civil courts, claiming damages for assault and negligence. The case came to trial in March of 1952, and will receive further mention later in this account.

Previously, in August of 1949, the experience of Joyce Dovey, aged nineteen, had already received some publicity. She was hypnotized by Casson as part of a stage demonstration, and a post-hypnotic was given that she and others would fall asleep, at a dance to be held the following night, every time the tune "So Tired" was played. This suggestion was successful in the case of several subjects. Later in the evening Casson called together all

those who had been affected, and after re-hypnotizing them went
to considerable trouble to eliminate any possible after effects of
his suggestions. Unfortunately Dovey had already left the hall,
before this was done. At work next day she collapsed, and then
continued to have periods of trance and automatism for a further
twelve days. Her doctor contacted Casson, who had returned to
London, and he was able to terminate the attacks after re-hypnotizing Miss Dovey over the telephone.

In March of 1950, at about the time that he accepted Diana
Rains-Bath as a patient, and perhaps influenced by this case, Dr.
van Pelt approached the Minister of Health and asked for the
introduction of legislation banning the use of hypnosis except by
medical men. In July of the same year he again asserted that the
"real menace of hypnotism lies in its use by the medically unqualified" and called specifically for the banning of stage demonstrations. The National Industrial Safety Committee for the Prevention of Accidents also called for a ban on stage demonstrations,
on the grounds that those who took part in them as subjects
might subsequently develop a spontaneous trance while at work,
to the probable danger of themselves and their workmates. There
was however little evidence at that time of any real disquiet,
either on the part of the public in general, or the British Medical
Association in particular.

The early part of 1951 passed without incident, and Slater was
playing to capacity houses at the London Coliseum. In July the
British Journal of Medical Hypnotism again called for a ban on
non-medical hypnotists, but there seemed little prospect that any
action would be taken. In September, however, there were widely published reports of serious after-effects experienced by two
school girls, both aged fifteen, following their participation in a
stage demonstration given by a lay hypnotist by the name of
John Brendan. Both felt "queer" after the performance, and one
of them collapsed. Brendan was called and alleviated the immediate symptoms, but next day one of the girls again felt dizzy
at school, and immediately after she had remarked on this, the
other, who was present, experienced similar symptoms. Both
were then somnambulistic for a period of forty-five minutes, during which time attempts to revive them were unsuccessful. On

learning of the incident, Brendan immediately visited the school, and awakened both.

In October the press gave prominence to the experience of another sixteen year old girl who developed about one hundred and fifty trances during the month following her participation in a demonstration given by Barrington, another hypnotist. This girl eventually had to enter a hospital, but there was no real improvement in her condition until Barrington himself was allowed to re-hypnotize her. In November there were headlined reports that two other girls who had also taken part in Barrington's performances had experienced similar after-effects. One of these had to enter a hospital.

These cases aroused a degree of public anxiety, particularly as several of those affected were still at school. In November, 1951, Dr. Barnett Stross, a medically qualified Member of Parliament who had himself had experience as an amateur hypnotist, asked the Minister of Health to investigate the cases which had been reported. In December, a further question from the same M. P. elicited the reply that one of the girls affected was still in the hospital. It was stated that the Government had no power to prohibit stage performances, and that it would probably be difficult to define hypnosis, legally, for the purposes of any Act of Parliament. It was agreed, however, that the Home Secretary should be consulted to see if anything could be done.

Matters then developed rapidly, although not at first with the official backing of the Government. A Bill proposing to forbid the use of hypnosis for purposes of public entertainment was put before the House of Commons by Dr. Somerville Hastings, and received its first reading before the end of the year. This Bill was introduced under arrangements which make it possible for a limited number of M.P.'s to propose legislation concerning matters of their own choosing, and which do not form part of the programme to which the Government itself is committed. The first reading of a Bill is little more than a formal notice that the House is prepared to give a matter serious consideration, and at this stage it still seemed probable that no legislation would result.

In February of 1952, a further case was reported in which a young woman collapsed at her work-bench eighteen hours after having taken part in a stage performance with a hypnotist by the name of Clark. She had to enter hospital for psychiatric treatment, and medical opinion was that, although the hypnosis was certainly not the sole cause of her condition, it might have contributed to it. Later in the month Mr. E. W. Short, M.P. asked the Minister of Health to investigate this case and to report on it. At about the same time the Variety Artists Federation, and the Theatrical Manager's Association, decided to take joint action to fight Dr. Hasting's proposals.

In March, the case of Rains-Bath versus Ralph Slater, to which reference has already been made, was sent for trial before jury. At about the same time it was revealed that two of the girls who had experienced spontaneous trances following Barrington's demonstrations were still far from well, and that this was also true of the two school-girls who had taken part in Brendan's performance. A number of Local Government Authorities decided at about this time that they would introduce measures to prohibit stage demonstrations of hypnosis in public halls which came under their jurisdiction, whatever the eventual fate of the Parliamentary Bill, which had just received its second reading, and therefore stood a reasonable chance of eventually becoming Law.

In the action against Slater, the jury awarded damages of one thousand pounds on the issue of negligence. They decided that the manipulation of the plaintiff's head, designed to re-establish trance, constituted an assault, and an additional twenty-five pounds were awarded on this count. There were also one hundred and seven pounds of special damages. Slater immediately announced his intention to appeal, and the results of the case stimulated a great deal of further controversy.

In June, Dr. Hasting's Bill was modified. As initially introduced, it sought to ban all public exhibitions of hypnotism for purposes of entertainment, throughout Britain. In its revised form it empowered each Local Government Authority to regulate, or ban, performances in its own area. A clause was also added, making it an offence for any person to use as a subject for the purpose of public entertainment, any person not having attained the age of twenty-one years. The Bill received the Royal Assent in August of the same year, under the name of the Hypnotism Act, 1952.

It is only fair to add that when Slater's appeal was heard in July, the verdict on the issue of negligence was quashed, and a retrial ordered. The damages for assault, and the special damages were, however, confirmed. The grounds for the judgment were that the judge had not properly put the case to the jury, as to whether Slater had implanted something of a frightening nature in the mind of his subject, and then failed to remove it. It was held that this issue was central to the question of negligence, and that the jury had not properly been instructed on this point. After some month's of indecision, the plaintiff decided not to initiate fresh proceedings.

It is of some interest that one of the three young women who experienced spontaneous trances after being hypnotized by Barrington had volunteered, and served as a subject, during three successive performances, while another later served as a subject for a different local hypnotist, in spite of her unpleasant experience, and then joined Barrington's act, being presented as "the trance girl." It also transpired that Clark's subject had previously developed a spontaneous trance after participating in one of Casson's performances. This hypnotist was called in, and after terminating the condition had urged her most strongly never again to participate in further demonstrations.

The full text of the Hypnotism Act is set out in this chapter. It will be noted that it is concerned only with public demonstrations for the purpose of entertainment, and that it makes no attempt to confine the practice of hypnosis to those with medical qualifications. It also specifically excludes from its provisions, exhibitions, demonstrations, or performances which are given for scientific or research purposes, or for the treatment of mental or physical disease. Auto-hypnosis, and other self-induced conditions of the same kind are also excluded.

Most Local Government Authorities at first used their new powers mainly to control the character of performances given for purposes of entertainment. In September of 1954, for example, permission for public performances was given at Margate, after the operator had promised not to stick pins in his subjects! With the passage of time, however, total prohibition was increasingly enforced. In September of 1959, Peter Casson was still playing to full houses in the large holiday resort of Newquay. It seems likely that this was the last place in the British Isles where such performances could be given, and by 1961 the ban was in operation there also.

The first prosecution under the Act took place in Northampton, in April of 1954. A lecture on hypnotism was given by a Mr. D. T. Watson, who addressed a meeting of the International Friendship League, and demonstrated some of the phenomena, using a young journalist (who was however over twenty-one years of age) as his subject. Permission to give the demonstration had not been sought from the Local Authority, as it did not take place in a hall licensed for purposes of public entertainment. Giving a demonstration designed as an entertainment, other than in such a hall, is specifically forbidden by the Act, so that the main point at issue, when the case was tried by local magistrates, was as to whether a serious lecture and demonstration, given before a private group, could reasonably be regarded as a public entertainment. The magistrates had no difficulty in deciding that it could not, and the case was dismissed.

The text of the Hypnotism Act of 1952 is reproduced below by kind permission of Her Majesty's Stationery Office, which owns the copyright. For this permission the author makes grateful acknowledgment.

HYPNOTISM ACT, 1952

An Act to regulate the demonstration of hypnotic phenomena for purposes of public entertainment.

(1 August, 1952)

Be it enacted by the Queen's most Excellent Majesty, by and with the advice and consent of the Lords Spiritual and Temporal, and Commons, in this present Parliament assembled, and by the authority of the same, as follows:—

    1.—(1) Where under any enactment an authority in any area have power to grant licences for the regulation of places kept or ordinarily used for public dancing, singing, music, or other public entertainment of the like kind, any power conferred by any enactment to attach conditions to any such licence shall include power to attach conditions regulating or prohibiting the giving of an exhibition, demonstration or performance of hypnotism on any person at the place to which the licence relates.

(2) In the application of this section to Scotland, for the reference to places kept or ordinarily used for public dancing, singing, music or other public entertainment of the like kind there shall be substituted a reference to theatres or other places of public amusement or public entertainment.

2.—(1) No person shall give an exhibition, demonstration or performance of hypnotism on any living person at or in connection with an entertainment to which the public are admitted, whether on payment or otherwise, at any place in relation to which such a license as is mentioned in section one of this Act is not in force unless the controlling authority have authorised that exhibition, demonstration or performance.

(2) Any authorisation under this section may be made subject to any conditions.

(3) If a person gives any exhibition, demonstration or performance of hypnotism in contravention of this section, or in contravention of any conditions attached to an authorisation under this section, he shall be liable on summary conviction to a fine of not exceeding fifty pounds.

(4) In this section, the expression 'controlling authority' means—

(a) in relation to a place in any such area as is mentioned in section one of this Act, the authority having power to grant licences of the kind mentioned in that section in that area;

(b) in relation to a place in any other area in England, the council of the county borough, borough, or urban or rural district where the place is, and in relation to a place in any other area in Scotland, the council of the county or burgh where the place is.

3. A person who gives an exhibition, demonstration or performance of hypnotism on a person who has not attained the age of twenty-one years at or in connection with an entertainment to which the public are admitted, whether on payment or otherwise, shall, unless he had reasonable cause to believe that that person had attained that age, be liable on summary conviction to a fine not exceeding fifty pounds.

4. Any police constable may enter any premises where any entertainment is held if he has reasonable cause to believe that any act is being or may be done in contravention of this Act.

5. Nothing in this Act shall prevent the exhibition, demonstration or performance of hypnotism (otherwise than at or in connection with an entertainment) for scientific or research purposes or for the treatment of mental or physical disease.

6. In this Act, except where the context otherwise requires it, the following expression shall have the meaning hereby assigned to it, that is to say:—

'hypnotism' includes hypnotism, mesmerism and any similar act or process which produces or is intended to produce in any person any form of induced sleep or trance in which the susceptibility of the mind of that person to suggestion or direction is increased or intended to be increased but does not include hypnotism, mesmerism or any such similar act or process which is self-induced.

7.—(1) This Act may be cited as the Hypnotism Act, 1952.

(2) This Act shall not extend to Northern Ireland.

(3) This Act shall come into force on the first day of April, nineteen hundred and fifty-three.

Additional Considerations (a)—Societies

The British Society of Medical Hypnotists: (President: Dr. S. J. van Pelt, M.B., B.S., F.R.S.M. Communications to: The Secretary, 126 Harley St., London, W. 1.) Of the several societies now extant, which cater for those with a special interest in hypnotism, the British Society of Medical Hypnotists is the oldest. It was established on March 22, 1948, by Dr. S. J. van Pelt. When it came into existence the activities of stage hypnotists, and other lay-practitioners, were receiving considerable publicity in the press, and it seemed to Dr. van Pelt that there was need for an organization which would promote the study and use of hypnotism in medicine, rescue the subject from the atmosphere of sensationalism with which it was surrounded, and campaign for the introduction of legislation to regulate the use of the technique. His personal view is that hypnosis should be used only by those with medical qualifications, and all the British members of the Society are fully qualified medical men who are also members of the British Medical Association.

Members have to sign an undertaking declaring that they will do their best to further the cause of hypnotism in medicine, and that they will not bring the Society into disrepute in any way by means of undesirable publicity, etc. There are fifty British members and approximately ninety in other countries.

The Society's activities include the making of instructional films, and the giving of lectures. Of major importance is the publication of the *British Journal of Medical Hypnotism*, which is the only British journal devoted entirely to work on hypnosis. This is published quarterly, and is available only on subscription. The editorial offices are at 4 Victoria Terrace, Hove 3, Sussex, England.

The Society for Medical and Dental Hypnosis: (President: Dr. J. A. Hadfield, M.A., M.B., Ch.B. Communications to: The Secretary, 91 Booth Road, London, N.W.9.) The first step in the evolution of this Society occurred in March of 1952, when a Wimpole Street dentist, Mr. E. Wookey, announced in various medical and dental publications that he was trying to form a group of dentists within the British Dental Association, to study the use of hypnosis in dentistry. The outcome of this initiative was that the

British Society of Dental Hypnotists came into existence in February of 1953.

An increasing number of medical practitioners were soon applying for admission to the Society, as they wished to attend the courses of instruction in the use of hypnosis, which it organized. These applications were accepted, and the proportion of doctors within the group rose so rapidly that a medical section was formed in April of 1955, when the Society changed its name to the Dental and Medical Society for the Study of Hypnosis.

In May of 1961, the former Hypnotherapy Group amalgamated with the Society, which then changed its name yet again, to the Society for Medical and Dental Hypnosis.

The organization's prospectus states that it was instituted for the study, advancement, and practice of hypnosis. The training of medical practitioners and dental surgeons to utilize the phenomena of hypnosis to the best advantage is considered of the greatest importance, and a study course has been designed to that end. This gives the beginner a basic understanding of hypnotic techniques, and of their applications. It includes individual tuition in technique.

Associate membership of the society is open to all medical practitioners and dental surgeons. There are nearly a thousand "full members,"—a status conferred only after the successful completion of a study-course. The Society is organized in four sections, which centre their activities on London, Manchester, Birmingham, and Glasgow.

In addition to the study-courses, meetings are arranged at which guest speakers talk on various aspects of hypnosis. A number of films, illustrating clinical applications of hypnosis, have been made by its members. There is no journal, but lectures by guest speakers are published in the Proceedings of the Society.

The Hypnotherapy Group: In the *British Medical Journal* for July 3 of 1954, appeared a letter signed by doctors and dental surgeons who were interested in "exploring the uses of hypnotism and hypnotherapy in all branches of medicine and surgery, with a view to obtaining an evaluation of the method by experts and practitioners in every relevant field." Readers who were interested in planning objective research, and discussing different methods and techniques, were invited to contact Dr. Gordon Ambrose, who was one of the signatories. A meeting was subsequently arranged, attended by seventy-nine doctors and students who had been interested in the letter, and the Hypnotherapy Group was formally inaugurated soon afterwards. The organization arranged lectures, discussions, and practical tuition, covering the induction of hypnosis and its clinical applications. About a hundred doctors attended courses, together with a few dental surgeons.

In 1961, the Group amalgamated with what is now the Society for Medical and Dental Hypnosis, and no longer functions as a separate organization.

The International Society for Clinical and Experimental Hypnosis (British National Division): (President: Dr. J. A. Hadfield, M.A., M.B., Ch.B. Communications to: The Secretary, 150 Harley Street, London W.1.) In 1958 the American Society for Clinical and Experimental Hypnosis became the American National Division of the International Society for Clinical and Experimental Hypnosis. At the same time preliminary arrangements were made for the eventual formation of National Divisions in many other countries. It was at one time envisaged that the Dental and Medical group might transform itself into the British Division of I.S.C.E.H. It would have been necessary for it to amend its constitution, however, so as to admit university-qualified psychologists to membership. After some debate it decided against this step, and in 1960 the British Division of the International body came into existence as a separate organization. Its first president was a distinguished psychiatrist, the late Professor Alexander Kennedy, and most of its members belonged also to the DMSSH.

The British National Division does not publish its own journal, but all members are entitled to receive the *International Journal of Clinical and Experimental Hypnosis.*

The British Society of Hypnotherapists: (President: Mr. T. G. Warne-Beresford. Communications to: The Secretary, 142 Harley St., London, W. 1.) The writer's intention in compiling this list of societies has been to make available, to those unfamiliar with British organizations, information which will help them to judge the status, bona fides, and intentions, of the various societies whose names come to their attention. It has therefore seemed entirely reasonable to include the British Society of Hypnotherapists among those which are considered. The writer would like to make it clear, however, that he has no personal knowledge of either the membership or the activities of this Society.

It was founded in 1955 by Mr. T. G. Warne-Beresford, whose object was to establish a body of trained hypnotherapists, who should be subject to ethical rules. Admission does not depend on the possession of formal qualifications, such as in medicine or psychology, but Mr. Warne-Beresford says that he was himself "an assistant Canadian Railway surgeon in Saskatchewan." All members must pass an examination, set by the Society, and must pledge themselves to abide by a number of rules, among which is one imposing the obligation to assure themselves, "before treating or offering to treat a patient, that he has been examined by his doctor, and that the condition from which he suffers has been diagnosed medically as a nervous condition." Courses of instruction are organized, each lasting about a year, during which prospective members receive "about two hundred hours of instruction in practical hypnotherapy."

The Society's examination is described as including papers in anatomy, biology, physiology, neurology, pathology, and a practical examination in hypnotherapy. Mr. Warne-Beresford has kindly made available a set of papers used for the 1962 examination. The easiest of the questions asked seem to assume a standard of knowledge similar to that required of candidates taking Advanced Level examinations in Zoology for the General Certificate of Education, which is usually attempted by grammar-school pupils of about eighteen years of age. The most difficult are at about the standard expected at the end of the first year of medical education in a British university. Occasionally, the wording appears to be somewhat bizarre ("what conditions would you expect from tension of the following nerves . . ."). So far as the present writer is concerned, their relevance to the practice of hypnotherapy is not always obvious, and they are certainly not adequate for establishing that a candidate has an adequate background in either normal or abnormal psychology. It is only fair to point out, however, that precisely the same criticisms could be made of the examinations leading to a first degree in medicine. No information is available about the syllabus covered by the course of instruction in practical hypnotherapy, or about the practical examination.

The Medical Hypnosis Association: (President: Dr. A. P. Magonet, B.Sc., M.D., F.R.S.M. Communications to: The Secretary, 10 Harley St., London W. 1.) This organization is quite different in function from those mentioned above. Its main object is to provide a service to doctors, who may wish to arrange a consultation with a hypnotist for one of their patients, but who require guidance in the selection of a specialist of this kind, or who may wish to know whether a suitable person can be found in some specified area. In furtherance of this objective the Association maintains a register of all properly qualified practitioners who are known to use hypnosis. It also collects as much information as it can about activities involving the use of hypnosis, even if these are carried out by people who are not regarded as being properly qualified.

The Association has no "members," in the usual sense of the word, nor does it organize lectures, study-courses, or meetings. The secretary is always glad to receive information from doctors who have started to practice hypnosis, and can sometimes make information available to doctors who are visiting Britain.

Additional Considerations (b)—National Health Service

General practitioners working within the National Health Service are free to use any form of treatment, including hypnosis. A general practitioner may refer a patient to a consultant who uses hypnosis, provided that the consultant also works within the Service. He is of course free to refer to *any* consultant, but those outside the Service will naturally charge the patient their normal fee. The number of Health Service consultants using hypnosis is small, and there is some evidence that this has provided the motivation for many general practitioners to learn the technique for themselves.

A practitioner may sometimes wish to call in a second doctor to assist him. If this second practitioner wishes to charge a fee for this service it must be paid in the first instance by the doctor who asked for his assistance. The latter may then recover the fee from the Service, but may under some circumstances be required to justify his claim. In 1957, a claim was submitted to cover the attendance of a second practitioner to give hypnotic anaesthesia while a patient's own doctor sutured the perineum after delivery. If a conventional anaesthetic had been used, the claim would have been met without question, but in this instance the Minister of Health referred the matter to a committee of the British Medical Association, which advises him on such matters. It was then agreed that the fee could properly be claimed in such cases, provided the doctor providing the service was accustomed to use hypnosis normally as part of his practice. This decision was influenced by the fact that the Anaesthetist Group within the BMA had previously decided that hypnotic anaesthesia induced by a medical practitioner could properly be classified as an anaesthetic.

Dentists within the Service frequently wish to call in a medical practitioner to administer a general anaesthetic. The ruling described in the previous paragraph suggests that if such a practitioner were to use hypnotic anaesthesia, then his fee could legitimately be claimed. However, a statement made by the Dental Estimates Board in 1959 made it clear that matters of principle have still to be settled, which might influence the extent to which dentists claiming fees from the Service can use hypnosis. The Board stated that it was prepared, in exceptional circumstances, to consider estimates involving the use of hypnotism, but that at present, decisions must not be regarded as creating precedents. It seems likely that there are points of difficulty in connection with the fact that the use of hypnotic techniques may involve several consultations, during each of which an attempt to achieve a satisfactory induction results in failure. Under such circumstances it would presumably be difficult for the dentist to succeed in his claim for a fee to cover these consultations, unless he could show that the advantages of hypnotic anaesthesia to the patient provided a sufficient justification for the additional expense.

FUTURE

It can be forecast with reasonable confidence that the medical and dental professions will continue to display a keen interest in hypnotism for some years to come. The subject has achieved a certain official status, the specialized societies have a large and increasing membership, and research into the therapeutic applications of the technique is being conducted with a high degree of competence by investigators of reputation and authority. There is already a fairly strong feeling that for women who are at least moderately susceptible to induction techniques, hypnotic training may be better than any other form of preparation for childbirth. It is also fairly safe to forecast that the technique will be accepted as affording the best method of symptom control in a proportion of asthma cases.

Members of the general public have a more realistic appreciation of the subject than ever before. In 1950, the only information available to large sections of the community was that which could be gleaned from the activities of stage hypnotists. In 1962, television programmes have brought reliable information to the majority of households.

All these developments are encouraging, and their influence is unlikely to be nullified in the immediate future. However, our increasing ability to make effective use of hypnotic techniques results to only a very small degree from advances in our knowledge of the fundamental nature of the hypnotic state. Techniques which are not properly understood tend to be at the mercy of fashion, and suffer periodic eclipse. If the mechanism of a cure is unknown it is sometimes difficult to counter the criticism that the cure may be producing effects which are less desirable than the disease, and there will always be a hard core of responsible and able men who refuse to use a procedure which cannot properly be explained. It is therefore very important that investigations into the nature of hypnotic processes, as opposed to the use which can be made of them, should be given a high priority.

There must be no illusion about the length of time that will be needed before a reasonably adequate "theory of hypnosis" can be established. Moreover, in the long run, only a multidisciplinary approach is likely to be adequate. There must be an intensive study of the workings of the endo-reticular system in the brain-stem, which will involve the combined efforts of psychologists and neuro-surgeons. We need to know much more about the way in which apperception can be modified by such factors as motivation, desire, and imagination, both with and without hypnosis. This will require the co-operation of experimental psychologists, who must also attempt to understand hypnotic behaviour in terms of learning theory and conditioning. Again, our ability to seek the right kind of explanation for hypnotic phenomena must depend on an accurate knowledge of just what these phenomena are. We do not have this knowledge at present, in spite of more than a hundred years of experience with the technique. Unambiguous evidence is available in respect of only a very few of the wide range of effects which have at one time or another been claimed. Here, too, both the clinician and the psychologist have a great deal of work to do.

Not only must representatives of many disciplines each make their own separate contribution, but they must also work in the closest possible association with one another. At the present time, many investigations involve a tragic waste of opportunity, and those who organize them do not realize that their value might often be enormously increased, at the cost of little additional effort. This fact is brought home to the experimental psychologist whenever he reads of investigations by medical practitioners in which no attempt has been made to partial out some of the psychological variables whose effects are already known to be important, such as suggestibility, personality factors, intelligence, and so on. Workers within other disciplines must undoubtedly have occasion to bewail lost opportunities of a similar kind, in the work which is carried out by psychologists.

At the moment, there is no strong pressure from any quarter for further legislation to control the use of hypnotism. This is not to say that everyone is satisfied with the present position, but suggestions for further control would certainly not receive the support of public opinion at present, and without this they would be unlikely to succeed. Even the control of stage hypnotism was not easily achieved, and it is generally believed that if Dr. Somerville Hasting's Bill had been put before parliament in its original form, at the time of its third and crucial reading, it would not have become law. The next objective of those who would like to see control extended is probably to promote legislation forbidding those without medical qualifications to use hypnosis for purposes of therapy. In framing legislation of this kind, arriving at a practicable definition of hypnotism would certainly pose difficulties. For the purposes of the Hypnotism Act, a rough and ready specification seems to have served well enough. So far as therapy is concerned, however, those with experience of the subject will recognize that there are innumerable ways in which a formal trance induction can be dispensed with. Any attempt to define the hypnotic state in a fashion so broad as to include all its possible variants could easily lead to a state of affairs where faith healing, training in the practice of Yoga, Christian Science, and the advertising of patent medicines would all involve transgressions of the law.

Although further legislation seems unlikely in the immediate future, debate about the desirability of different kinds of control will undoubtedly continue, both inside and outside the medical profession. No rational conclusions can be possible until reliable evidence has been collected about the nature of the dangers which may attend the use of hypnotic techniques, and the frequency with which they are likely to be encountered. It is possible, for example, that an ill-advised hypnosis may activate a latent psychosis in a few unfortunate subjects. If this is true, then any hypnotist whose training does not equip him to detect prepsychotic conditions must run a certain risk. Refusal to accept this risk, however, would make it necessary to forbid the use of hypnotic techniques to all dentists, and to most general practitioners. But there is ample evidence that these two professional groups can use the technique to the great benefit of innumerable patients, and it is obviously necessary to balance the possible harm against the demonstrated good, as is indeed the case with all forms of therapy.

It is not only in therapy that this problem arises. It is sometimes asserted that even an innocent-seeming experiment with a hypnotized subject may occasionally precipitate a condition which calls for immediate psychiatric attention. If this is true, then experimental psychologists working in this field, and their subjects, also run risks. To avoid them, it might be suggested that only specialists in psychological medicine should be allowed to conduct experiments involving the use of hypnotism. However, the study of the fundamental nature of hypnosis, as opposed to its therapeutic applications, ceased long ago to be a branch of psychopathology. Specialists in psychological medicine receive training which equips them to diagnose and treat the wide range of psychiatric abnormalities. Very few have more than a nodding acquaintance with experimental psychology, or research techniques. This method of avoiding the risk, if it exists, would thus hit certain kinds of research activity very badly. Here again, an estimate of its magnitude is obviously a necessary antecedent of any rational decision. Until opinion is replaced by knowledge, on this and many related questions, there will be much sterile controversy, and many prejudices will be able to masquerade as carefully considered opinions. There is just as much need for effective research on questions of these kinds as there is for a continuation of investigations into the therapeutic value of hypnotism.

Many lines of argument therefore converge to support the view that more and more research is needed into every aspect of hypnotism: a subject which many psychologists feel is among the most complex, and the most potentially rewarding of all those which engage their attention. This research must be organized after the fashion of a prolonged siege of a difficult position, rather than as a series of skirmishes, and it must be in every sense a combined operation. Unfortunately, there are few indications that appropriate facilities will be available in Britain in the immediate future. The research foundations normally take the view that their function is to accept the risk involved in opening up a new field, but that once the value of a particular kind of study has been established it should be continued under the auspices of institutions which can offer more permanent support. In the present context, only the universities might in theory fill this role. In practice, however, it is very unlikely that they will be able to do so. For example, there is probably no university department of psychology in Britain at the moment where the departmental head is able to earmark part of his limited resources for the use of an investigating team made up of members of his permanent staff. Even should the desire be present, it is very difficult to free lecturers from teaching duties to the extent necessary to make a fruitful investigation possible. What seems to be needed is an organization having some of the characteristics of the Institute for Research in Hypnosis in the USA, and nothing of this kind exists.

There are of course problems other than research. The hypnotist and his subject stand in a relationship which demands an unusual degree of responsibility from the former, and of trust from the latter. Such a relationship should be guarded by an appropriate code of ethics. Hypnotists all have their own personal standards, which are usually adequate for the protection of their subjects. However, the medical and dental professions have a code which can effectively be enforced. It is a punishable offence, falsely to claim membership of these groups, and they have themselves accepted the responsibility for maintaining proper standards. It is very much to be hoped that this will soon be true of psychology also. At the moment, anyone can claim to be a psychologist, and even one who is properly qualified is controlled to only a limited degree by the code of his professional society, and of the organization within which he works. There does at last seem to be a real possibility that this rather unsatisfactory position will be improved in the not too distant future. Co-operation between the several disciplines which must inevitably be concerned with the study of hypnosis will then be very much easier than it is at present.

Another problem is that of training. Little is being done to implement those sections of the BMA's 1955 report which recommended instruction about hypnosis for medical undergraduates, and even graduates specializing in psychological medicine normally find it difficult to obtain an adequate education in this field. Practical training, in particular, is exceptionally difficult to acquire. The position is a little better for psychologists, so far as theory is concerned, but practical instruction is a problem for this group also. We already know enough to suggest that hypnotism may be the treatment of choice for some patients with some disorders, and it is regrettable that so many must be denied its benefits until the problem of education has been solved.

There is perhaps some danger that contributors to a volume such as this may slip into a role more suitable to proponents of a new world religion. They are of course surveyors of only a little corner of scientific and medical activity. Nevertheless, hypnotism is a study of peculiar interest. It is concerned with a subject almost impossible to define, and with effects which sometimes seem almost magical. It can help one man, but not another. It has potential uses in almost every field of human activity and yet can be applied reliably to hardly any. It promises to provide a research tool of quite exceptional power, and yet attempts to use it may sometimes involve extraordinary complications. It engenders in one a ridiculous enthusiasm, and in another an irrational distaste, while those who might use it the most effectively are often completely indifferent to its possibilities.

The hypnotized subject manifests behaviour at least as complex as that of a normal individual, and the theoretical framework needed to explain it will certainly be no less intricate than that needed to explain normal behaviour. It is in this that the challenge of the subject lies. Hypnosis will never properly be understood until people are understood, and it seems reasonable to believe that achieving this understanding will keep a lot of people very busy for a very long time!

IMPORTANT REFERENCES

Eysenck, H. J.: *Dimensions of Personality.* London, Kegan Paul, 1947.

Heron, W. T.: Hypnosis as a factor in the production and detection of crime. *Brit. J. Med. Hypnot.,* Spring, 1952.

Neustatter, W. L.: *Psychological Disorder and Crime.* London, Johnson, 1953.

Radzinowicz and Turner: *Mental Abnormality and Crime.* London, MacMillan, 1944.

Weatherhead, L. D.: *Psychology in Service of the Soul* (2nd ed.). London, Epworth Press, 1938.

HYPNOSIS IN HUNGARY

By

Francis A. Völgyesi, M.D.

*(Autobiographical data may be found in the
body of this chapter)*

RECENT PAST AND PRESENT

THE TURN of the twentieth century saw the beginning of an enthusiastic interest in Hungary in hypnotism (mesmerism) and in
medical hypnosis. Aristocrats (Counts Szápáry and Mailáth) and
laymen both became interested in hypnotic phenomena. Amateurs performed on the stage, at parties, and at the same time
physicians such as Z. Sebök (Head Surgeon of the Budapest Voluntary Ambulance Association), P. Ranschburg (neurologist),
G. Décsi, M.D., etc., used hypnosis extensively. Their ideas involved animal and medical magnetism. In the course of time
hypnosis based on science and neurophysiology became clearly
distinguishable from such occult phenomena as telepathy and
spiritism. With this development, applications confined to strictly medical ends began. In this way scientific hypnosis became
a clear demarcation between psycho-organic facts on the one
hand and superstitious mystical beliefs on the other. Such progress has not been easy.

The Neukom-Salamon case and its consequences were at the
time (1895) famous all over the world. Neukom, a well known
well-digger in southern Hungary, and still better known as an
amateur hypnotist, had read many technical books on hypnosis.
His practice included many patients who came from afar, for his
work with hypnosis had been unusually successful. His method
of induction was to put a silver spoon in the patient's hand and to
have the light from a candle reflected from it. The patient was to
fixate his gaze upon the sparkling light and then sleep was sug-

gested. However later even this procedure proved to be unnecessary, for the pre-hypnotic suggestive milieu about Neukom was so powerful that it was sufficient for him to merely extend his hand toward an open window, whereupon all patients, waiting outside, would fall into a deep somnambulistic trance which would last for many hours. It happened that while Neukom was a guest in Count Forgách's castle where his fame had attracted a number of medical officers and private physicians (from the neighbourhood and from Vienna) who wished to check on his results, he performed the following experiment on one Ella Salamon. She was twenty-two years of age and a relative of the Count. Her complaints involved the symptoms of tuberculosis and for this she had been under Neukom's care for some years. Symptomatic curative results, to this time, had been encouraging. On this occasion he employed a deep state of trance and suggested, for purposes of experimentation, that she put herself in the place of her relative (N.J.) in a far distant village and tell him what she felt. This relative was, at the time, suffering from cavernous tuberculosis accompanied by hemorrhages. When Salamon received this suggestion she winced but did not answer. Neukom further increased the depth of the hypnotic state and repeated the question. Eventually the girl collapsed and could not be resuscitated. The autopsy indicated, and the criminal court decided, that the girl "had not died of hypnosis." Neukom was subsequently acquitted but as a consequence of this incident a decree was issued and in 1895 Hungary became the first country to adopt legal provisions whereby "only professional physicians are permitted to apply hypnosis for therapeutic purposes and only in the presence of a third person." This regulation is no longer rigidly enforced in Hungary today.

James Braid, in his publications of 1842 and 1843 had been first to give the field a decidedly neurophysiological interpretation. He was also the first to introduce the term hypnotism in the technical literature of the day. His followers in France were E. Azam, A. A. Liebault (1823-1904), H. Bernheim (1837-1919) who initiated the first clinical school of hypnosis in Nancy, and J. M. Charcot (1825-1893) who initiated a school in Paris. Under the direct influence of these individuals were H. Laufenauer, E. Moravesik, K. Schaffer, E. Högyes, J. Donát, E. Jendrassik, E. Frey, P. Ranschburg, K. Lechner, G. Décsi, J. Schuster, J. Göttler, L. Benedek, Z. Papp, B. Horányi, E. Nemes and F. A. Völgyesi. These men were engaged in intensive theoretical and experimental research in medical hypnosis in Hungary. These individuals, (professors and neurologists, etc.), had had competent scientific training and their writings were welcomed in international circles.

Up to the turn of the century medical hypnosis and verbal suggestion had been identified with psychotherapy in almost all of the civilized world. Generally speaking indications for hypnotherapy or psychotherapy were confined to a narrow field, i.e., they were restricted to diseases regarded as purely functional such as the hysterias, neurasthenia and the psychic neuroses. Conservative clinicians held that it was only in such cases that hypnotherapy was ethically permissible. In the more severe cases, involving the psychoses, hypnotherapy was said to be definitely contraindicated. Whenever a neurologist, for example, applied hypnotherapy for serious organic ailments, certain circles would term such application as charlatanism and would vehemently criticize, by means of official disciplinary measures, the physician involved.

In evaluating the status of hypnosis at this time, it should be remembered that there was no uniform or adequate scientific definition of hypnosis, and that almost every specialist had his own meaning for the term. In addition it should be remembered that amateur hypnotists (in circuses, in fairs, on the stage, and at private parties) had seriously discredited hypnotism which still had its burden of mystical elements. It was also true that at this time Hungarian specialists, who had been enthusiastic about hypnotism as young men, acquired fame and high positions in universities and clinics, etc., and as a result, had practically abandoned hypnotherapy because it entailed the possibility of failures and criticism. It was also true at this time that frequently, in the course of hypnotherapy, hypochondriacs, hysterics, psychopaths, or paranoiacs would often harass the physicians and also that promoters would often find subjects for cabarets, etc., in the office of the physician using hypnosis.

As early as 1860, mesmerism (hypnotism) began to be characterized in the international literature by the appearance of many thorough reports. These at first had been written by Hungarian specialists who were in the forefront of this development, but subsequently there developed a serious lag in the progress and application of medical hypnosis. This was attributable in part not only to the aforementioned factors but also, and possibly more importantly, to the criticisms which came from two other quarters.

Some materialistic and mechanistic clinicians viewed hypnotism, as well as psychotherapy in general, with contempt. They considered them to be mystical and atavistic remainders of the past. In their reductionist monistic view they wished to eliminate the concept of psyche entirely for, according to their belief, the mind was nothing but the direct secretion of the brain, like bile from the liver or urine from the kidneys. They expected the radical cure of any disease to be by pharmaceutical means or by some material intervention. People at this time said that the sick in Vienna had two situations confronting them: they could be examined by the famous internist Skoda and then could be dissected by the equally famous anatomist Baron von Rokitansky! However the progress of civilization has convincingly shown that diagnosis and surgical intervention, no matter how precise and excellent, are just not sufficient. The doctor's personality, it is now realized, is one of "the most important drugs" in medicine. The psychical relation between physician and patient, i.e., the psychotherapeutical process was now seen in a new light. The patient was considered to be in as a great a need of psychical calming by the doctor as he was in need of mechanistic treatment for his somatic complaints.

Another criticism of hypnosis was levelled by representatives of ecclesiastical spiritual influences—the clergy and the "medici pastoral." These people have in fact largely surrendered their role to the modern secular physician who has been trained in a clinical and a psychotherapeutic setting. Despite this fact however, ever since the days of Father McNeil, who in 1842 labelled J. Braid as an agent of Satan, segments of the church have attacked hypnotherapy as well as psychotherapy in general—especially when these were aimed at clearing up sexual conflicts.

Beginning in 1895, such psychological concepts as the subconscious, catharsis, deep personality, etc., were expropriated by S.

Freud and his followers. These significant ideas were used in biased fashion by a large number of orthodox as well as neo-Freudians. Freud, together with Breuer, had abandoned hypnotism chiefly because of the fact that they had encountered failures in the course of their practice, and because "they had been unable to hypnotise everybody in the same way." In 1921, at a meeting on psychoanalysis in Budapest, Hungary, Freud stated that "if hypnosis is silver, then psychoanalysis is gold." In dogmatic and scholastic style, in which he ignored somatic etiological factors, he elaborated his pansexual theory which regarded all mental anomalies as neuroses which could be traced to the suppression and transformation of infantile libidinous conflicts. Based on this theory Freud developed his method of treating the "deep personality" by means of free association. His technique, he said, was a passive one which resulted in the eliciting of catharsis.

At first Freud's teachings were regarded by progressive-minded young intellectuals as revolutionary—a trend for the future. Wasn't it wonderful, they in effect said, to grub freely in the subconscious in mental and sexual libidinous experiences which allegedly play such an important role in every manifestation of life. Wasn't it also wonderful to tear open, with a freely rambling imagination, the mental wounds that had been inflicted by a forgotten past and as well to interpret dreams in such a myriad of ways. Characterizing the instincts as being atavistic, hostile, warring, and unalterable, they were considered as being decidedly effective in behaviour. The psychoanalytic school of thought attempted to trace all social anomalies to the Oedipus, Coriolanus, or similar libidinous conflicts. They kept asserting that the universal remedy for these evils was psychoanalysis. All this was very pleasing to the youth and to the belletrists for it was in conflict with the clergy and was popular, not only among doctors but among thousands of amateur psychoanalysts.

The professional psychoanalysts, e.g., Ferenczi, Adler, Jung, and Alexander, Feldmann, Szalai, Herrmann, Gartner, Farkásh-azy, Szinetár in Hungary took an uncompromising stand against hypnosis and called it pseudo-scientific. Neo-Freudians, as well as orthodox Freudians, all over the world, launched a vigorous, overt, propaganda campaign against medical hypnotism. They proclaimed, for example, that hypnosis "was able to achieve only temporary symptomatic curative results, and this only with some hysterics." To achieve really causal and therefore permanent recovery, in cases of psychic ailments was, according to their view, possible only through psychoanalysis.

By the turn of the century, psychoanalysts had drawn the attention of the civilized world to the psychotherapy of mental ailments (and this fact might be considered its only true merit) for by now the concepts of the subconscious and the deep personality had become popular. However their false teachings, which were harmful were propagated in the widest of circles. These teachings eventually came to a deadlock, but had in the meantime infected large portions of the English, Hungarian, and German-speaking scientific world. This is not to suggest that certain psychoanalysts, by means of their individualized procedure, did not achieve some beneficial results with some neurotics when their treatment was applied with unending patience. However, it is a well-known fact that the thousand-year-old psychocatharsis of the Roman Catholic Church (confession and communion) have also frequently brought abatement of symptoms. It is a known fact, in professional circles, that the term neurosis (improperly and wrongfully expropriated by Freud) had been used as a fundamental concept by others before him. P. Joire and later I. P. Pavlov, for example, had used this very term with much more scientific precision. No one challenges the importance of such concepts as: deep personality, libido, conflict, etc., nor is the fact denied that the abreaction of stress is important. Objection essentially is to the meanings that may be attached to these terms, i.e., there should not only be the interpretations that Freudians had monopolistically given to them.

My report would be incomplete were I not to mention other harmful side effects that were entailed in psychoanalysis and were rather widespread. These factors may also be important in the lag which medical hypnosis encountered in Hungary. I refer here to its effect on pedagogy which harmed society. Restriction and control of children were not countenanced, sex instruction by example was belittled and a rise in juvenile crime occurred. There was in general a failure in child education and this was especially noticeable in the western world.

In 1910, as a grammar school student, I started experimenting with hypnosis, being influenced at this time by the tricks performed in circuses and fairs. I succeeded in putting a young girl into a deep hypnotic sleep, such that neither I nor other doctors who were called were able to awaken her. Eventually Dr. Sebök, in the presence of two other physicians, succeeded in doing this by means of passes, intensive skin stimulation and suggestion. As a university student I commenced the scientific study of hypnosis, now being influenced by the writings of A. Forel and V. M. Bechterev. I was surprised by the sequence of successes which surpassed all my expectations. In 1912 I was among the founding members of the Ujpest-Rakospalota Voluntary Ambulance Association where I was able to find the time and opportunity for systematic investigation with the help of my young colleagues. In this capacity I encountered many patients to whom first aid had to be given and minor operations performed—all with hypnosis as the analgesic. However in the "wave-trough" of interest in medical hypnosis which started in 1912 and has lasted to the present day, few clinics or hospitals were open to me and whatever progress I made in theory or application was autodidactic and gleaned from the compilation of data obtained from my private practice.

The outbreak of war in 1914 took many of the doctors to the front. Due to the shortage at home, I had to replace many doctors who had previously practiced in various hospitals. At this time I was resident assistant in the Anatomical Institute of the University of Budapest. Whenever possible I employed "vigil-hypnosis" (light hypnosis of short duration) applied to groups. Such a procedure proved quicker and more effective than the use of a narcotic or an injection. Later, still more patients and greater opportunity presented itself to me after I enlisted for the front. This was true both at the aid posts in the front lines and behind the fronts. As a result of my experience I was again made only too painfully aware of the following facts: (1) how little was being taught about hypnosis at the Universities, (2) that what was being taught was generally biased or incorrect, (3) that much mystical superstitious prejudice was shown toward scientific hypnosis in general and medical hypnosis in particular, (4) that despite all this the practical beneficial facts about hypnotherapy were accumulating rapidly (extractions of teeth, operations, painless child-birth, etc.).

As a result I became increasingly convinced that a serious mistake had been made in the evaluation of hypnotism. The Academy of Science in Paris had denounced Mesmer and mesmerism in their entirety and were not willing to deal with the problem at all. Possibly the fluidistic or animal magnetistic theory of mesmerism was wrong and imagination did play a significant role. It was not, however, considered necessary to study how and why imagination resulted in the undeniable cures that occurred. Thus it happened, in many parts of the world, including Hungary, that so-called impartial experts only too easily disposed of and belittled the immense importance of hypnosuggestive hypnotherapy.

Meanwhile events outdid expectations, for patients who were being treated by hypnosis for minor nervous ailments reported, most thankfully, that simultaneous with their treatment, chronic symptoms of organic illnesses, purulent tuberculotic abscesses on their legs, gastric and intestinal ulcers, heart and respiratory complaints, sciatica, stubborn wet eczema, hypertension, etc., disappeared. It would seem that organic ailments as well as mental ailments were *de facto* cured by the use of hypnosis.

I soon became aware of the pressing need for greater specificity in terminology; such as prognosis, nosology, and especially concerning hypnotic techniques, for I am unaware of any two specialists who would be able to give definitions of wakefulness and sleep that would be acceptable to the other (but the facts of wakefulness and sleep exist nonetheless). With hypnosis the case is the same. Wakefulness, hypnosis, and sleep, can only be appreciated scientifically in their close interrelationships. All three phenomena play an important role in man's life from birth to death. In connection with hypnosis no one is fully able to give adequate explanation as to why its manifestations are so varied, or as to why there is so much individual difference in susceptibility. This individual variation seems to be largely dependent on the person to be hypnotised, his innate individual characteristics, his neurotypological constellation and the professional skill of the hypnotist. With regard to typology I have been developing, since 1918, my "psychoactive-psychopassive neurotypological constellation complex." This theory has stood the test of time, and as a result of it, I am now able to predict more accurately the susceptibility of the patient, and to integrate such knowledge with the diagnosis. Consequently I am able to develop a dependable "fiasco-free" technique for medical hypnosis. This theory also has the advantage of indicating to me when contraindications exist.

Specialists, who utilize hypnosis enthusiastically and systematically, were believed to be living in "another world" by those whose only knowledge of hypnotic phenomena had been obtained from second-hand sources or from amateur demonstrations. Realistically I was only too aware, that while investigation of hypnotic problems was worthwhile, I would have to face a fight with medical opinion. So I entered the fight which was not without danger to me personally. My program was to: specialize in hypnosis, rid hypnosis of mysticism, define basic terms, develop adequate techniques, and point out indications and contraindications in hypnotherapy. To do this I at first carried on many kinds of experiments and these included work with mediums, etc. My findings were both positive and negative. However by 1940 I decided to respect the clear dividing line which existed between occultism, on the one hand, and hypnotism with its scientific foundation, on the other. I have, consequently, abandoned the "swampy" territory of mysticism and concentrated all my activities on medical hypnosis and psychotherapy.

Prosperity in the medical profession, as well as the central geographical location of Budapest, made it possible for me to obtain and study both ancient and modern literature on hypnosis in the east and in the west. At the same time I also compiled, from my own practice, as a defense against criticism, a large number of clinical cases, with their anamnesis, where recovery was achieved by means of the use of hypnosis. Exposed to a barrage of personal attacks and criticisms, the large number of my hypnotically improved or cured cases has always been my ultimate defense.

These cases I had been collecting with great élan, ever since my days as a medical student and later during the war.

In 1917, I had been resident surgeon and radiologist at the Budapest Central Hospital of the State Asylum for Children, and at the same time, had been working in other hospitals. I was now under the direction of experienced specialists and was able to continue my use of hypnosis in connection with urological etc. operations and treatments. Around this time I entered private practice as a neurologist, and surgeon of the Courts of Justice, but before long was at the Roumanian and Russian fronts. Here, as head surgeon, I was able to work with larger groups and consequently could apply hypnosis more freely. Some time later I was transferred to the war theatre of the Hungarian Soviet Republic, now in the capacity of Commander and Head Surgeon of a division. Together with Dr. I. Fekete, my assistant and pupil, we treated and operated on hundreds of the wounded and sick, using hypnotic analgesia. Our patients were both military and civilian, for it often happened that, at the request of other physicians, I assisted at births (behind the lines), applying hypnotic analgesia.

A great "leap forward" occurred when a number of daily papers in 1920 carried long articles about my successful results with hypnotherapy with cases of serious organic disease. As a consequence of this my consulting hours ran from morning until 11 P.M. I was treating on the average about eighty to 100 patients per day. Three secretaries daily listed the names of at least twenty new patients, who desired consultations, which required a wait of three months. My successes had been publicized in foreign papers as well, and professors and doctors sent many patients from abroad. In addition, many individuals came who wished to evaluate my practice and study my technique. They keep doing so today.

My first book *Place and Application of Hypnosis in Modern Therapy,* was published in Hungarian in 1920, and my first long treatise on hypnotherapy was published in the periodical *Therapy.* In my book I described 3,800 cases of serious organic disease which were remarkably successful in their outcome when hypnosis had been used. Notwithstanding the devastation caused by wars, revolutions, counter-revolutions, and the siege of Budapest,

I had succeeded in preserving many documents, e.g., those concerned with etiology, letters of recommendation from doctors, correspondence, medical certificates, etc. My records, which have been kept since 1918 to the present, contain 61,500 cases treated by hypnosis and psychotherapy.

My consultations took place at maximum speed, in a sportsmanlike manner (it was the only way for my wife and me to endure overwork) however in all this I observed the strictest adherence to ethical and professional conduct. Where I achieved remarkable hypnotherapeutic success in patients suffering from serious organic disease, I reported these to the medical associations. In making these reports I encountered bitter personal and scientific attack on the part of colleagues who held different views, belonged to another school of thought, i.e., were imbued with different clinical ideas. But I entered the fight and fought tirelessly. I had not been put to the stake to be burned, but for twelve years my books had been! It was the large number of my cured or improved patients that supported me in my fight. In 1920, the chief medical officer (E. Csordás) in Budapest ordered me, in an official decree, to discontinue my hypnotic consultations. The daily papers carried an article saying "the hypnotist-doctor has been put to sleep!" At noon, on the same day as the prohibition, Dr. Agoston Benárd, Minister of Public Welfare and Health, called on me during my consulting hours. As a surgeon he had himself used hypnosis and had studied the techniques that I myself used. He interviewed patients that were present in my office. Meanwhile, three hundred of my former patients, who had been cured or improved, demonstrated in front of the Prime Minister's office and demanded repeal of the ban against me. They were filmed for the weekly newsreel. Dr. Benárd, who had the highest jurisdiction in these matters, authorized me to inscribe on my door the fact that I was permitted to carry on consultations. The newspapers now reported that "the hypnotist-doctor has been awakened."

At the beginning of my hypnotic practice I realised that progress in psychotherapy could not be based on the practice of the Freudians or neo-Freudians. It had to be based on the rules of hypnosuggestive insight, and active reeducation. Again, in opposition to Freudian practice, it required close *cooperation* with other significant somatotherapeutical (pharmaceutical, etc.) procedures. This is to say there must be cooperation with the family, with the laboratory, with the doctor, and possibly with consultants. I had come to realise that the expensive, passive, free association technique of psychoanalysis did not in any way meet the requirements of our time. This was especially true when it was carried out by individuals who did not possess the requisite diploma, or had in effect only been trained in short analytical courses, and were really amateurs. Psychotherapy, no matter what kind, like the surgeon's scalpel, requires skill and a sense of responsibility. Notwithstanding the adverse opinion of critical scholars, the well-organized psychoanalytic movement became quite popular in the press and in the literature of the day.

Whenever possible I travelled abroad and visited places where it was possible to study other hypnosuggestive practices. At Munich, I visited the clinic of Professor Isserlin at Dresden, W. Brown at Oxford and that of J. H. Schultz, M.D., etc. I was glad to see the systematic application of hypnosis at these Institutes. At Lourdes my observations were reported in one of the Hungarian Medical Journals as well as in my book *Hypnotherapy in Cases of Organic and Mental Disease* (1924). At this place undeniable cures occurred as a result of the hypnosuggestive atmosphere. In the summer of 1923, I sailed around Europe and wrote my book, *Soul and Natural Science—Miracle or Natural Law.*

The following year I was a guest of Emil Coué at Nancy. In the years following World War I, Coué's popular method of simplified autosuggestive training, (couéism) was hotly debated, and I considered the procedure well worth investigating. The truth was that Coué had called public attention to certain empirical facts, and had really pioneered. He had been responsible for the founding of the "Association for Applied Psychology" and the "Second Nancy School of Hypnosis." On the basis of his simplified autosuggestive exercises he developed a group hypnosis psychotherapy at the Nancy Institute. I later arranged for the publication in Hungarian of Coué's book. Many people, all over the world, have experienced for themselves how it is often possible to ease or cure all kinds of physical or mental sufferings by systematically repeating Coué's autohypnotic and autosuggestive verbal prescriptions, e.g., "ça passe, ça passe, ça passe" "I feel better every day," "it does not hurt at all," "my will power is getting stronger every day," etc.

In the summer of 1926 I visited New York, Philadelphia, and Atlantic City, in the United States. Here I studied, among other things, the forced tapering-off cures for alcoholism at Welfare Island, New York, and some of my papers on the psychotherapy of alcoholism, and other organic illnesses, were published in medical periodicals of the U.S.A. In the same year I was married and my wife took over as my assistant secretary. She has been my irreplaceable associate without interruption except for some difficulties such as wars, revolutions, counter-revolutions, and the birth of three children. She herself has written several books, one of these dealt with animal hypnosis (*The London Zoo*, written with Julian Huxley). She is now preparing a book entitled *Psychology of the Waiting Room*.

As a former anatomist I have always been interested in morphological (neuro-anatomical and neuro-biological) definitions of hypnotism. This interest had in fact, led me to develop the aforementioned neurotypology. It was partly due to experiences with such neurotypological constellations (relating as previously indicated to hypnotisaability) that led me to make a detailed study of cerebral-circulatory conditions and the state of the cerebral spinal fluid in hypnosis. In my 1920 book I devoted a special chapter to these findings, according to which (and in contradiction to opinions prevailing at that time) it is not only the special cerebral blood circulation, but also the cerebral lymphatic circulatory conditions that play an important role in providing the metabolism of cerebral cells and in regulating all changes occurring in the waking, the hypnotic, or the sleep state. In sleep, and partly in hypnosis too, excitation and inhibition alternating in the nerve cells are regulated by the blood vessels. In hypnosis and sleep when cortical excitation processes are partly concentrated and inhibition is being irradiated simultaneously, the regenerative processes of the nerve cells are ensured by the cerebral spinal fluid. On the basis of these findings I have set up my (figuratively named) *partial, reversible, vasomotor decerebration theory of hypnosis.*

Ever since 1926, the morphological illustrations provided by V. M. Bechterev and I. P. Pavlov's (hypnosis) experiments on animals have indicated that, in my fight against psychoanalysis and mechanistic interpretations of hypnosis, I had been proceeding in the right direction. I realised from the very beginning (relatively few shared my views until the 1950's) that I. P. Pavlov's discoveries and teachings, based on his rigorously conducted analytic and synthetic experiments, were destined radically to modify all views that were then held on hypnosis, psychology, psychiatry, psychotherapy, medicine and anthropology. This was due in good part to his findings connected with hypnosis, internal inhibition and sleep. No one before or since has produced such a mass of data, based on scientific explanation, and related to the medical importance of hypnosis, as I. P. Pavlov.

Early in 1935, I corresponded with Pavlov who invited me to read a paper at the Fifteenth International Congress of Physiology, which was being held both in Leningrad and in Moscow in honor of his 85th birthday. The world's leading physiologists who attended this event were addressed by Professor G. Barger of Edinburgh. The paper I presented at this meeting was entitled Beeinflussung der vegetativen reflexe und der sogenannten autonomen organfunktionen durch hypnosetherapie (Influencing vegetative reflexes and so called autonomous functions of organs through hypnotherapy, *Sechenov Journal of Psychology of the U.S.S.R.*, 1936, 21, No. 5-6, or see *Proceedings of the Fifteenth International Physiological Congress* Leningrad-Moscow, August 9-16, 1935, State Biological and Medical Press, also see F. A. Volgyesi, Pavlov and Hypnotism, *Journal of Physiology of the U.S.S.R.*, 1938, 24, No. 5.) In my paper I showed morphological illustrations which demonstrated on the basis of my anatomical and physiological data how one is able to exert a decisive influence on vasamotor, trophic, endocrine, humoral, vegetative, and visceral regulators. Then through the influence on these regulators one might affect almost all normal and pathological phenomena of life. This may occur not only through direct (mechanical, chemical or electrical) unconditioned stimuli but also through the spoken word, i.e., by conditioned verbal stimuli of the secondary signal system. It may also occur through the neocortex, by means of reasoning and persuasion and in the case of certain ailments by means of verbal hypnosuggestions, i.e., by a temporal avoidance of the supreme intellectual sphere—the "psychic barrier." It is thus possible to exert a separate influence on the functions of discrete organs and to a certain extent on the entire personality (these ideas had been previously published, see: Die seelische konstitution und die indikationen der psychotherapie ((Mental constitution and indications for psychotherapy)). *Zentralblatt für Psychotherapie und Grenzgebiete*, 1934, 8, No. 3, Hirzel Publishers, Leipzig. An article on the same topic may also be seen in the *Zentralblatt für psychotherapie*, Vol. VIII, No. I. This paper was entitled Psychische gradualitat und progressive cerebration ((Psychic graduality and progressive cerebration)). Reference may also be made to my book *Human and Animal Hypnosis with Special Regard to the Phylogenesis and Ontogenesis of the Brain* ((Budapest 1937 in Hungarian; Zurich 1938 in German)).).

My experiences were in complete accord with Pavlov's basic theses that the conditioned reflex theory showed the way to exact experimentation with internal organs and with all higher nervous activities in both animal and man. Medical hypnosis also provides experimental and therapeutical opportunities of investigating such phenomena both in normal and pathological behaviour. I could not comprehend why it was that Pavlov, who had been awarded the Nobel Prize in 1904 for his work on the salivary response, was so seldom mentioned in the medical literature in this country and in the west during the years 1910-1920. Even when mention was made of him the more significant findings about hypnosis that he had published were not discussed until the 1950's. Ever since the beginning of his research work Pavlov had been actively interested in hypnosis. During his travels, as a young man, he had studied hypnosis both at Ludwig's and at Heilenhain's Institutes. Later on he repeatedly mentioned that to clarify the complications arising in animal experimentation, he and his associates had to conduct experiments on internal inhibition in sleep and in hypnosis. Since 1930, I have regarded myself as an enthusiastic disciple of Pavlov and his associates.

At Diestoie Selo, where Pavlov and those attending the Fifteenth Physiological Congress were gathered, I had a personal encounter with Pavlov. Someone tapped my shoulder with a stick from behind, turning around I saw short, laughing Pavlov with his entourage. "Are you the Vengerski doctor?" he asked me in his Russian-tinted German and invited me to have a vodka with him in celebration of his "death anniversary." It was then explained to me that *Révai's Great Encylopedia* (Budapest 1927) and several major western encyclopedias described him as being born in 1849 and dying in 1916. "Since then," he said, "I have celebrated my death anniversary every year." A little later he pointed to two groups of scientists saying, "Look, these are people who know what hypnosis is all about and like to engage in it, and there you see those who are against hypnosis." The former group was headed by K. M. Bikov, and K. Maria Petrova, while the leader of the latter group was Orbelli.

The possibilities that may be realised from hypnosuggestive rules which are in accord with individual neurotypological constellations are so immense that persons who are not familiar with them are unable to comprehend or even believe in them. Thus it happens that some specialists, excellent in their own fields, often display an emotionally tinted, or even aggressive attitude toward therapeutical facts present in the field of hypnotherapy. However the majority of unprejudiced medical experts (surgeons, internists, gynecologists, pediatricians, dentists, etc.) are by no means reluctant to apply the benefits of medical hypnosis even in cases of obvious organic disease. It is incomprehensible why it is that so many physician-psychologists, psychiatrists and psychotherapists are reluctant to extend the benefits of hypnosis to their patients. As a consequence of the idealistic (purely physical or psychological) mechanistic (purely physiological) controversy, there has been a temporary decline in the use of hypnotherapy all over the world and this is still being keenly felt in Hungary.

Additional books published after 1920 included: *A Message to the Neurotic World; The So-called Mysteries of Hypnosis; Man's Soul, Woman's Soul,—the Yung-Yin Principle in Nature; The*

Soul is All—From Superstitious Healing Methods to Modern Hypnotherapy; Psychosomatic Psychotherapy; Active-complex Psychotherapy and the School for Patients Movement; Medical Hypnosis; I. P. Pavlov and Hypnosis, and the Technique for Psychic Influencibility; etc. These books were published in Hungarian (Tudományos Könyvkiado, Medicina, etc.), in English (Hutchinson, London), in German (Orell-Füssli, Switzerland) in Germany (West, Hippokrates; East, Volk und Gesundheit) in French (Vigot Frères), in Spanish (Franklin, Louis de Caral), etc. I am at present editorial staff member of *Acta Psychotherapeutica* (Basel-New York), *Journal Nervopatologii i Psichiatrii,* Imenji S. Korsakova (Moscow); *Journal of British medical hypnotism* (London); member of Hungarian Association of Neurologists and Psychiatrists; corresponding member (since 1949) of the British Royal Medico-Psychological Association; founding member of the International Association for Psychotherapy; and Honorary Member of the German Psychotherapeutic Medical Association; etc. The development of hypnotherapy, the establishment of its appropriate place and application in the therapy of the future, is by no means simple. Development in this field, at present, is far from complete although there are many signs of international progress.

The coming of a full renaissance of hypnotherapy may be attributed to many factors, some of which are of recent origin. These are; technical and scientific progress, increasing social responsibilities, stressors burdening the nervous system as never before, the rise of living standards, and the appreciation of psycho-organic interrelations. These factors have all greatly accelerated the demand, all over the world, for adequate medical treatment on the psychic side by means of hypnosuggestion—when the latter is indicated. I believe that I have provided, via my neurotypological theory, an almost complete protection for the physician against the possibility of failure. This makes it possible for him to meet the exacting requirements involved in treating a large number of patients, in a relatively short time, without hospitalization, and inexpensively.

Suggestion itself is not a "phantasmagoria" nor is it an influence of "transient superficial effect" but rather it is essentially a neurohumoral influencing technique which, while it is corticovisceral, possibly avoids the intellectual area, i.e., the human neo-cortical centre. It has, as a conditioned response, certain structural and organic consequences.

It is wrong to suppose that the depth of hypnosis determines its effectiveness. Frequently, in my practice, light hypnosis (vigil-hypnosis) is perfectly adequate for achieving satisfactory recoveries. Moreover, extremely psychopassive and hypersuggestible individuals should only be lightly hypnotized. The following constitutes a simple but useful "trick of the trade," which is especially suitable for cases of highly psychoactive persons. After calming the patient, the hypnotic technique need not be started with unnecessary and lengthy preparatory explanations, but with the resolute statement "I am certainly *not* going to hypnotize you today. I am just preparing for treatment." In this way "the wind is taken out of the sails" of possible critical opposition.

In the case of the psychoactive neurotype, preference is to be given to the method of intellectual insight and autogenic psychagogic training, whereas with psychopassive individuals, systematic vigil-hypnosis techniques are to be preferred. The patient, in either case, should be strengthened both physically and psychologically and all deficiencies of a psychosomatic nature remedied by means of direct hypnosuggestion. When in the course of therapy the patient becomes independent, further safeguards for permanent recovery should be placed in his and his family's hands. Consequently, in order to ensure a permanent recovery and resocialization, the practitioner of medical hypnosis has of necessity to mobilize a number of additional forces. The criticism advanced by Freudians and neo-Freudians, that hypnosis results in an irrational regression to a lower animal level is completely erroneous. Insofar as man's brain is different from that of the animal, so too is his waking, hypnotic and sleep state. Even an oligophrenic idiot is not irrational in a regressive sense, but is merely different from other humans. His characteristics are those of a sick human and inasmuch as the characteristics are of a human nature they vary qualitatively from even the highest animal. In its first phase it is true that hypnosis is characterized by partial irradiation of the protective inhibitions of the cortex, but it could only be classified as a partial regression if sleep itself, with its extensive cortical protective inhibitions, were to be classified as a regressive phenomenon. In short, sleep and hypnosis are neuro-biological processes whose character and purpose are entirely different from regression.

In his valuable book on *Pavlov-Freud* (New York, International Publishers, 1959-60) H. K. Wells states, on the basis of detailed analysis, that the whole structure of Freudian psychology and psychopathology rests on irrational speculations, while Pavlov's teachings, based on rigorous scientific experimentation, represent a cortico-anatomical biological psychology. It is in this sense that the fight against mental and physical disease are the targets of modern psychosomatic practice. This is also true of medical hypnosis (an aspect of psychosomatic medicine) which, when embedded in an *active complex psychotherapy,* provides an effective means of realisation. The word *active* is used because it is diametrically opposite to the Freudian and neo-Freudian deep psychotherapy which is lengthy, expensive, oneirocritcal and passive in nature. It is *complex* because its therapy is embedded in the entire armament of Gesamtmedizin, and as previously indicated it cooperates with all other specialties. This is in contrast with the basic procedure of most Freudian and neo-Freudian schools.

In obstetrics it is a serious error to say that psychoprophylaxis is needed only to ensure delivery free of fear and pain. Psychoprophylaxis is needed after as well as during delivery in a preventative sense. Deaths occurring during narcosis, administered for any reason, are frequently psychic deaths in which incorrectly autosuggested phobic mechanisms may play an important role. Furthermore in the use of hypnosis as an anaesthetic a considerable amount of the drug might not be needed if the anaesthetist were to pay more attention to the possibility of utilizing hypnosuggestion.

In my book *Medical Hypnosis* (1962) I have devoted many chapters to the wide variety of hypnotic techniques required, if one is to avoid failure, due to the different neurotypological constellations of different individuals. I have dealt with the phenomena of the "moist hand" which in itself reveals (at the first shake) that we have to deal with an individual who is not only hypersensitive, labile vegetatively, but also one who is extreme-

ly psychopassive. By means of the "faradic hand" it is relatively
easy to calm quickly extremely psychoactive individuals (or individuals who are refractory for other reasons) on whom it is impossible to apply hypnosuggestion. The method of the "faradic
hand" is more than a suggestive aid. The repeated slight faradi-
sation of certain cervical and other nerve endings may have soothing and curative effects on the patient. I should like to mention
that, for decades, I too was of the belief that we might content
ourselves with only verbal-suggestive influences from the field of
hypnosis. However knowledge acquired about the varied character and extreme energy of recently discovered radiations war-
rant the view that the time has come for a posthumous rehabilitation of certain of Mesmer's ideas.

The modern era of a renaissance of neo-animal magnetism has
begun. Invisible, complex, and intense radiation energies (Hertz,
Roentgen, cosmic, etc.,) act above us, about us, within us, and
through us. Today it is possible to tap currents not only through
EKG or EEG, but in normal and pathological electrical and magnetic flows connected with life phenomena in the stomach, intes-
tines, internal organs, retina of the eye, etc. All these may easily
be amplified and demonstrated. Certain animals, (bats, fish, but-
terflies, etc.,) are provided with intricate biological communication
systems (via; radar, ultraviolet waves, infrared waves, ultra-
sonic frequencies, scent stimuli, etc.) whose complexities are at
present being investigated by scientists. Even now it appears that
such systems are decidedly superior, both quantitatively and qualitatively, to man's normal physiological abilities and organs of
this nature. The human neo-cortex has created devices which
have made possible astonishing results such as space ships, com-
puters, etc. It has been known for a long time that there exists a
number of "special" phenomena which have been scientifically
classed under the term hypnotism. During the last century we
have come to know a number of facts and have availed ourselves
of the opportunities they provided for science. Yet these facts
were not so long ago belittled or denied by exact scientists. They
were considered to be the speculative product of a superstitious
imagination. Without abandoning rigorous scientific technique
and without regarding hypnosis as a regressive dynamism (in the

psychoanalytic sense) it must be pointed out that scientists have been guilty of neglecting the very branch of science which has produced so many achievements, made possible by hypnosis.

Spirit and soul have to this day connoted something immaterial and transcendental, i.e., things independent of the body in a dualistic sense, something "unearthly, from beyond." Hence both concepts are philosophically ambiguous. Originally these have been antithetical to matter or nature. Science, however, has advanced enough to say that these concepts, i.e., soul and spirit, can be scientifically defined—allowing at the same time for the preternatural. Both terms, according to science, should be purified of all mystical, magical and theurgical remainders and tied to the cortex and neo-cortex. It does not alter the case that Ranson and Penfield as well as others have, over the last three decades, contributed valuable information on the cooperative functions of the hypothalamus and the visceral subcortical brain which also regulates consciousness (see article by G. Jefferson, Die anatomie des bewusstseins, Triangel-Sandoz, 1961, 5, 96-100).

At present, especially in western scientific literature, it is considered "scientific" to attack Pavlov's cortex-domination principle on the basis of recent information concerning subcortical nerve organizations. There is also said to be encouragement for the supporters of the Freudian principle of unconscious domination in morphological conceptions. It was against this obsolete and incorrect view that F. V. Bassin, Soviet academician, has written his latest book *Consciousness and the so-called subconsciousness* (Philosophical Institute, the Academy of Moscow, 1962). The cortex-activating rule of the reticular formation, the centrencephalon (integrating system) and the diencephalon in their decisive regulation of vital functions admit of no doubt. This however confirms rather than refutes Pavlov's teachings on cortex-domination. The same may be said about my own thesis, according to which conscious vigilant activities, developed on the basis of neuro-humoral regulations are impossible without the human neo-cortex.

Man's neo-cortex has even now created *cybernetical brain models* which, as calculating and translating machines, have already far surpassed, in certain respects, the performance of the human brain—their "creator." As a result of development in work (production, transportation, communication, etc.) and in social conditions, the "good old family doctor" has yielded to his well-trained successor the "social doctor." This latter individual meets present-day requirements. We can no longer content ourselves with medical work confined to the four walls of surgery, excellent though it may be. In this sense I developed the "School for Patients Movement" which provides for the close cooperation of nurse, doctor, psychologist, family, school, place of work, and the social environment. They are all important in the prevention, treatment and post-treatment of disease.

In his lecture to the Hungarian Academy of Science in Budapest (1962), Hans Selye, the Hungarian-born scientist now residing in Montreal Canada, mentioned that the stimulus for his highly important endocrinological research had been provided by an observation he had made in his youth. He had observed that the most varied, specific and aspecific etiopathogenetic factors (injuries, physical and psychical traumas, conflicts, stressors, intoxicants, etc.) are able to produce a phenomenon-ensemble, which he termed the "general disease syndrome." As an antonym to Selye's definition, I have chosen the term "general health syndrome" for a group of phenomena which usually emerge from adequate hypnosuggestions. It is possible in a large number of cases to retune the patient psychically (Gesamtumstimnung) and physically (Gesamtumstellung). Thus the patient who has just conveyed to one the overall impression of being a psychologically depressed and a physically wrecked "sick man" will suddenly appear as a smiling hopeful person who seems to be healthy or at least on the road to recovery. In a relatively short time his whole personality structure has undergone a change for the better—he is literally getting younger. This is so in about 60-70 per cent of the cases treated by adequate medical hypnosis.

There are those who warn of possible dangers or complications in hypnotherapy. An important piece of counter-evidence to this (and also a great personal satisfaction) is the fact that, despite a record number of patients and treatments and despite the fact that I have been practising for over half a century, there has never been any substantial complaint against my use of hypnosis, (or any other medical treatment) made by a patient or member of his family. It is only possible for those who have systematically treated serious cases of depression, suicidal mania, neurotics, raving psychotics, etc., to appreciate this.

I have added to Pavlov's definition of higher nervous activity the concept of cortical representation and regulation implied in the close connections of wakefulness hypnosis and sleep. I have also emphasized the indispensible role of the specifically human neo-cortical nerve organization of the top hierarchical rungs of the "brain-ladder" which dominates man's life. This is in sharp contradiction to Freudian and neo-Freudian teachings which have recently endeavoured to prove (even admitting the close connections with subcortical centres) that it is the archaic instinctual life that dominates behaviour, both "downwards" in the vegetative system and "upwards" in neo-cortical-psychic relations.

Standards of medical training in Hungary have been high for decades. Ethical, critical and disciplinary safeguards have been very strict. Hypnotism is not tolerated for stage entertainment, for sensationalistic purposes, or in the practice of charlatans. These restrictions do not obviously apply to certified psychologists who may, as an extension of medical work, practice hypnosis scientifically and experimentally in the various institutes.

Among my pupils in Hungary, József Király, psychologist and György Danis, physician, have best identified themselves, both in theory and practice with my resolute uncompromising anti-Freudian stand based on Pavlov's teachings.

FUTURE

True, a considerable lag appears in the universities and in postgraduate medical training in both hypnosis and active psychotherapy in Hungary. However important bodies (ministries, universities, medical centres, etc.,) are now attempting to eliminate these shortcomings by means of special extension courses which endeavour to remove the discrepancy which favours somatotherapeutic rather than psychotherapeutic developments.

In 1962, at the Commemorative Czechoslovakian Purkinje Medical Congress, I presented a paper concerned with hypnotherapy at the symposium on "Experimental research in higher

nervous activity in man." During the same year my book on animal and human hypnosis was discussed at a symposium in Professor G. Klumbies' clinic (Friedrich Schiller University, Jena).
In this year there was also a congress on hypnosis convened by
the German Medical Psychotherapy Association. Its theme was
"Objektivierung Psychischer Befunde." At this Congress called
by D. Müller-Hegemann and H. K. Kleinsorge I discussed, in my
paper on hypnotherapy, organic disease and the role of the
human neo-cortex. I would predict rapidly improving theoretical
and practical prospects for "active-complex psychotherapy." I
would also predict that medical hypnosis will, in the future, be
used both widely and wisely. All this applies to Hungary proper,
but also, as encouraging signs indicate, to the international scene
as well. The future of that branch of science, concerned with the
phenomena and problems in the area of hypnosis and hypnotherapy, is promising.

HYPNOSIS IN INDIA

By

J. P. DAS, PH.D.

*Jagannath Prasad Das; born 1931; M.A. Patna University, India,
Ph.D. London University, England; Member, India Science Congress; Samaja (Society), Cuttack, S. Sahu, 1955,* Manasika Byadhi
*(Mental Illness), Cuttack, Mac Books, 1962, Conditioning and
hypnosis, J. exper. Psychol., 1958, 56, 110-113, Learning and recall under hypnosis and in the waking state, A.M.A. Arch. gen.
Psychiatry, 1961, 4, 517-521, etc.; present position, Reader in
psychology, Utkal University, Bhubaneswar, India.*

PAST

THE PAST is sometimes glorious while the present is relatively
eventless for many things, so too for hypnosis in India, where the
past is more important than the present. Hypnosis and like phenomena were not only known, but were systematically produced
in ancient India. These were often backed by intricate systems
of philosophy. The *Yoga* and the *Tantra* are the best known
examples of this. *Yoga* is relatively more philosophical whereas
Tantra is ritualistic.

YOGA

The original Yoga system is ascribed to Patanjali, a saint-philos-
opher. Many variations of this system are now available. But
here, attention is given only to Pantanjali's system and specifically
to those parts which deal with processes analogous to hypnosis.
The original Yoga system consisted of 195 mnemonic rules esti-
mated to have been written sometime between 300 A.D. and 500
A.D. It is divided into four parts, the first two being concentration and means of attaining concentration. These are of interest
to us and shall be described at some length.

Yoga by definition is a state closely resembling hypnosis be-
haviorally. It is a withdrawn state where all passions are checked
and the psychological reactions to both internal and external stimuli are absent. In this state, the "mind" ceases to fluctuate, but
nevertheless is quite alert and discriminating. Concentration, at
first, may be achieved through thinking about a single external or
internal object and then it may pass on to a still higher stage
where the object is no longer necessary. The person here does not
even make an effort to concentrate. This is called the shut-in state
(Niruddha).

How does one achieve concentration? In other words, how
does one make the mind retreat from external objects and turn
inwards? First, the person becomes disinterested in objects and
desires. This is then followed by an active search and rejecting
any passions or desires that may still be present as well as the
destroying of even their latent roots. Such detachment can only
come through continued practice.

Concentration or Samādhi is first conscious and then unconscious. Unconscious concentration is achieved by first concentrating on gross objects and later on some subtle element of the gross
objects. A typical illustration in skeletal form of the gradual process of concentration from the Yoga system is as follows:

Suppose a person is concentrating on an earthern jar ("ghata").
In the beginning he is conscious of the name "ghata," of the
sounds "gha-a-ta," of the characteristic shape of the jar and of
the meaning of "ghata." Gradually, with deeper concentration,
he becomes conscious of only the meaning of "ghata" devoid of
its name, sound, and shape. In a still deeper state of concentration or Samādhi, the person fails to discriminate between the jar
and himself. The object and the subject form an integrated
whole. He experiences a *feeling* of "oneness" with "earth" which
is the element of the earthern jar. Even here, however, the concentration is conscious, for it still has this feeling to concentrate
upon. It is comparable to visualizing a plant from its seed, for the
jar in its complete form may be reconstructed as long as this
feeling is present. Therefore it is called seeded (Sabija) Samādhi. However, when even this consciousness is blocked or in-

hibited, the highest possible state of Samādhi is reached. It is called seedless or unconscious (Nirbija) Samādhi.

Some physical and psychological factors are the enemies of Samādhi. These are: illness, low intelligence, hesitancy, doubt, indifference, and laziness. In addition, if the person is unhappy, frustrated or restless, he cannot achieve the required level of concentration. Mental agitation which is opposed to concentration is often produced by the emotional state accompanying joy, sorrow, virtue and vice. Even if a person does not experience these in himself, he may still be distracted by coming across instances of these in others. For example, happiness in others may arouse jealousy, this can, however, be eliminated by developing a friendly attitude towards the happy man. Pity for one in sorrow removes aggressive tendencies. Virtue in others can bring pleasure and thus eliminate envy and so on. By the above procedures the mind is purified and concentration then becomes possible.

With pure consciousness, the mind can concentrate on any sense organ and experience its specific sensation in a sublime fashion. For example, concentration on the tip of the nose can bring the experience of sublime smell; concentration on the tip of the tongue generates sublime gustatory sensation. In fact, from concentration on gross objects, the mind can move on to concentration on subtler and subtler objects. As a result of such specific concentration, the mind becomes stable at a point. This is also a method by which one can achieve higher stages in concentration. Apart from sensations, there are two other experiences which make Samādhi deep—concentration on some beautiful image seen in a dream and recall of the happiness of a deep sleep.

The seedless state of Samādhi may be theoretically puzzling. If in the ultimate state of Samādhi, even consciousness is blocked, and the mind cannot feel the presence or absence of anything, is it not dead? And if the mind is dead, it is not concentrating, for it will cease to exist. How then can the person break this insular state? How can he come back to normal life? The answer is that even in unconscious concentration, there are latent impressions of the mind—analogous to the retention by a piece of thread of characteristic shape even after it has been burnt. Such latent impressions are not objects of unconscious concentration; but are characteristics of a living person. When these latent impressions are revived, the mind descends from the state of seedless concentration by the same steps through which it (Nirbija Samādhi) was attained.

Aids to Yoga

There are eight aids to reach the supreme stage in Yoga. These are abstentions (Yama), observances (Niyama), postures (Āsana), regulation of breathing (Prānāyāma), withdrawal of the senses (Pratyāhara), fixed attention (Dhāranā), contemplation (Dhyāna) and concentration (Samādhi). Postures are different ways of maintaining the body; in such positions the person feels undisturbed by external changes. Perfection in postures comes with prolonged practice. Once a perfect posture is assumed, the person cannot discriminate between environmental changes such as heat and cold. Specific postures are recommended for contemplation, regulation of breathing, etc. Regulation of breath or Prānāyāma involves expiration, inspiration and the holding of breath. In each of these forms, normal breathing is suspended. When protracted these help the attainment of concentration (Samādhi). Fixed attention, contemplation and Samādhi are three direct aids to Yoga whereas the first five are indirect aids. How are these three direct aids related to each other? They are successive stages leading to a state of true and illuminating knowledge. How does one attain fixed attention? After eliminating anger, envy, etc., and filling the heart with friendship, appreciation, and other beneficial emotions, one has to practice various abstentions and observances. Later on, breathing is regulated, when one is in a certain fixed posture, and the person is no longer disturbed by conflicting thermal stimuli of heat and cold. The sense organs are now withdrawn from their specific objects and lose their activity. Then the mind, as it were, is brought to focus within a very limited region such as the tip of the nose. This way of holding the mind is Dhārāna or fixed attention. With further practice, the mind can be fixated for a long time without any fluctuation and one can experience a sense of union with the object of focus. This is called Dhyāna or contemplation. When contemplation becomes deep, the mind is lost in the object of concentration and is not conscious of its own identity. That is, the person does not even have the consciousness that he is concentrating and thus he attains the state of Nirbija Samādhi.

The true knowledge that follows the attainment of Samādhi is exceptional in the sense that it confers supernormal powers to the Yogi (i.e., the person practising Yoga), for knowledge is power. The ultimate aim however of Yoga is not to attain supernormal powers but to attain a state of pure consciousness in which matter is not represented. Such a state does not have any attributes; it exists by itself and does not register any change. This state is called Kaivalya or "onlyness." Those who have attained this state in their lifetime become free from any obligation to enter into the chains of birth and death after they forsake their body.

From the above account, it is apparent that concentration (Samādhi) and hypnosis have points of similarity and difference. Subjects under hypnosis may not be properly oriented to time and place. They are not bothered by relatively slight changes in the environment—although it is doubtful that one remains insensitive to changes in temperature without a specific suggestion to that effect. A person in hypnosis is surely not dissociated with regard to social and moral standards in general, for hypnotic suggestions, which threaten the ego break the trance and the individual wakes tense and anxious. Apparently in Samādhi, however, one can become completely dissociated from one's physical as well as psychological environment. Dissociation in the sense of loss of memory for the events during trance may be present in deep hypnosis, but if amnesia is not suggested loss of memory may be only partial. On the other hand, in Samādhi, it is said that the Yogi has a distinct memory of the joy and bliss he experiences and the Yogi likes to return to that state of blissful contemplation. Whether in hypnosis this is so may be debated. Persons who had experienced a deep trance, describe it as extremely pleasant (except when unpleasant suggestions had been given), and wish to have the experience again. It may well be, that in Samādhi, there are no *events* to forget, because it is a state of concentration without any object of concentration, and hence what the Yogi experiences is a general feeling of well-being, perhaps analogous to that following a deep dreamless sleep.

Positive and negative hallucinations can be produced in deep hypnosis. Similarly, in a somewhat higher state of concentration in Yoga, the stage in which mind has stopped fluctuating, sensory hallucinations may be produced. As it has been mentioned earlier, focusing the mind on the tongue can bring about sublime sensations of taste. But according to Yoga, sense organs are only gross objects and such concentration on sense organs is only one of the ways to deepen Samādhi. In hypnosis, too, positive and negative hallucinations facilitate the development of somnambulism. There appears to be some similarity between the means of attaining Samādhi and hypnosis. Postures and regulation of breathing are two indirect aids to Samādhi. There are many postures which the Yogi must practice, but ultimately he must choose one for use during concentration. Usually, this is the "lotus-posture" in which the right foot is placed on the left thigh and the left foot on the right thigh while the person sits erect. For hypnosis, the individual is asked either to sit in a relaxed manner or to lie down on his back. The purpose is to minimize movement and to maximize relaxation. Although the "lotus-posture" does not appear to be comfortable, it becomes so with practice and it definitely restricts movement. Probably it also prevents an easy development of sleep. In hypnosis deep breathing is often recommended and deep and regular breathing is taken as a superficial sign of trance. It involves relatively prolonged inspiration and expiration. In Samādhi, in addition to regulated inspiration and expiration, prolonged retention of breath is also prescribed. Breathing and its control occupy an important place in Samādhi.

TANTRA

Tantra has both a philosophy and a method of practice. For the philosophical basis of Tantra, a popular but authentic reference is Avlon's *Principles of Tantra* (1914). The ritualistic aspects of Tantra consist of mantras (incantations) for invoking Goddesses as well as specific rites for influencing or controlling any person of the worshipper's choice. These rites are of special interest to us. A person can be made restless, can be attracted, can be injured or obstructed by performing rites specific to each of these purposes.

However, the rites of Tantra do not appear to have any rational basis. This is in contrast to Yoga where the methods for achieving Samādhi, for example, are quite rational. A Tantric worshipper has to undergo rigorous training in order to obtain the necessary power over others. But nowhere in the study of Tantra does one find a rational basis for these rites. In order to clarify this point examples of two such rites are given below.

How to Attract

The Kamalakshi charm should be written on a bhurja leaf. The ink for writing this should be prepared from the blood of the second finger of the worshipper and should be blended with musk, and other sweet smelling substances like aguru and gorochana. Recite the charm "Om Shrim Kamalakhsi attract such and such person, hum, phat" a thousand times. Then tear this bhurja leaf into small pieces and smear them with mud from the feet of the to-be-attracted person and roll them into small balls and dry these balls in the sun. Build a figure of the to-be-attracted person (usually a woman) with three hot substances like red-pepper, pippali, and sunthi as ingredients. Put these balls in the stomach region of this statue. Then place this statue in a pot and let it face the direction in which the desired woman lives. This should be done at night and should be accompanied by the recitation of the Kamalakshi charms. If this is done properly the woman should present herself before the worshipper being impelled by sexual passion.

How to make a Person Restless

Bring some leaves from the neem tree (the leaves have a very bitter taste) and write the name of your enemy on the leaves using the feather of a crow as a pen and the dung of buffalo and horse as ink. Chant the charm "Om, obesiance to Kakatundi (a Goddess), etc." Then prepare a holy fire using a crow's nest on a neem tree as firewood. The fire that is used to ignite the crow's nest must have been brought from a funeral pyre and be fed by oil from human fat, etc. There are pots present which bear the names of the worshipper's enemies. When the ashes from the holy fire are put in a specific pot, the person to whom the pot has been assigned, experiences restlessness. During this ceremony, the Goddess to be meditated upon has the following description: She is of smoke colour, has three eyes and is very thin. She has a crescent on her forehead, her hair is knotted and she wears a tiger's skin. Her eyes are sunken, her teeth are terrible to look at and her belly is a hollow. There may be a sound philosophical basis for these rites, but they certainly appear weird and grotesque in the background of contemporary culture. Even so, many in India believe in Tantric phenomena and they are often publicized by newspapers. There are recognized Tantric worshippers in many parts of India and they are consulted when someone is attacked by an illness whose cause cannot be readily traced. For example, if a child for no apparent reason cries most of the time or has a sudden attack of diarrhea, many villagers would call in a Tantric worshipper. He is most successful in curing traumatic neurosis.

The elaborate procedure adopted by the Tantric worshipper has much the same effect as that produced by hypnotic suggestion.

ESDAILE'S WORK

India accidentally became the working place for one of the pioneers in hypnosis—James Esdaile. He used hypnosis for surgical anaesthesia, and performed a number of varied operations. He found a number of filaria patients at and around Calcutta needing leg amputations, and operations for hydroceles. It is reported that the British government in India was initially pleased with his work and permitted him to establish a Mesmeric hospital. But his enemies tried to disgrace him. He left India in 1851, and was barred from practice by the British Medical Society. He thus was a follower of Mesmer not only in an academic sense. The unjust and ungrateful treatment he received high-lighted the fact that his views, as those of Mesmer, did not suit the spirit of the times.

PRESENT

With a rich past, it should be expected that psychologists, psychiatrists, and the medical profession would be actively concerned with hypnosis. This is not so. In each of the above fields, the West is followed closely. Consequently innovations which occur in these fields originate in the West and take time to reach India. The wide use of hypnosis in the fields mentioned above is recent, and has not yet been introduced into the corresponding fields in India with the possible exception of psychology.

ATTITUDES

Medical

There is no indication that hypnosis has gained a foothold in medical research or practice. The All India Institute of Medical Sciences at Delhi seems to have only one Indian reference on hypnosis; it is by Anand, Chhina, Mears, and Singh on EEG activity under hypnotism published in January, 1961, in the *Indian Journal of Physiology and Pharmacology*. Likewise, in the field of psychiatry, only a few use hypnosis professionally. Some of them are attached to the All India Institute of Mental Health at Bangalore.

Dental

Hardly any researcher or practitioner is concerned with the application of hypnosis in dentistry. The All India Dental Association at Bombay publishes a standard journal and reference to this reveals only that articles on hypnosis written by foreign authorities are occasionally reproduced in this journal. Hypnosis "is rarely taught in any of our Dental Colleges and is very seldom practiced in our country" (personal communication, Editor of the *Dental Journal*).

Legal

No outstanding legal cases concerning hypnosis seem to exist. Consequently the existence of specific laws with regard to the undesirable use of hypnosis is not generally known to lawyers.

Psychological

In Indian Universities, the theoretical aspect of hypnosis is included in the courses of study for psychology, but special instruction in hypnosis is not available. Universities and Medical Schools are not averse to the study and practice of hypnosis. In fact, there is hardly any opinion either in favour of or against the use of hypnosis. This is also true of the attitude of the general public with regard to hypnosis.

Additional Considerations—Learning

Practicing psychologists sometimes use hypnosis as a psychotherapeutic method, but seldom report their findings in the standard journals. As for research by psychologists in hypnosis, the present author appears to be the only one (an unenviable position!) who has published work in this field. The areas of research being investigated are: eyelid conditioning and hypnosis, learning and memory in the hypnotic state, hypnotically induced anxiety and learning, vigilance and hypnosis, verbal satiation, and hypnotic susceptibility and the personality correlates of hypnosis. Some of these findings are summarized in the following paragraphs.

One of the earlier findings (Das, 1957) was a moderately high positive correlation ($r = .51$) between the frequency of conditioned eyelid responses to a tone and the degree of susceptibility to hypnosis. Hypnotic susceptibility was scored following the usual procedure of counting the number of suggestions that the subject accepted. If he accepted none, his score was zero, whereas if he accepted all suggestions, including post-hypnotic amnesia and a simple post-hypnotic suggestion, he was scored six. Following Pavlov, hypnosis had been regarded as a state of selective cortical inhibition. Subsequently the positive relationship between hypnosis and conditioning led the author to hypothesize that in hypnosis, the subject learns to develop a state of cortical inhibition and the extent to which he may be successful determines his susceptibility.

If hypnosis is a state of cortical inhibition, higher nervous activities like learning and retention should be affected in some manner. A relatively better controlled experiment was designed to investigate this. It was found that although there was no difference in the strength of learning in hypnosis and wakefulness, retention of material learned under hypnosis was weaker than that in the waking state. Thus the manner in which hypnosis affected intellectual processes could be complex and indirect and any attempt to observe a simple and direct relationship between them may not be fruitful.

Further work into the nature of hypnosis has been carried out and recent findings give evidence of specific relations existing between hypnosis and vigilance as well as hypnosis and verbal satiation. The vigilance task was a standard auditory vigilance test where the subject was required to detect groups of three odd numbers (signals) occurring irregularly in a random series of odd and even numbers. Error in vigilance was the difference between the number of signals detected by the subject and the number actually presented. Satiation referred to the loss of meaning of a word following its massed repetition. Osgood's Semantic Differential Scale was used to measure the extent of satiation. Subjects, before experimentation, rated a word on nine seven-point graduated scales varying for instance, from extremely good to extremely bad. They were again required to rate the same word immediately after repeating it continuously for 40 seconds. If the initial rating of the word was "extremely good" and its final rating was neither good nor bad then meaning of the word lost three units, and indicated high satiation. But if the ratings were reversed, low or lack of satiation was implied. It was observed in these experiments: (1) that poor vigilance and hypnotic susceptibility were positively related, and (2) that good hypnotic subjects appeared to have low verbal satiation (the correlation between lack of satiation and hypnotizability was .67).

Hypnotizability and rigidity (intolerance to ambiguity) was correlated positively. Thus it appears that susceptibility to hypnosis goes with poor vigilance, lack of satiation for verbal stimuli, and intolerance to ambiguity. From previous studies, hypnosis was found to have no significant relationship with intelligence (Nufferno Speed Test), extraversion and neuroticism (Maudsley Personality Inventory). In a recent study similar results were again obtained for extraversion and neuroticism.

Hypnosis had been used as a tool for designing crucial experiments in learning. In one such experiment, the relation between anxiety and rote learning was investigated. Anxiety and non-anxiety were induced under hypnosis and rote learning was carried out under such conditions. The advantage of using hypnosis was that each individual could act as his own control since he can be made anxious and nonanxious on separate experimental sessions. No differences in learning emerged.

A factor analytic study concerning the nature of hypnosis revealed that running through the various hypnotic and post-hypnotic suggestions, a single prominent factor was detectable. This could be named as a general factor of hypnotizability which seems to be more or less unitary.

The research on hypnosis reported here cannot be justifiably described as Indian, for it does not stem from an indigenous Indian background. Obviously, also, the merits or demerits of work by a single individual who happens to be an Indian cannot be generalized to research in hypnosis in India.

FUTURE

The future of hypnosis in India, like its present, is very much linked with its future in Western countries. It is unlikely that in India, an indigenous trend with regard to research or application of hypnosis will emerge. Universities and the Medical Schools do not seem to have any inherent prejudice against introducing hypnosis into their studies. Little opposition from any other quarter is anticipated. The clergy, as a class, do not have any influence in this regard. Among the Hindus, the clergy is neutral to such things. On the other hand, a favourable atmosphere for a scientific study of hypnosis may be created by the current revival of interest in the practice of Yoga. Incidentally, the recent Western interest in Yoga is at the root of this revival in India. However, the interest in hypnosis coming as it does through an interest in Yoga may acquire an orientation unsuitable for rational research into hypnotic processes. Such an orientation may impel a researcher only to prove that what was said by our saints and seers was basically correct. Such research would be regressive and useless, for, fruitful research should be pursued regardless of narrow nationalistic interests.

IMPORTANT REFERENCES

Avlon, A.: *Principles of Tantra*. Madras, Ganesh & Co., 1914.

Behanan, K. T.: *Yoga, a Scientific Evaluation*. New York, Dover, 1937.

Das, J. P.: *An experimental study of the relation between hypnosis, conditioning and reactive inhibition*. Ph.D. thesis, London Univ. Library, 1957.

Woods, J. H.; *The Yoga—System of Patanjali or the Ancient Hindu Doctrine of Concentration of Mind*. Cambridge, Mass., Harvard Univ. Press, 1927.

HYPNOSIS IN ISRAEL

By

Solomon Kugelmass, Ph.D.

Solomon Kugelmass; born 1926, Ph.D. Columbia University, New York, U.S.; Member, American Psychological Association, Israel Psychological Association; The variability of vibratory perception in the sensorimotor induction syndrome (wtih L. Halpern), Acta Psychiatrica et Neurologica Scandinavica, 1958, 33, 181-192, etc.; present position, Acting Head of Department of Psychology, Hebrew University, Jerusalem, Israel.

Any evaluation of professional development in Israel should take into account the relative youth of the country. First of all only fourteen years have passed since the State has achieved independence. In addition, it must be stressed that most of the adult population are immigrants who have arrived after the founding of the State. Professional training in medicine, dentistry and psychology has only very recently been developed at the University. It should be borne in mind, then, that training and attitudes toward professional technique are not essentially Israeli in development and have for the most part been brought here from primarily European training centers. Only a very small proportion of the professional workers were born in Israel, and most of these received their training in Europe.

During the past three years during which the author served as Israeli representative for the I.S.C.E.H., he became impressed with the relative lack of professional activity in this field. In order to obtain a more thorough objective basis for the present report, letters were sent to the medical, dental, neuropsychiatric and psychological professional organizations requesting information on the use of hypnosis by members of these organizations.

Answers from the dental and psychological organizations indicated no specific knowledge of use of hypnosis by their respective members. While the author would be in a position to state that this is in line with his own knowledge of practice in the case of the psychologists, it is more difficult to interpret this for the dental profession. I personally have heard of a few dentists who employed hypnotism in their practice, and know of one dentist, currently in the United States for further professional training, who had intended to study the use of hypnosis for dental practice. The author was referred directly to a number of psychiatrists by the secretary of the Israeli Society for Neurology and Psychiatry. Two of them, directors of Mental Hygiene Clinics, reported no use of hypnosis. Very limited use of hypnosis was reported by individual psychiatrists who are members of the Department of Psychiatry of the Hebrew University—Hadassah Medical School, the Talbieh Mental Hospital, which is also affiliated with the Medical School, and the Department of Psychiatry of the Tel-Hashomer Government Hospital. These departments report the use of hypnosis in very special cases. It might be added that the general tone of these reports was reserved. There was little knowledge in any of these institutions of the possible use of hypnosis by other institutions.

The most detailed and enthusiastic report was received from Dr. Meir, Director of the Beer Yaacov Government Mental Hospital. He reported clinical use of hypnosis for both therapeutic and differential diagnostic purposes. In addition, he has used hypnosis in his work with neighboring general hospitals. His team conducted a course for the doctors of these hospitals stressing the use of hypnotism in childbirth and psychosomatic problems.

In the Department of Psychology of the Hebrew University there is the usual student interest, and term papers are written on the topic. One small research attempt was undertaken by the author in collaboration with Dr. Edelstein of the Talbieh Mental Hospital. The Department is interested in offering a seminar on the use of hypnosis in psychological research during the coming academic year. Since there is a lack of trained personnel in this area the introduction of this seminar will depend upon the expected presence of a visiting expert.

Two events during the year (1961) had a stimulating effect on the professional use of hypnosis. Dr. William S. Kroger lectured on the use of hypnotism in childbirth in Jerusalem and Tel-Aviv. These lectures, accompanied by films, stirred interest, particularly in gynecological circles. In November 1961 Dr. Edelstein was invited to run a short seminar on hypnosis by Dr. H. J. Birkhahn, the Chief Anesthetist at the Rambam Government Hospital in Haifa. Twenty doctors and dentists attended this two day seminar.

The legal authority contacted indicated that there are no particular restrictions on the use of hypnosis, as long as no specific criminal act is involved. A representative of the Ministry of Religious Affairs said that he knew of no special attitude toward hypnosis on the part of the clergy. I would be of the opinion that hypnotism would be a topic of high general interest to the public. A number of stage performers have had successful tours here during the past few years. To summarize briefly, it would appear that there is little professional use of hypnosis in Israel. Most of the limited activity takes place within a psychiatric setting. On the other hand there are some recent signs of increasing interest in hypnosis in certain medical branches, in dentistry and in research psychology.

HYPNOSIS IN ITALY

By

ANDREA ROMERO, M.D.

Andrea Romero; born 1907; qualified for university teaching in neurology, psychiatry, Universita di Torino; medals Universita di Torino, national scholarship to Salpêtrière Hospital (France); Member Società Italiana di Fisiologia, Fellow and National Representative of Italy for the I.S.C.E.H., President of the Associazione Medica Italiana per lo Studio dell'Ipnosi (A.M.I.S.I.): L'Ipnosi in Psicoterapia, Torino, Minerva Medica, 1960, L'Ipnosi come ausilio psicoterapico sue possibilita e limiti, Medicina Psicosomatica, 1961, 6, 3, L'Ipnosi nella medicina contemporanea, 1961, 52, 79, etc.; present position, Chief Resident Physician in Neurology at the Ospedale Mauriziano, Turin, Italy.

RECENT PAST

THE OBSCURITY which now cloaks hypnosis in Italy contrasts sharply with the luxuriant flourishing of publications and monographs on the subject which appeared during a time span which, roughly speaking, goes from 1875 to 1900.

The names of famous researchers linked with these valuable studies are: Lombroso, Morselli, Tamburini, Seppilli, Dal Pozzo, Silva, Mantegazza, Belfiore, etc.

From 1900 on, the emphasis on hypnosis in Italy inexorably declined. And yet it is at this very time that we meet up with some research which passed unobserved at the time, but which in the light of our present knowledge seems full of revealing predictions. I am alluding to the work of Professor Vittorio Benussi, Director of the Psychology Institute of the University of Padua. This work was the object of a long report at the Fourth National Congress of Psychology which was held in Florence in October 1923. Later, in 1925, selections from this work appeared in a volume entitled *Suggestion and Hypnosis as Tools of Real Psychic Analysis.*

While many earlier works stayed strictly on the paths opened up by previous great theoretical thinkers concerning suggestion, that by Benussi really had something new to say.

By taking respiratory behavior as the indicator of emotional situations, Benussi obtained from every respiratory tracing what he called a "respiratory outline." After studying this, he arrived at certain important conclusions which we are wont to consider as recent discoveries. First of all, the hypnotic state, he said, is not at all comparable to nocturnal sleep, but rather is a state of apparent sleep in which the intellect is awake.

On the basis of experiments, he states the indestructibility of memory traces, in the sense that nothing can be forgotten so completely as never to be able to recall it. The importance of hypnotic hypermnesia in personality exploration for therapeutic reasons is strongly indicated. He firmly declares that all functions of the intellect remain unharmed and intact during hypnosis. He then affirms the autonomy of the emotional functions, since it is possible to create directly by suggestion the most widely diversified emotional situations without relying on any indirect thought process, either externally suggested by the therapist or internally suggested to oneself by the subject or patient.

Among the fifty situations which were studied, we find for example: dislike, pity, envy, happiness, disappointment, liking, etc. It is further shown, again experimentally, that such situations are not dependent on objective situations which are traditionally considered to be directly tied up with them. Examples of these "pure" intellectual situations, created by hypnotic suggestion, are: understanding, evidence, doubt, indecision. Finally, from data now recorded and from experiments showing that the cancellation of thought causes a sense of pleasure and well-being, important conclusions may be drawn for the understanding and the elucidation of so-called mystical experiences, such as we find described in the pages of Saint Teresa of Jesus, Saint John of the Cross and Saint Francis of Sales.

PRESENT

The writing of a paragraph concerning the present development of hypnosis in Italy is most embarrassing.

Practically speaking, to talk of medical hypnosis today in Italy is like talking of a ghost. One can scan neuropsychiatric magazines, consult the minutes of psychological and psychiatric congresses and the name of hypnosis either never appears or is found used improperly for narcosis or to designate chemically induced states of twilight consciousness.

It is symptomatic that in the twelve volumes of the great *Italian Medical Encyclopedia* (published by Sansoni, Florence, 1953) and compiled through the collaboration of the greatest names in Italian medical science, the item "Hypnosis" is edited by a foreign author—Professor Heinrich Koch of the neurological clinic of Tübingen (Germany). This work does not even contain one Italian bibliographical citation. Two supplementary volumes of this *Encyclopedia* were published in 1961 and 1962 and contained recent findings on many important subjects, but the publishing house did not feel it necessary to revise the chapter on Hypnosis.

The very sparse development of studies and applications of hypnosis in our country can be attributed partly to a spontaneous and exuberant defense against magic—mystical excesses to which the passionate Latin spirit might be very prone. It is mostly due however, to a conscious brake used by the traditional biologico-somatically oriented neuropsychiatric school. This school, which boasts of great names and made valuable contributions in the past, is confirming with its unbending attitude, the historical paradox stated by Alexander, i.e., that the greatest conquests of the past in the scientific field often become the most serious obstacle to further progress. They tend to suffocate all new trends at the moment of birth, denying their collateral and complementary value.

I confess that I was tempted to give up the task of reporting on the present state of hypnosis in Italy after having perceived the difficulty of sounding out the attitude of various representatives of medical specialties and of the social classes. Many were annoyed at being asked their opinion on a subject which they considered so out of date, and they looked patronizingly at those interested in it, almost as if to rebuke them for not dedicating themselves to "more serious things." But the start of the inquiry into hypnosis came unexpectedly and spontaneously, because of a deplorable event. Toward the end of October 1961, a nineteen-year-old maid from Veneto was operated on for appendicitis in a Milan clinic, in a state of hypnotic analgesia. The hypnotist was not a physician, but a professional hypnotist, who called himself a "hypno-anaesthetist" and boasted of his particular hypnotic power. The operation was conducted in an atmosphere like that of a country fair, and the publicity drum was beaten in all the daily and weekly newspapers, with many photographs and sensationalistic articles.

The A.M.I.S.I. (Italian Medical Association for the Study of Hypnosis) made its voice heard by condemning the event and denouncing its incorrectness to the Milan Medical Association, who are now deciding about this and making provisions for the future. But one cannot say that all the consequences were evil. Public interest, aroused by the rash press campaign, caused many questions to be raised, which stimulated an equal number of answers from persons who otherwise would never have revealed their attitudes. Thus one again discovers that even in the highest spheres of medical culture the most ancient prejudices and misunderstandings about hypnosis still flourish.

ATTITUDES AND MISCONCEPTIONS

I do not think it is useful to subdivide the most important ambiguities about hypnosis into different paragraphs each dedicated to a different category, e.g., physicians, university professors, lawyers, judges, priests, uneducated persons, etc. I believe it is more effective to mention the various erroneous ideas one by one. These unfortunately are pretty much the same, even if they have different structure and color, depending on different degrees of education and culture in the particular group under discussion.

Moral, Volitional and Religious Questions

Preconceptions about the moral aspects of hypnosis are always the hardest to die. They certainly constitute the most serious barrier against the acceptance of hypnosis as a medical instrument. People fear that hypnosis cancels the will and inhibits critical power thus allowing the overturning of moral or religious principles. It is believed that by making use of hypnosis, one can easily induce, with later total amnesia, the perpetration of the most nefarious crimes during a state of unconsciousness. Since the description of this widespread prejudice which I have just given may seem exaggerated, I repeat here word for word what a very eminent physician and priest, an exponent of Italian academic psychology, wrote in August 1957 to a colleague who had asked him about his attitude toward hypnosis: "I believe that hypnosis is neither convenient nor advisable for any type of medical treatment whatsoever. First of all, it cannot be used on all subjects, secondly, it gives rise to serious problems which have been brought to light by those who have studied hypnosis. In the third place, hypnosis puts the subject in the hands of those who practice it, in such a way as to completely take away from them all freedom of action. Is doing this right? I do not think so, even if the patient consents. Those subjects who allow themselves to be hypnotized are mostly neurotic or emotionally unstable. They are put into the physician's hands, and he can then do as he wishes with them. Therefore the action of hypnosis is quite different from that of chemical anaesthetics. The latter it is true takes away consciousness, mobility, and the activity of the senses, but in using them one cannot do what one wishes, as happens in hypnosis."

There is no objection by the clergy *per se* to the practice of hypnosis if the latter is scientifically and ethically carried out.

Power

Another widespread misconception is that which says that the induction of hypnosis requires that the hypnotist possess a mysterious power. A valuable treatise on neuroses, recently, written by an eminent neurologist, says: "Hypnosis requires that the operator have personal hypnotic power, and can consequently only be used by neuropsychiatrists who possess this power." A director of a neuropsychiatric clinic, a world-famed scientist, wrote as follows in a magazine, concerning the controversy about hypnotic anaesthesia: "Hypnosis has fallen into disuse because it is believed to be neither very serious nor scientific. But since it appears to give excellent results with some subjects, I do not see why it should be opposed. Naturally hypnosis is not generally practiced by the surgeon, but by a third person who has the required abilities. The resulting loss of consciousness is similar to that encountered in normal surgery with chemical anaesthesia."

Fraud

Another unfounded but extremely common idea is that everything in hypnosis is a trick and/or a fraud, so that the physician who practices hypnosis cannot avoid the charge of quackery. A recent work by a famous neuropsychiatrist (whose concepts have a strictly somatic stamp, and who gives a very small place among the methods of psychiatric therapy to psychoanalysis, and even this with a thousand reservations) states, with obvious allusion to hypnosis, "I shall say nothing of other methods which have nothing scientific about them, but are completely histrionic, and do not lead to a lasting scientific cure, but to fleeting deceptive improvements."

The author of this article, when he began his hypnotic studies many years ago, was warned by an official representative of neuropsychiatry as follows: "All of us now and then have to tell our patients fibs for reasons of treatment; but be careful not to dedicate yourself to that kind of therapy which is only based on deception and boasting."

Sleep

The confusion between hypnosis and sleep is unfortunately inherent in the very name of hypnosis. Modern works on "waking hypnosis" are not known, and the older ones by Benussi which I mentioned above have been completely forgotten. Everyone expects that in order to recognize a hypnotic state, one should be confronted with "hypnotic sleep." One imagines the state of "deep trance" as a condition of complete unconsciousness.

Pathological State

On a par with the preceding misunderstanding is to conceive of hypnosis as a pathological state—abnormal and exceptional. Reminding people that hypnosis is a normal and often a spontaneous aspect of psychological activity, and that accidental states of spontaneous hypnosis are met with in everyday life, creates reactions of disbelief and mistrust.

Trance Depth

Hypnotic therapy is generally considered to be of little practical use, because it is erroneously believed that a deep degree of hypnosis, which can be reached by only a few individuals, is indispensable. People do not understand the difference between experimental and therapeutic suggestions. They do not know that the latter may be obtained with only a superficial degree of hypnosis which would not allow for or just barely allow for the carrying out of the simplest experimental suggestions, described in classic scoring systems for the measurement of trance depth.

Gullibility

The false statement that receptivity to hypnosis, or hypnotizability, means gullibility, has resulted in a strong resistance to the spread of medical hypnosis. Even a physician who prides himself on having an open mind for the newest ideas and professes to be an advocate of hypnosis, may often boast that he cannot be hypnotized and has resisted repeated attempts to hypnotize him. He obviously mistakes what is really a lack of imagination, concentration, and emotive reactivity for intellectual, volitional, and moral superiority.

TEACHING AND RESEARCH

Italian devotees of medical hypnosis are grouped into one society: A.M.I.S.I. (Associazione Medica Italiana per lo Studio dell'Ipnosi), and the present chairman is the writer of this article. The Society was founded on April 12, 1960, by Professor Silvio Palazzi, who was then director of the Odontological Clinic of the

University of Pavia. He deserves the credit for having bravely broken the silence which had surrounded medical hypnosis in Italy for more than thirty years. The origin of the A.M.I.S.I. goes back to a series of lectures on hypnosis given by Dr. Piero M. A. Pavesi to a small group of doctors who had expressly invited him to Reggio Emilia in the spring of 1957. Dr. Pavesi is a physician from Parma, an odontologist, who has been practicing in London since 1950. He was then requested by Professor Palazzi to teach a course in Medical Hypnosis and Psychosomatics at the Odontological Clinic of the University of Pavia. From 1958 on, he periodically gave several educational courses for physicians. Similar courses were given, also by Dr. Pavesi, in Milan, Reggio Emilia and Pavia. When Professor Palazzi resigned as president of the A.M.I.S.I. for personal reasons in 1960, the Executive Board of this Association offered the presidency to the author of this article. The latter had been connected with the I.S.C.E.H. since 1955 and in 1958 was nominated Fellow and National Representative for Italy. Professor Palazzi was then offered the honorary presidency of the A.M.I.S.I. The Board of Directors of this organization has been made up of the following members since the assembly in 1960: President: Professor Andrea Romero, neurologist and psychiatrist; Vice-President: Dr. Piero M. A. Pavesi, odontologist; Secretary: Dr. Giampiero Mosconi, obstetrician-gynecologist.

The A.M.I.S.I. acts as a National Division of the I.S.C.E.H., and its president and secretary are both members of the latter's committees. It is also connected with the American Society of Clinical Hypnosis, and has, since 1960, been part of the Federacion Latino-Americana de Hipnosis Clinica.

The A.M.I.S.I. now has about one hundred active members, representing different branches of medicine. Its program is the study of hypnotic phenomena and the application of hypnosis as a diagnostic and therapeutic method in various medical specialties. It avoids any kind of publicity with the public and adheres strictly to spreading knowledge among physicians. So far it has set up seven theoretical and practical courses to bring individuals up to date on hypnosis. Since the sixth course, held in 1961 in

Milan, the meetings have been in the nature of Symposiums and it has published in its Proceedings works of importance. The voice of the A.M.I.S.I. is beginning to make itself heard. At the time of the controversy about hypnotic anaesthesia which I mentioned earlier, medical magazines and newspapers with large circulations expressly asked for and published the opinions of Pavesi, Mosconi, and the present author. Two treatises on hypnosis were published in 1960, one by Pavesi and Mosconi dealing with medicine and one by the author of this article dealing with the uses of hypnosis in psychotherapy. Articles and contributions by members of the A.M.I.S.I. are appearing in Italian and foreign scientific magazines. The Italian medical associations ask for information and invite our people to give lectures and to tell them of recent developments. For example, the last lecture which the author of this article gave during 1962 for the United Hospitals in Leghorn (by invitation of the Leghorn Medical Association) attracted many physicians from different parts of Italy. It then gave rise to some sustained, interesting and informative correspondence.

Academic courses in hypnosis for the medical student are few, for the non-medical student they are non-existent. In part this situation has resulted from the complete lack of interest in hypnotic research shown by non-medical disciplines.

It really seems that there are good signs of an awakening scientific interest in medical hypnosis, and that the aura of suspicion and hostility which surrounds hypnosis is about to be dissolved.

LAWS

At present, we cannot—fortunately—go to a hypnotic show in Italy. The spectacular period toward the end of the nineteenth century, when Donato the hypnotist (the Belgian d'Hont) went up and down the peninsula arousing hysterical excitement and fanatical admiration in the largest of theatres, is finished forever. The Supreme Health Committee had intervened even then and had interrupted performances because they were "dangerous to the public." A new wave of hypnotic shows came in the early twentieth century with Pickman (stage name of Alberti, an

Italian, and a pupil of Donato's), Helman, Gabrielli, and Mira-
bello (who had a degree in medicine).

Two separate provisions of the law, concerned with protecting
public health, regulate public exhibitions of hypnotism for show
purposes. They are:

> (a) "Whosoever places someone, with his consent, in a
> state of narcosis or hypnosis or treats him in such a way as to
> suppress his consciousness or will, may be punished if any
> danger to the safety of the person arises from this fact; by
> arrest (from one to six months in jail) or a fine of from 300 to
> 5,000 lire ($5-$80). This provision does not apply if the action
> is done for scientific or curative purposes by someone who is
> part of the medical profession." (R.D. October 19, 1930, N.
> 1398 C.P.)

> (b) "Entertainment by hypnotism (magnetism, mesmer-
> ism, fascination), fakirism or other similar things are not
> allowed if they can disturb the impressionability of the public
> but where they involve only harmless games they are exempt.
> Such exceptions must be decided however by the physician
> of the province." (R.D. May 6, 1940, N. 635).

These decrees are remarkably unclear. They confuse hypnosis
with mystical shows and with other definitely criminal acts, they
impute miraculous powers to hypnosis, and finally, they make
all restrictions useless by not indicating how and when a procedure is a lethal weapon or a harmless game.

Because of the loopholes in these ambiguous and elastic legal
provisions, scattered hypnotic shows run by magicians still take
place. They call themselves illusionists, and consequently are not
considered to be breaking the law despite the fact that they frequently sneak in a few hypnotic acts. They do this until their
game is revealed and their license revoked. Recent attempts to
give hypnotic shows, despite impressive publicity, were not successful. Ceccarelli's "tour" in 1958 did not arouse much public
interest. Since then there has not been any publicity in Italy for
hypnotists "with eagle eyes and irresistible fluids." One of my colleagues from the United States, a member of the I.S.C.E.H. told

me, on a recent trip to Italy, that he was sorry that medical hypnosis was so poorly developed here, but that he was glad to note the complete absence of theatrical hypnosis. Traveling through the Italian Peninsula, he had not even seen one poster announcing a hypnotic show.

One might say that the old abuses had saturated the atmosphere, and that the public, in contrast with the fanaticism of an earlier time, is now completely detached and disinterested, and this saves it from succumbing to charlatans. But a more subtle danger is waiting in ambush. The campaign about hypnoanesthesia (mentioned above in the operation for appendicitis) showed how sensitive the public is to news about health. It can resist the allurements of theatrical hypnosis, but risks falling into a snare when hypnosis is described as medical by incompetent or profit-seeking people. Therefore it is imperative to anyone that has knowledge of truth and has the public welfare at heart to endeavor to prevent the rising interest in medical hypnosis in Italy falling into the hands of irresponsible persons.

FUTURE

What future can be outlined for medical hypnosis in Italy? It may seem Utopian to think about it, present difficulties being what they are, but it is precisely in clarity of plans and soundness of decisions that the possibility for future development lies. The A.M.I.S.I. is strongly endeavoring to have hypnosis officially recognized in Italy, as a diagnostic and therapeutic medical instrument along with other pharmacological, physical and psychotherapeutical methods as it already has in England, in the United States and in Soviet Russia. The major points of the A.M.I.S.I. program, which its members are undertaking to disseminate among physicians through publications, lectures and interviews, are: (a) absolute prohibition of any publicity and profit-oriented form of hypnosis with the lay public, (b) exclusive reservation of the study and application of hypnosis to doctors, (c) setting up of theoretical and practical courses to teach hypnosis to doctors, (d) prohibiting doctors who use hypnosis calling themselves "hypnotists" or "hypnosis specialists" (since hypnosis can be of aid in all fields of medicine it should not be the exclusive instrument of any of them), (e) peremptory prohibition of public exhibitions of hypnosis for entertainment purposes, (f) restrictive legislative provisions similar to those which regulate the use and suppress abuses of drugs and medical and surgical aids in general.

Resistance does not consist entirely of ignorance, nor mental laziness nor of definite stands taken. The surprising oscillation between the two opposite poles of denying all reality to hypnosis or considering it a mundane trick, and accusing it of all sorts of misdeeds and declaring it a very dangerous method, makes us suspect that the judgment of those who oppose it is dictated by obscure and irrational motives. We begin to think that the struggle to make the truth known in a field like hypnosis, touches the deepest secrets of the human mind and has many points in common with the fight against mental illness. The real enemy to be conquered, and the one which disguises itself in the most unsuspected forms so as not to be recognized, is fear.

The A.M.I.S.I. is confident that the dignity of its attitude and the seriousness of its studies will enable it to succeed, in the not too far distant future, in overcoming the resistance against the proper use of hypnosis.

IMPORTANT REFERENCES

Belfiore, G.: *Magnetismo e ipnotismo.* (6th ed.) Milano: Hoepli, 1922.

Benussi, V.: *La suggestione e l'ipnosi come mezzi di analisi psichica reale.* Bologna: Zanichelli, 1925.

Mantegazza, P.: *Le estasi umane.* (2nd ed.) Firenze: Marzocco, 1943.

Pavesi, P. M. A., and Mosconi, G.: *L'ipnosi nella medicina moderna.* Pavia: Cortina, 1960.

Wundt, W.: *Ipnotismo e suggestione. Studio critico.* Milano: Sandron, 1923.

HYPNOSIS IN JAPAN

By

GOSAKU NARUSE, PH.D., M.D.

Gosaku Naruse; born 1924; Ph.D., graduate Tokyo Bunrika University, M.D., Niigata University, Tokyo; Chairman, committee on Hypnosis in Psychology for the I.S.C.E.H., Honorary Fellow, American Society of Clinical Hypnosis, Member Japaneese Psychological Association, Member Japaneese Association of Psychiatry and Neurology, Executive Member Japaneese Society of Hypnosis; Saimin-Mensetsu no Gijyutsu (Techniques of Hypno-interview), Seishin, Tokyo, 1959, Saimin (Hypnotism) Seishin, Tokyo, 1960; present position, Associate Professor Kyushyu University, Fukuoka, Japan.

PAST

HYPNOTIC PHENOMENA have been familiar to the layman in Japan for a long time. Various techniques of hypnosis-induction were developed by Japanese priests. It seems to have had its origin in Shamanistic ceremony. "Miko" (female medium), "shyugenjya" and "gyojya" (male medium) are still known as the priests of "Shyugenkyo" which is the oldest native religion in this country. They are able to fall into a state of "kamigakari," a sort of self-induced trance, by themselves through a characteristic ceremonial procedure seeking communion with the dead.

There is also another technique for inducing a self-trance in Japan. It is "Zazen" or Zen-meditation which has its origin in Indian Yogi and Buddhism.

Some priests of "Hokkekyo," which at present is the most popular sect of Japanese Buddhism were trained not only in self-hypnosis but also in hetero-hypnosis. They are called "genjya" or "genza." They try to cure believers who are in trouble in their daily life, by a sort of cathartic method under hypnosis. Sometimes, miko and shugenjya utilize the same technique.

Even if, in the long history of hypnosis, it was not always possible for hypnotic operators to avoid introducing mysticism and
irrational explanation, it seems to be fairly true that they tried
to treat it as sincerely and to understand it as suitably as possible. Hypnosis in this country, therefore, has not been as largely
spoiled by the so-called stage-hypnotist or amateur hypnotist as
in Great Britain or the United States. One may say rather that
this phenomenon (hypnosis) has been better accepted in most
instances by Japanese physicians and psychologists as a field of
scientific study.

It was in this atmosphere that the first book *Saiminjyutsu Oyobi
Suggestion Ronso* (*Archives of Hypnotism and Suggestion*)
brought to the attention of Japanese scientists the western concept of hypnosis. Two Japanese scientists performed highly significant work: one a psychologist, Fukurai Tomokichi (1870-
1952), and another a psychiatrist, Kokyo Nakamura (1881-1952).
The former published a textbook, *Saimin-shinrigaku* (Psychology
of hypnosis) in 1905 which included his experimental results together with a history and a theory of hypnosis from a western
point of view. The latter studied the use of clinical hypnosis,
especially in fugue patients, and published a book, *Nijyu-jinkaku
No Onna* (*A Double Personality Woman*) in 1937.

PRESENT

Despite these notable books, the tempo of research in hypnosis
had been very slow in this country until World War II. The situation that then obtained, occurred not only in the field of hypnosis, but in the fields of abnormal and clinical psychology as well.
For after the war, many psychologists found interest in these
fields. A renewed attention to hypnosis was thus developed in
this favourable atmosphere.

Since the year 1950, modern research was performed by an
active and rising generation of psychologists and physicians who
utilized both careful experimental design and scientific procedure. At this time the following studies were published: A study
of memory in hypnosis by Satoru Kawai, perceptual alteration in
hypnosis by Hitoshi Kati, EEG in hypnosis by Katsumi Kaketa,

Tonanosuke Oguma, et al., and post-hypnotic hallucination by Gosaku Naruse. Tonao Obonai and Gosaku Naruse reviewed international and national studies of modern hypnosis in their book *Jikken-saimingaku (Experimental Hypnosis)* in 1953, and this in turn stimulated further investigation of this field in Japan.

Following such experimental psychological studies, clinical hypnosis began to be developed by physicians and clinical psychologists. About 1950, Tsunehisa Takeyama introduced his therapeutic technique, the present author discussed the role of hypnoanalysis and the question of symptom removal by hypno-therapy, Toranosuke Oguma reported on his clinical experience with hypnotic therapy of "writer's cramps," and Hirokazu Kurauchi, a physician, began his excellent study of hypnoanalytic therapy of the fugue state. It was fortunate for hypnotic study in Japan that these experimental and clinical studies occurred in the laboratories and clinics of the foremost universities in the country. As a result, there was a greater acceptance of hypnosis as a scientific area of study in Japan.

As a result of the renewed study of experimental and clinical hypnosis in Japanese universities, institutes and hospitals, a society "Saimin Kenkyukai" (Japanese Society of Hypnosis) which had an annual meeting and a journal *"Saimin Kenkyu"* (Japanese Journal of Hypnosis) was established in 1956.

This in turn stimulated further study in the various fields of hypnosis. Some of these studies included: psychosomatic investigation by Jujiro Ikemi and his collaborators, dental practice by Yasuhide Takahama and his colleagues, investigation of Schultz's autogenic training, and the study of self-hypnosis by the present author and his collaborators. The present author also published a book on clinical hypnosis *Saimin-mensetsu no gijyutsu* (Techniques of hypno-interview) in 1959, and another on experimental hypnosis *Saimin* (Hypnotism) in 1960. Hirokazu Kurauchi and Jyuji Maeda, both physicians, published an introductory book on medical hypnosis *Gendai-saimingaku* in 1959. In this same year the Japanese Society of Hypnosis had a one-week workshop for physicians and psychologists which created interest in the study of hypnosis.

ATTITUDES

Medical

Among the majority of physicians in Japan, the prevailing attitude regards hypnosis as a kind of medical charlatanism or camouflage to cover up deficiencies in technique. Many physicians who were interested in hypnotic treatment hesitated to study hypnosis openly or to declare that they utilized hypnosis in their practice. The curtain of secrecy in medical practice was, however, raised by psychiatry.

In psychiatry, toward the beginning of this century, Shoma Morita and his colleagues at the Jikei Medical College attempted to use hypnosis in psychotherapy. They later gave it up because it was too reminiscent of symptom removal. They were converted to another type of therapy, an original and ingenious technique called "Morita Ryoho" (this therapy involved social isolation, occupational therapy, anxiety-positive-acceptive-attitude). After this abandonment, interest in hypnosis was cooled in its ardour rapidly in Japanese psychiatry. The other leader in the field, K. Nakamura, a professor of psychiatry at the Chiba Medical College, was incapacitated by an unfortunate illness.

After World War II, however, under the influence of American psychiatry, interest in psychoanalysis began to grow. Hitherto, Japanese psychiatry had been influenced mainly by German psychiatry. Some of the psychiatrists attempted to follow in Freud's footsteps by going back to his studies in hypnosis. They began to understand hypnotic phenomena and to cooperate with psychologists. At first they investigated the field of hypnosis experimentally and then extended this area to clinical practice— especially psychotherapy. The eye of this typhoon of renewed interest was in the Department of Psychiatry, Kyushyu University. Here they studied the various techniques of hypnotherapy described in two of Wolberg's books, *Hypnoanalysis* and *Medical Hypnosis*, the latter, being in two volumes.

Hypnoanalytic technique proved its excellent efficacy in the treatment of fugue patients. This was done under the supervision of H. Kurauchi and his colleagues. Jiro Kaneko, professor of psychiatry at Osaka University and his co-worker Noboru Takaishi, studied hypnosis with special reference to its effects on chronic urticaria and allergic reaction. Tsunehisa Takeyama and his pupils, were, and are, treating their neurotic and psychosomatic patients by a form of suggestion therapy at the Jikei Medical School. At Keio University, Mitsuo Shizume and others treat their patients, under Professor Taiei Miura's supervision, by hypnoanalysis at the Psychiatric Department of Keio University.

Apart from the above mentioned clinical applications, Haruo Akimoto, professor of psychiatry, and his colleagues at Tokyo University, began an examination of the physiological characteristics of the hypnotic state with particular reference to the electroencephalographic (EEG) record, galvanic skin reflex, and other indices reflected by polygraphic recording. Izurh Shibata examined the EEG pattern obtained from his neurotic patients by an EEG wave-analyzer under H. Kurauchi's supervision at the Kurume Medical School.

Reports of hypnotherapy are also received from time to time from hospitals and private clinics, not associated with universities or medical schools, however, their number is not very large. This indicates the fact that while hypnosis is fairly well accepted in the universities it does not prevail in private offices as a field of psychiatric practice throughout Japan.

In the field of internal medicine, the most outstanding leader is Yujiro Ikenie. He and his colleagues have studied many psychosomatic phenomena by hypnotic suggestion; e.g., bowel function, excretion, anti-bacteriological function in the blood, etc. His achievements were so excellent, that in 1961, he was appointed Professor at the Institute of Psychosomatic Medicine, Kyushyu University. This institute is supported by the Japanese Government. Other physicians in this field are studying in their private offices the application of hypnosis to clinical practice in internal medicine. There is, however, a difficulty, in that most physicians other than psychiatrists, are not at present very familiar with the psychodynamics or the human relationships involved in hypnosis. The system of post-doctoral training for the physician is poor and few, and this is especially true in the field of medical psychology. It is expected that such a shortcoming will be met by the introduction of such psychological courses that will enable them in the future to utilize hypnosis more suitably in their practice.

Interest in the use of hypnosis in gynaecology and child-birth in this country is very low. One of the reasons for this is the Japanese gynaecologists' poor knowledge of psychology and hypnosis. Another reason is the feeling of fear, uneasiness and distrust of hypnotic treatment on the part of most women, especially the gynaecological or the pregnant patient. It would seem that this fear is stronger than their fear of gynaecological disease or painful child-birth. No university department at present utilizes hypnotic practice for obstetrics or gynaecology. There are, however, a few private hospitals and clinics in which some physicians are treating gynaecological patients with hypnotic suggestion. One of these is Senoo's Clinic in Ono-City. Seiki Senoo, in the last decade, has published papers on his experiences with hypnotic operations in this area. For painless child-birth Velvovski's method (waking hypnosis) is better known at the present time than sleep hypnosis. Many pregnant women want to learn the former because they believe that training in a waking state with full consciousness is safer than the latter which represents treatment in a trance or sleeping state with unconsciousness. Recently a few physicians in Tokyo have started using hypnosis in child-birth in co-operation with psychologists. One of them, Tadahiko Ozaki is comparing the effects of heterohypnotic with self-hypnotic child-birth, especially when Schultz's autogenic training is involved.

In the field of anesthesiology the
Japan who is studying the effect of h
operation. His name is Yoshio Suzu
area at the laboratory of Tohoku Uni
sive work in this area would lead one
in this field will be reported on in the

Dental

Interest in the application of hy
recent in this country. In the year 1
troduced hypnotic research in psych
department of dentistry of the Tokyo
(the best known government dental

his colleagues did research not only in the psychosomatic field but in all fields of dental practice as well. The Japanese Society of Orthodontics in 1960 officially sponsored a meeting for the discussion of the role of hypnosis in dentistry. At this conference professors of dentistry evinced an interest in the utilization of hypnosis. At the departments of orthodontics and dentistry for children at the Tokyo Medical and Dental College both Y. Takahama and K. Kurosu have played leading roles.

In the city of Kyoto a few years ago a society of dental practitioners was formed, whose members have studied the techniques of hypnosis as applied to dentistry. At present they number, i.e., those who have met the standard requirements, about forty. In Tokyo there also is, at the present time, an equal number of dental practitioners interested in the use of hypnosis.

Legal

In 1906, the former time of the full tide of hypnotic interest, an unfortunate incident occurred. A patient in whom hypnosis had been induced died some days after the trance, not as a result of the hypnosis, but because of her illness. Her family, however, believed the physician to be guilty, and public opinion, misunderstanding the real nature of hypnosis, sided with the family. As a result of this, in 1908 a decree was enacted which prohibited not only laymen but also psychologists and physicians from an unreasonable induction of hypnosis. This law "Keisatsuhan-Shobatsu-Rei" was enacted, it was said, because of the dangers in hypnosis. This incident had the unfortunate effect of putting a sudden stop to interest in hypnotic phenomena.

In the years after World War II, the above law was repealed because it was thought to infringe upon basic human rights. In 1948, as a consequence of this decision, a new law "Kei-Hanzai-Ho" was enacted. In this new law prohibition of hypnosis was omitted, however, the reason for this was not too clear. It would seem that the legal drafting committee considered hypnosis a dead issue at this time, and therefore did not mention it in their new law. There was in fact very little interest shown in hypnosis at that time in any part of the country. It was difficult for the legal committee to foresee the coming prosperity of hypnosis even in the same year!

The Japanese Society of Hypnosis is considering the adoption of a law regulating the practice of hypnosis. This, however, is not easy because of the difficulty in deciding qualifications for hypnotic practice. In Japan there are no diploma boards as in the United States for deciding whether or not an individual is competent to use hypnosis in medicine, dentistry, or psychology. At present, we do not even have licensing for clinical psychologists. However, an effort is being made to approach this situation.

Psychological

Hypnotic phenomena were demonstrated by K. Nakamura before the members of the Japanese Society of Applied Psychology at its annual meeting in 1948. Several of the psychologists present had their interest stimulated by the unusual phenomena demonstrated and these individuals may be said to have contributed to the renaissance of Japanese hypnosis. They had often, however, in the early days to encounter obstacles in the form of taboos which in effect said that no man should come in contact with hypnosis if he wanted to be a psychologist in a Japanese university. This situation was created in part by the unfortunate episode which befell T. Fukurai who had been a symbol of research in the field of hypnosis. He was forced to resign as associate professor of psychology at Tokyo University because his public speech on spiritualism was judged to be too unscientific.

Psychologists, active in the area, tried to overcome this taboo by the use of careful design and scientific method in their research in hypnosis. They were successful and were rewarded by its wide acceptance in universities. One study (Naruse and Obonai) was judged by the Japanese Psychological Association as the most excellent paper, among all of the Japanese psychological research papers, for the year.

As Naruse has stated the Department of Psychology at Tokyo University of Education was for several years the research center for experimental hypnosis. However, later, an interest in, and a concern with hypnosis prevailed in many other leading psychology departments in Japan. Such departments had many new

graduate students and well-established and outstanding professors of psychology. Some of the latter are at present engaged in
experimental studies and clinical practice with hypnosis. Several
psychologists have received grants to pursue studies in the field of
hypnosis from the Japanese Ministry of Education. In 1962, the
education faculty of Kyushyu University began its first lectures
on hypnosis for psychology students.

For the last fifteen years research in experimental hypnosis has
been performed by Japanese psychologists. They have been concerned with: hypnotic scales, measurement of suggestibility and
hypnotizibility, the effect of suggestion on apparent size, hypnotic
dreams, post-hypnotic hallucinations, the effect of suggestion on
social attitudes, age regression, human motivation, hypnotically
induced experimental neuroses, EEG in hypnosis, sleep, intoxica-
tion, psychosomatic change by hypnotic suggestion, etc. Other
areas of experimental interest can be found in a paper by Naruse
in 1959.

In Japan, clinical psychology is not as popular as in the United
States, and consequently, clinical hypnosis was slower to develop.
Therapeutic techniques in hypnosis are however gradually advancing. Many of these are similar to those in psychiatry and
will be described later on. Two clinical techniques which have
been recently developed, and which are frequently used are,
educational hypnosis, and self-hypnosis.

Some teachers, as well as school psychologists, are trying to
apply hypnosis to the educational field, not for therapy but for
curriculum learning and guidance. These individuals studied the
possibilities of educational hypnosis under the supervision of a
physician or clinical psychologist. While results have as yet been
few, it seems to be a hopeful field of hypnotic application for the
future.

A two-year project of correcting the diet of school children by
Obonai and Naruse at the Psychological Clinic (Tokyo University of Education) was supported by a grant from the Japanese
Ministry of Education. This stimulated the refining of the so-
called mental rehearsal technique under hypnosis which, by its
utilization of vivid imagery, had the children mistaking the suggested imagery for their own preferences. This procedure yielded

excellent results in correcting habits of like or dislike of certain foods.

The technique was also applied to withdrawn boys and girls in order to encourage in them an active attitude in reading or oral expression before their classmates. Some school counselors also attempted to apply the mental rehearsal technique of hypnosis to motivate curriculum-learning, swimmers in training, as well as using the same technique to rehabilitate enuretics, stutterers, motion-sick individuals, etc.

There is a fairly wide-spread favourable disposition to self-training or self-observation in Japan inasmuch as such a procedure adheres to the idea of Zen-meditation, Indian Yogi-training, or Shamanistic ceremony. Quite a few patients in this country ask for self-hypnosis in psychotherapy. While the data of self-hypnosis in general are sparse, it has an excellent method, i.e., J. Schultz's autogenic training. In addition there are also the instructions contained in old Japanese documents. Recently a group of Japanese psychologists and psychiatrists studied the training process, the clinical application and the physiological effects of autogenic training. This procedure had excellent results especially for anxiety neurotics as claimed by Schultz. Its application to stage-fright and sports events indicated its possibilities.

It seems that the state induced by a well-trained subject from the standard exercises of autogenic training is similar to that of "Zammai" or "Zenjo" in Zen-meditation. Electroencephalographic records show a physiological similarity between the two, i.e., alpha waves are dominant in both states when the eyes are open. The author and his colleagues are now studying other similarities as well as differences between autogenic training and Zen-meditation. It is their hope that there will be found a relationship between self-training in the trance, for purpose of psychotherapy, and the foundations of a Weltanschauung understanding for the self-training of personality.

Clerical

As stated in an earlier section, the Shamanistic medium who has been trained to go into a trance by herself, may in this state relate to her believers words from the Shamanistic God, from the dead, from the person who is living though far away, or even from animals (dog, fox, snake, horse, etc.). This custom has been

FIG. 1. "Mikos" and their believers, Mt. Osore-zan.

FIG. 2. "Genjya" and group hypnosis, Hokke-ji Temple.

very popular in Japan and the medium had had an official position in the government during ancient times. It was believed that the Japanese Emperor was a descendant of one of the great mediums.

However, modern Japanese people do not believe in mediums, and this kind of custom only survives at the present time in certain rural areas and particularly among aged people. Nowadays, in such places, the "Miko" or "Shyugenjya" are not so much magicians as they are poorly trained counselors! A "Miko" gathering is shown in Figure 1. This picture shows a typical Japanese medium and her believers on their sacred mountain Osore-zan in northeast Japan. Hetero-hypnosis in the Japanese clergy is seen in its typical form in the Temple of Hokkekyo, a sect of Buddhism. The clergy must be trained by thirty-five days of religious austerity before being qualified as "Genjya." When so qualified they may induce in their believers a kind of trance. In this state the "Genjya" may treat his subjects in a manner similar to the use of prestige suggestion or catharsis in hypnotherapy. A scene of the ceremonial induction of hypnosis is shown in Figure 2, which was taken at the Temple of Hokke-ji, Chiba prefecture, a major training center of "Genjya."

Almost all Japanese modern religions even "Shyugenkyo" and "Hokkekyo," vow that they do not rely upon hypnosis and that they abjure any kind of magic. It seems, however, to the present author that all of them do in fact utilize some aspects of hypnotic phenomena, albeit in an unrefined or rather primitive way. He is at present attempting to indicate the hypnotic factors in their practices. One such study concerns the comparison of the physiological nature of Zen-meditation and Schultz's autogenic training.

Public

There are two types of public response to hypnosis in this country; the one is negative and the other is too positive. In the former hypnosis is considered as unnatural, nonsensical, meaningless, unscientific, fictitious, deceptive, charlatanistic, etc. In the later, hypnosis is seen as supernatural, highly reliable, a panacea, etc.

Both of these attitudes have resulted in a misrepresentation of the true nature of hypnosis and in so doing have harmed its cause. These attitudes have been cultivated not only by those who are unfamiliar with or who had little knowledge of hypnosis, but also by those hypnotists who talk too much about its superiority, treat it too dramatically or attribute all manners of things to hypnosis and in the process of so doing project their own unconscious wishes or attitudes.

The responsibility for the artificial implantation of unfavourable public attitudes toward hypnosis has also to be taken by the media of mass communication, like the radio, T.V., or the newspapers. They treat hypnosis in a dramatic or sensationalistic fashion in order to achieve startling effects. It seems also that another cause of a distorted attitude is elicited by the undesirable attitude of the hypnotist, i.e., he may make his patients undergo many unusual experiences in the trance state.

However, it is believed that the Japanese people are gradually getting a realistic and reasonable attitude toward hypnosis. Several books on hypnosis which have been recently published have contributed by giving the public a true understanding of hypnosis. It is possible to appreciate the extent to which they exerted an influence on public education from the fact that one of these books (Fujimoto, H.) had been on the best seller list for eight weeks during the year 1959. Many of our universities are now giving as great an opportunity as possible, not only to students of psychology and psychiatry, but also to those in general medicine, dentistry, and other fields of science, art and education, to see and study what hypnosis is all about.

There are amateur hypnotists who are not as proficient as the psychologist, physician, dentist or other qualified individual for research. These tyros, are however, too inadequate in their knowledge, method and reputation to run rampant. Consequently the problem of the amateur stage hypnotist in Japan is not great. There is, however, the real problem of raising standards and providing more training facilities for the study of hypnosis by qualified scientists.

FUTURE

The renaissance of hypnosis in Japan was initiated at the department of psychology at the Tokyo University of Education. This institution became its training centre for scientific research. More recently Kyushyu University also became a centre for research in the area of hypnosis. Even though the number of individuals doing research in hypnosis is not large, any qualified scientist can, at present, study hypnosis at any of the leading departments in psychology, medicine or dentistry.

At present, Japanese research in hypnosis faces a forward step in the greater progress of their movement. This development closes an initial or introductory chapter in the field of hypnosis. It is not easy to foretell the fortune that confronts Japanese hypnosis. However, one is safe in saying that it is spreading a healthy root in the scientific ground. Its growth may not be rapid but it is gradual and steady. We may expect a good harvest in the future. The author, as a relative, cannot help praying for good luck and a rich harvest for the future of hypnosis in this country.

IMPORTANT REFERENCES

Fujimoto, H.: *Saiminjyutsu nyumon* (Introduction to hypnosis). Tokyo, Kobunsha, 1959.

Fukurai, T.: *Saimin shinrigaku* (Psychology of hypnosis). Tokyo, Seibido, 1905.

Kokka-Igakukai: *Saiminjyutsu oyobi suggestion ronso* (Archives of hypnosis and suggestion). Tokyo, Kokka-Igakukai, 1904.

Kurauchi, H., and Maeda, J.: *Gendai saimingaku* (Modern hypnosis). Tokyo, Keio-Tsushin, 1960.

Nakamura, K.: *Nijyu-jinkaku no onna* (A double personality woman). Tokyo, Daito-Shyuppan, 1937.

Naruse, G.: Recent development of experimental hypnosis. *Psychologia*, 2: 20-26, 1959.

Obonai, T., and Naruse, G.: *Jikken saimingaku* (Experimental hypnosis). Tokyo, Nakayama, 1953.

HYPNOSIS IN THE NETHERLANDS

By

BERTHOLD STOKVIS, M.D.

Berthold Stokvis; born 1906; medicine Amsterdam University, medical psychology, psychiatry and neurology Leyden State University, psychoanalysis Amsterdam Psychoanalytic Institute; Gold Medal Leyden Psychiatric University Clinic; Member, Academia del Mediterranea di Palermo, Honorary Member American S.C.E.H., Sociedad Argentina de Hypnotherapia; Hypnose in der arztlichen praxis (Hypnosis in medical practice), New York, Basel, Karger, 1955, Suggestion (with M. Pflanz) New York, Basel, Karger, 1961, Der Mensch in der entspannung (Man in relaxation, with E. Wiesenhutter), Stuttgart, Hippokrates Verlag, 1961; present position, reader in medical psychology, Head Psychosomatic Center Leyden State University, Netherlands.

PAST

THE DEVELOPMENT of hypnosis in the Netherlands clearly shows the changing way in which medical working methods may be successively appreciated in the course of the years. The big struggle that went on in France between the so-called School of Nancy and the Paris School, also found its reflection in the Netherlands. The seemingly unbridgeable gulf between Bernheim on the one side, and Charcot on the other, is well known. What was here at stake was, in fact, the existence of two completely different points of view. According to Bernheim—who had previously consulted Liébault—the hypnotic state should be regarded as an exceptional condition which any normal person might be brought into by anybody else; Charcot, on the other hand, in his well-known *leçons du mardi* in the Salpêtrière, propounded his opinion that hypnotic phenomena were, in fact, of a hysterical nature. His subjects were, as a rule, hysterical female patients, who did indeed express the symptoms that were suggested to them while in the hypnotic state, in a hysterical manner. A lively, if maybe rather too affective description of these sessions was given by Axel Munthe in his well-known book *San Michele*.

While these prominent clinicians were beginning to concern themselves with hypnosis, interest in the subject was also aroused among contemporaneous students of medical science. In the Netherlands, too, hypnosis suddenly stood in the center of general interest, *vide* the article by Bollaan in the *Nederlands Tijdschrift voor Geneeskunde (Dutch Journal of Medicine)* in 1888. It is remarkable that scientists of the greatest ability had let themselves be tempted, in those days, to write books on hypnosis containing miracle-stories. It is not easy to sift the large quantity of chaff in the hypnotic literature at this time from the small amount of grain. Without the slightest feeling of chauvinism, I would here mention that Van Renterghem's critical publications constituted a welcome exception in this respect. In this connection I may also mention the writings of Frederik van Eeden, who, apart from being an author of repute, was also a physician. These two investigators were the pioneers of hypnosis in the Netherlands. There soon followed some further publications on hypnosis: Van Boekhoudt, Reeling Brouwer, Van Effen, Filatheles, De Jong, Nolen, and Wijsman. However, apart from these authors, only little was being written about hypnosis at the time in the Netherlands—at any rate when compared with writings in other countries. In Germany the periodical *Zeitschrift für Hypnotismus* was founded in 1891. But by that time the general interest in hypnosis had practically had its day.

Meanwhile, however, the hypnotic method of treatment had become a recognized therapeutic aid in medical practice. In these years, Van Renterghem, together with Frederik van Eeden and Van der Chijs, founded a clinic in Amsterdam, which was called Instituut Liébault. In this clinic he treated patients according to the method of "simultaneous treatment." The present writer, when he had just taken his medical degree, once visited Van Renterghem (then a very old man) at this clinic. The latter treated the patients according to the method described at the time by Wetterstrand. In a large round room the patients were laid on beds, and the hypnotist walked from patient to patient, whispering suggestions into his or her ear. This method of treatment has since been completely abandoned in the Netherlands. The fact is, after all, that the moment the hypnotist had departed, one patient will ask another: "Are you asleep?" and his neighbor will say: "No, are you?" etc., etc. Notwithstanding these drawbacks, Van Renterghem's clinic enjoyed a general renown, and even attracted many patients from abroad. The interesting library which Van Renterghem had collected was presented by his son to the present writer upon his father's death. The clinic has been closed for many years.

During the first two decades of the present century only very little work has been done on hypnosis in the Netherlands. In the beginning of the 1920's Dutch scientists issued protests against the occult conceptions that were being put forward in other countries concerning hypnosis, e.g., by Alrutz (1920), Löwenfeld (1922), and Kindborg. It was notably Van Rijnberk who rightly remarked that the existence of any force radiating from a human being has never been objectively demonstrated. In the course of the 1920's the Amsterdam nerve specialist S. Koster made a beginning with his publications on hypnosis. For the rest of his life he made valuable use of hypnosis in treating various neurological afflictions, as well as many neurotic disorders. He has written a large number of articles on hypnosis, both in Dutch and in foreign periodicals, as well as a textbook of hypnosis, from which his great experience as a clinician is clearly evident. There is no doubt whatever that Koster, who is now dead, may be called a pioneer; for as early as the nineteen thirties the Professor of psychiatry in Leyden, D. E. Carp, in a textbook on neurosis, was able to state: "hypnosis has come into its own." In the course of the thirties we started with experiments on hypnosis in our medical-psychological laboratory in Leyden, and made a beginning with our publications in this field,

It is not our intention to present a complete review of the entire literature on hypnosis which has been published in the Netherlands. Of historical interest and importance are the conceptions of the renowned G. Jelgersma, who declared that hypnosis is a condition of lowering and narrowing of consciousness, in which only that which is directly linked with the genesis of the hypnotic state is mentally incorporated. In this respect the hypnotic state would seem to evince an unmistakable resemblance to the hysterical state.

Summarizing, therefore, the situation in regard to hypnosis as it existed in the past, we may say that, following the great interest in hypnosis during the 1880's, there came a recession, coupled with a more unfavourable general judgment. When, during World War I, the importance of hypnosis as an analgesic means (Levy-Suhl) became evident, interest was once again aroused; and gradually—in the 1930's—interest in academic circles in the Netherlands was also awakened in this ancient form of psychotherapy.

PRESENT

As mentioned above, a growing interest in hypnosis was shown especially at the University of Leyden, during the nineteen-thirties. At that time we made numerous experiments in our medical-psychological laboratory. In addition to these experimental-psychological and clinical-psychological investigations (particularly our phenomenological investigations relating to hypnosis), we also conducted psychodiagnostic structure-analytical examinations, and physio-psychological experiments. We furthermore endeavored to assess the clinical value of hypnotherapy.

ATTITUDES
Medical

Speaking generally, we may say that the attitude of the present day Netherlands physicians towards hypnosis as psychotherapy is less skeptical than used to be the case in former times. This may be partly explained by the fact that, during the last few decades, the present writer devoted a number of lectures, in the college courses in psychotherapy at Leyden University, to the significance of hypnosis, and partly by the fact that, thanks to the publication of articles in the medical periodicals and a number of textbooks in the Dutch language, physicians in this country have become more familiar with the nature of hypnosis. But this is not to say that hypnosis is now being generally applied in medical practice in the Netherlands—although we have been making propaganda for it from Leyden for years. There are, however, a number of general practitioners who have made a study of the applications of hypnosis; but the majority feel reticent towards the use of this particular therapy in general practice. Nonetheless, patients are referred to the psychiatrists every day, with the question of whether hypnotic therapy is indicated. Obviously, hypnosis must be applied in the right way. More than once we have found that its faulty application may have very bad consequences. If a doctor uses hypnosis in the wrong way it may cause him to abandon its regular use. It is therefore essential that the physician be given an opportunity to learn this method correctly. We shall revert to this point anon.

We are opposed to the specialization of a medical man, or even a psychiatrist, into becoming a *hypnosis-doctor*. Who is going to wield this hypnotic practice? Should it be the general medical practitioner? Can hypnotherapy be put in the hands of every doctor? Or is the other extreme valid: would it be only the hypnosis-doctor, i.e., a specialist among specialists, who is to be entrusted with the performance of this form of psychotherapy? As I said above, this latter question must be answered in the negative. We consider the very concept of *hypnosis-doctor* downright odious. The physician who applies hypnosis is and remains a psychotherapist who ought to be able, and to possess the inner preparedness, to play the whole of the keyboard of psychotherapy. It is untrue to say that the medical man who applies hypnotic treatment lacks the qualities of the psychoanalyst. This is nothing but a dogmatic contention. Do not let us forget that it was Ferenczi who applied hypnosis and Schilder and Kauders, who wrote a book on hypnosis when the former was already a psychoanalyst. Levy-Suhl, too, was an analyst, and finally, Freud himself was a pupil of Bernheim. We ourselves have applied hypnosis in Leyden for years, while we are also orthodox Freudian psychoanalysts.

Every experienced therapist knows that it is not only the method which causes the patient to improve, but that the personality of the physician who uses a method is of the greatest importance. On this truth rests the fact that one doctor will have greater success with a given method, possibly hypnosis, or even with one medicament than another. The practitioner in a large town will find it advisable to call in the assistance of the psychotherapist when necessary. In the villages and the countryside, however, the physician may sooner be led to apply hypnotherapy himself. Medical men who possess an adequate mastery of the technique of hypnosis will find it a valuable addition to their arsenal of psychotherapeutic aids. It is difficult to give a complete and generally valid list of indications for hypnosis. In this respect it is, of course, necessary to individualize. The patient's personality structure is often the deciding factor. The same things apply to hypnosis that apply to all forms of psychotherapy; viz., its application depends upon: (1) the personality structure of the patient; (2) that of the doctor; (3) the nature of the disease; (4) psychosocial factors, and (5) the transference and counter-transference situation.

Hypnosis may be applied as a form of "covering" psychotherapy. Indications for this are, in the first place, all hysterical conversion phenomena (motor conversion symptoms, such as disturbed coordination; sensible and sensorial phenomena; vegetative disorders, such as disturbances in circulation, respiration, in the gastro-intestinal system, the urinary tract, or the genital organs); skin infections, vaso-neurotic symptoms and sleep disorders. In the second place: anxiety-hysteric reaction forms, depersonalization neuroses, some cases of involutional melancholia, and some forms of torpor (alcohol, nicotine).

Hypnosis may further be applied in connection with uncovering psychotherapy. We here point to the use of hypnosis as hypnocatharsis. Use of hypnosis and the orthodox psychoanalytic method in one and the same patient is not meaningful for the two are irreconcilable. It is also possible to apply hypnosis as a psychagogic method, i.e., by conveying certain suggestions to a patient in the hypnotic state; however, we ourselves are not in favor of this method.

The application of hypnosis in partial or entire replacement of narcotics or anti-neuralgics is nowadays fairly infrequent. In former times hypnosis was sometimes used in complete replacement of narcotics; but this as indicated is at present an exception. Hypnosis during childbirth is hardly ever applied in the Netherlands. This, however, does not include the Read method, and other relaxation treatments, which are definitely and frequently used in this country. Hypnosis linked with electric shock treatment, occasionally recommended abroad, is never applied in the Netherlands, any more than protracted hypnosis (the so-called "Dauerhypnose"). Hypnosis, however, is sometimes used as a partial replacement of narcotics, for example in cases of violent pain (phantom pains). In those cases where administration of narcotics is not possible or advisable, hypnosis is occasionally applied.

Very little value is attributed in the Netherlands to the significance of hypnosis as a differential diagnostic aid.

Dental

On the attitude of the dental profession towards hypnosis we may be brief. Speaking generally, Dutch dentists do not apply hypnosis, although there are one or two exceptions. The medical profession in this country take the stand that hypnosis is a *medical* method, and as such should be applied exclusively by physicians. We ourselves are in agreement with this opinion.

Legal

We may say the same as above about the attitude of Dutch lawyers with respect to hypnosis. Application of hypnosis in forensic practice simply does not exist in the Netherlands. We regard the application of hypnosis in court, in agreement with Dutch law (Article 29, Criminal Code), juridically inadmissible, ethically wrong, and scientifically unreliable.

One must here consider different possibilities such as: (a) The commission of a crime or misdemeanor which occurs during hypnosis. Here, the hypnotized person may be either the victim (sexual offence), or the delinquent committing the crime. With respect to this we hold the view that a sexual offence can only happen to a person during hypnosis if the hypnotized person is also inclined that way. The same applies, *mutatis mutandis,* to the commission of a crime or misdemeanor under hypnosis. In that case the person committing the offence must have been already previously inclined to commit the offence in question. In our view, responsibility, and the feeling of responsibility are not diminished in the hypnotic state. (b) In obtaining evidence of crimes by hypnosis one must differentiate between those cases in which the hypnotized person was unaware of the facts while in the waking state, and those cases in which he or she was aware of the facts while in the waking state. In the first case it is, in fact, possible—as we know from our own experience—to eradicate an amnesia. When, on the contrary, the person was aware of the facts while in the waking state, it will be impossible to induce him to communicate the facts—unless he wishes to do so himself.

Psychological

Generally speaking, reputable opinion at Dutch universities is not averse either to hypnosis as a medical-psychological method of investigation or as a psychotherapeutic technique. Here too, however, the general view is that hypnosis belongs to the sphere of action of the medical man, and that the psychologist should fight shy of its application. In accordance with this view, there is hardly any interest in hypnosis among psychological circles in the Netherlands.

Clerical

We shall here briefly summarize some ecclesiastical points of view in the Netherlands regarding hypnosis.

On the part of competent quarters (J. Waterink) I was told that the general opinion prevailing in Dutch Reformed Calvinistic circles is difficult to describe. Some prominent Protestants' attitude is one of diffidence towards hypnotic phenomena; they are afraid of the influence of the Devil, and prefer to hold aloof. The number of Reformed persons who absolutely reject hypnosis as a medical aid is very small. As early as 1901-1905, Geesink declared that hypnosis, providing it is applied by a competent medical man, cannot meet with any objection from Reformed quarters. If applied for a criminal purpose it is, of course, evil; and no one—unless ill—should let himself be brought under the power of another. The fundamental idea among this group is that every gift of God is good, providing it is accepted with gratitude. This means, therefore, that, according to the Dutch Reformed conception, if it is true that in hypnosis we have to do with a real gift from Creation, this possibility should be taken advantage of, providing this is done *sub specia boni*, i.e., with the aim of helping human beings, and fighting evil and disease.

According to Mr. Rector A.A.M. Sanders, Pr. (personal communication) there is no objection in official Roman Catholic quarters against the application of hypnosis by physicians. As early as 1846, Bishop Mgr. Lacordaire approved magnetism (mesmerism), and later, hypnosis was approved by Rome as a method of healing. Nonetheless, some Roman Catholic priests in the Netherlands disapprove of hypnosis.

As I was told on behalf of the Rabbinate of the Netherlands Israelitic Chief Synagogue at Amsterdam, the Jewish precepts do not contain any objection against hypnosis as a medical form of therapy.

The medical man in the Netherlands, therefore, experiences no hindrance whatsoever from any ecclesiastical quarters against the application of hypnosis. Only in a few sectarian circles are occasional objections raised.

Public

There is a great deal of interest in hypnosis among the Dutch public. This interest is manifested not only in a morbid appetite for sensationalism, caused by witnessing hypnotizers on the variety stage, but also in the wish to have hypnosis applied to themselves for therapy. Patients often call upon their doctor with the request to be treated hypnotically. In that case they have usually been reading popularly written booklets in which the therapeutic significance of hypnosis is presented in a strongly exaggerated style. As a result the psychotherapist usually has to disappoint them in their expectations.

Apart from this, people often have quite wrong ideas concerning the nature of hypnosis. They believe that medical hypnosis implies a kind of narcosis-like state, and patients are often disappointed when they find that hypnosis causes only a partial lowering of consciousness.

It would therefore definitely be a good thing if, with the aid of radio talks or via the television, the public were given proper guidance on the subject. We have in the past endeavored to clear up these misunderstandings by means of newspaper articles; but these have to remain nameless, because they would otherwise be regarded as (prohibited) advertising.

TEACHING AND RESEARCH

In the Netherlands opportunities are available to qualify in the application of hypnosis in the universities. As explained above, it is notably at Leyden University that some hours are devoted to hypnosis during the college courses of psychotherapy, and annual demonstrations are given. When Koster, whom I mentioned above, was still alive, he organized private courses for doctors and dentists, which aroused considerable interest at the time. These courses are no longer being held. The late Koster was, at that time, President of a Dutch society of doctors and dentists who were interested in hypnosis.

With regard to the literature available, there exist two textbooks on hypnosis in the Netherlands language, e.g., that by the eminently experienced Koster, (which I referred to above), and more recently a book by the present writer: *Hypnose in de Geneeskundige Praktijk (Hypnosis in Medical Practice)* 1955. Both these books were written for the benefit of the general practitioner and may be called supplementary. Koster's book is perhaps written somewhat more enthusiastically than the latter one, which shows a degree of skepticism, and advises caution.

MISCONCEPTIONS

A number of misconceptions have already been partly explained. They exist notably among the lay public, and to a lesser degree among physicians. The latter sometimes overrate the value of hypnosis; for instance, in cases of sexual aberration, and in stammering.

CONTROL OF STAGE AND AMATEUR DEMONSTRATIONS

Control of stage demonstrations does exist in the Netherlands. There are no legal regulations governing them; but there are local police by-laws which regulate the appearance of a stage hypnotist in the municipality concerned. In most cases hypnosis on the stage is permitted, providing the variety artist brings along his own assistants to experiment upon. There are no regulations governing demonstrations by amateurs within private circles.

Before these police measures existed we often had an opportunity in the Netherlands to study the behavior of those among the audience who had placed themselves at the disposal of the hypnotist. Again and again one is led to wonder what kind of state these people were in; whether they really had amnesia for their remarkable conduct, or whether they merely simulated this amnesia. In order to find this out, we had, in our laboratory, asked many persons some pertinent questions about their experiences at the time who, on the stage had apparently quite willlessly, complied entirely with the sometimes exorbitant demands of the artist. We then found that various factors were involved in calling forth their behavior and mannerisms. On the one hand it was the hypnotist's authority, his name and fame, his dress, tone of voice, or his personal charm. On the other hand it might be the effect of intimidation. Many a boastful swanker who exchanged his very inconspicuous figure as a lone spectator lost in the crowd in the auditorium, for that of a helpless subject on the glaringly lighted stage, with the eyes of the audience on him, told us that he lost his self-assured attitude at that moment, and fell in with the variety artist's instructions. The persons we examined told us that they nearly always obeyed the commands of the hypnotizer because they wanted to please him. They were vaguely aware that he was, after all, trying to earn his living, and practically all of them were quite aware that they had behaved in a strange way on the stage. Later on they exhausted themselves with all sorts of absurd excuses in the attempt to explain their bizarre conduct. On the ground of our introspective investigations we are of the opinion that we have here a certain unconscious simulation. There exists a certain analogy in the external resemblance of hypnosis and stage-acting, on the one hand, and that between hypnosis and the propensity to react with hysterical mechanisms, on the other hand. Naturally, the term simulation must be used with caution, since we here have to do with not fully conscious thoughts and actions.

On the grounds of our experience we are of the opinion that the use of hypnosis on the stage is an extremely reprehensible activity. The technique which these people use is often a method of taking a person off his guard, (and therefore resembles rape), and deserves severe reproval. Many variety artists with whom we have come in contact confided the secret of their technique to us, and practically always we were confronted with psychologically injurious *modi procedendi.* As regards the application of hypnosis in the form of amateur demonstrations the same applies as what is stated above about variety artists. *Hypnosis is not a kind of entertainment, but a medical-psychological method to be handled only by competent medical men.* In the course of over thirty years as practising psychotherapists we have been able to observe countless injurious consequences following the misuse of hypnosis, and the application of hypnosis by incompetent persons. These results may be: troublesome erotic relationships with the hypnotizer; all sorts of complaints of dizziness, headaches, faintness, and sometimes even hallucinatory experiences; and conditions of mental twilight.

Additional Considerations
(a)—Investigations at Leyden

Here follows a summary review of our investigations covering the last thirty years or so.*

In 1937, we were first able to work with the tensiograph—an instrument designed by ourselves as a method for the uninterrupted automatic registration of the systolic and diastolic human blood pressure. This made it possible to register the blood pressure as part of a psychophysical examination, in which both

---

*I wish to express my grateful thanks to my colleague Mrs. S. M. de Boer (nee Siccama) for her assistance in drawing up this report.

neurotically disturbed persons and normal persons acted as subjects. The results of this investigation were as follows:

(a) In an emotional state the blood pressure appears to be
considerably higher than under normal circumstances.

(b) In this state the person's reaction to strongly affective stimuli is weaker than is normally the case.

(c) During the stadium decrementi (decrease in the severity
of a disease) the blood pressure falls below the level at
which it stood before the examination.

These findings are theoretically important with a view to the
emotional determination of essential hypertension. Linking up
with the above data, an investigation was made into the therapeutic importance of hypnosis in cases of essential hypertension.
On the basis of fifteen patients who were hypnotized five times
per week, for a total of twelve times, we came to the following
conclusions.

The reactivity of the blood pressure in sufferers with essential hypertension depends upon many factors. Notably those patients who are readily suggestible and hypnotizable, and who
belong to the sentimental temperamental group in Heymans' typology, are particularly suited to being treated by hypnosis. An
incongruity is thereby found between the subjective and the objective symptoms of the disease; and while the lowering of the
blood pressure—which is more considerable systolically than di-
astolically—continues only a few weeks, the lessening of the complaints lasts more than six months.

Also, in 1937, B. Stokvis and N. Speyer made an investigation
into subjective phenomena occurring during hypnosis, in which a
female and a male colleague, both of whom were familiar with
hypnosis, were hypnotized. The purpose of this experiment was
to examine more closely the psychological backgrounds of hypnosis. Our male colleague related his impressions immediately after
the hypnotic state was over. Following this verbal communication, which was taken down, he also wrote what he had remembered. After this our female colleague was hypnotised by a
(male) doctor, and the same procedure was again followed. This
examination showed that the hypnotic state is a contraction of

consciousness preceded by a lowering of consciousness; that the subject under hypnosis adopts the suggestions to please the hypnotist, and finally, that the action of every suggestion travels along the road of autosuggestion.

During the succeeding years these experiments were extended, and the physical chemistry of the blood during the hypnotic state was determined. Changes in the hemoglobin content, and in the number of erythrocytes and leukocytes were studied. Apart from an emotional leukocytosis and hyperglobulia, we could not determine any specific changes.

In 1940, Stokvis and Fortanier experimented with daydreams. During sleep, caused artificially with the aid of evipan tablets, the influence of various stimuli was studied. After waking up the subjects communicated their dreams. There appeared to exist a connection, with the nature of the stimulus, with the person's experiences during the day, and with his total personality. At the same time the blood pressure was registered uninterruptedly, so that one also received an impression of the vegetative changes that occurred during the dream, and was able objectively to determine their structure.

In 1956, in an article entitled Experiences with the narco- and hypno-analytical method, results were given of extensive investigations into hypnosis induced by chemical stimuli. It was found that narco-analysis offers no advantages over hypno-analysis; only its technique is simpler. But the drawbacks of narco-analysis are: (a) that the lowering of consciousness cannot be properly regulated, (b) the subject's consciousness is not clear afterwards, and (c) the chance of possible injurious side-effects is much greater.

Investigations into the emotional determination of paroxysmal tachycardia, during the war-years, brought to light that hypno-suggestively the pulse rate may be accelerated up to 220 per minute, even coupled with a complete angina pectoris-like attack. Patients with paroxysmal tachycardia were taught, under the influence of certain stimuli (counting) to lower their pulse frequency autosuggestively; later on they learned how to lower the frequency, by ideational self-stimulation to 56-80 beats per minute.

Experiments with hypnosis and organic diseases, e.g., mammary carcinoma showed that hypnosis is indicated in those cases where the patient reacts neurotically to the organic deviation. The patient's general condition then usually improves under hypnotic treatment.

In 1958, experiments were made in Leyden with respect to the psychological changes on the Szondi and the Thematic Apperception Test that occur under hypnosis, with neurotic patients and with students. These tests show a regression in thinking, willing and feeling. Even the sense of time changed—as was also found by Cooper and Erickson. As regards the subject's intelligence we found no change. The Goodenough test (drawing) showed that the subject under hypnosis may, through autosuggestion, imagine himself in a former period of his life, i.e., indicated the possibility of regression. Handwriting analysis in which ten subjects under deep hypnosis were given various suggestions, after which they were to write down a few words, yielded no distinct changes which might point to any real changes in the affective condition of the persons to whom the suggestions had been given.

In the years around 1955, we also studied the psychology of post-hypnosis. We came to the conclusion that the performance of post-hypnotic suggestions is dependent upon the autosuggestive conception which the hypnotized person has concerning them. When the post-hypnotic instruction is felt by the subject to be unpleasant or morally inadmissable, he shows a tendency to fall into a hypnotic sleep—evidently in order to escape responsibility for the act. Regression in thinking, willing and feeling is no longer present during the post-hypnotic state; but notwithstanding this the hypnotic suggestion remains effective. In some cases the instruction is carried out at once (immediate post-hypnotic suggestion); in other cases much later (deferred post-hypnotic suggestion). We may therefore conclude that there are no general rules as to the extent to which hypnotic suggestions are implemented post-hypnotically. For this, a sound knowledge of the subject's personality structure would be necessary.

Other experiments taught us that patients suffering from hysterical twilight conditions, who had wrongly been hypnotized, could be brought back to a normal state of consciousness by causing this autohypnosis to pass into a normal hypnotic state.

We have also conducted investigations with respect to hypnosis as a method of studying the fundamentals of psychosomatics. Since, in psychosomatics, an emotional process is manifested in a mental reaction, and at the same time in one or more physical symptoms, hypnosis is eminently suited for its scientific investigation. When various data have been obtained by anamnestic and psychological examination, different fragments of the patients life can be presented to him or her again under hypnosis. By means of the polygraph it is possible to ascertain:

1. The typological nature of the patient, as regard the manner in which he experiences these things;
2. The degree of his emotionality;
3. The extent to which he represses his affect.

This enables us to determine the degree in which certain events acted psychotraumatically.

Here follows our final examination of the psychotherapeutic results of hypnosis. Here, in a comprehensive examination of the results of uncovering and covering, methods of psychotherapy applied to sufferers from psychoneurosis and somatoneurosis, we obtained the following figures: Results of hypnosis in twenty sessions (1958)

10 per cent   socially very well adapted
20 per cent   socially well adapted
20 per cent   socially adequately adapted
25 per cent   socially doubtful result
25 per cent   result either nil or negative

Additional Considerations (b)—Danger

One of the dangers which we have come across when hypnosis is wrongly applied is addiction to hypnosis. We found that this "hypnosophilia" occurs only in persons with strongly developed masochistic traits who, in an intense feeling of dependence, coupled with a lustful emotion, surrender themselves to the hypnotizer. It is especially this feeling of being dependent that gives these persons their lustful gratification. We were able to make some interesting observations in this respect in the course of our practice.

Additional Considerations
   (c)—To Whom One May Refer

The same thing applies to hypnosis as to the whole of medical science, and, for that matter, to all branches of science and literature. Before World War I, Dutch authors were mainly oriented towards the German-speaking linguistic area; but after 1945 there came a complete switch-over to the Anglo-American literature. Before this war the old books by Forel, Schilder and Kauder, and the excellent works by J. H. Schultz were considered the classic works to which one referred in the Netherlands. Since the end of the war books by Brenman and Gill, Erickson, Kline, Marcuse, Schneck, and Weitzenhoffer have been, more particularly, the works which are considered in the Netherlands as being the leading literature on hypnosis. As stated above, there also exist textbooks on hypnosis in the Dutch language, viz., the textbook by the pioneer S. Koster, now dead, and a textbook by the present writer, *Hypnose in de Medische Praktijk*. The latest edition of the latter work has meanwhile been published in Switzerland under its German title *Hypnose in der Ärtztlichen Praxis*, and will soon be published in English and Spanish.

FUTURE

With regard to the future of hypnosis in the Netherlands, we may say that the general interest in the subject is moving in an upward curve. As we said in the beginning of this chapter, hypnosis is no longer regarded as a form of quackery, and it is now accepted as a medical method by non-psychotherapists. Only a sharp clear determination of indicants, a critical and technically correct handling of hypnosis both as a psychotherapeutic aid and as a psychological method of investigation; a skeptical attitude towards all unduly enthusiastic propaganda, and finally, the publication of writings which can stand scientific criticism, can alone safeguard the future sound development of hypnosis in this country. We in the Netherlands look forward to this development with every confidence.

IMPORTANT REFERENCES

Boekhoudt, W.: *De beteekenis van hypnotisme en suggestie in ons strafrecht en strafproces.* Leeuwarden, Diss. Coop. Handelsdrukkerij, 1890.

Bollaan: *De hypnose in de practijk.* Ned. T. v. G., 1888, I, vol. 24, 346-355.

Carp, E. A. D. E.: *De neurosen.* Amsterdam: Scheltema & Holkema's Boekhandel en Uitg. Mij. N. V.

Eeden, F. van: *Psychotherapie* (litt. summary). Ned. T. v. G., 1890, II, vol. 26, 441-446.

Effen, Van: *De hypnotisch suggestieve therapie bij pas ontstane distorsies.* Ned. T. v. G., 1890, II, vol. 26, 350-352.

Filatheles: *Een gevaarlijk geneesmiddel.* W. A. Morel, 's-Gravenhage, 1888.

Jelgersma, G.: *Leerboek der psychiatrie,* part I, gen. part. Amsterdam, Scheltema & Holkema's Boekhandel, 1911.

Jong, A. de: *Het hypnotisme als geneesmiddel beschouwd.'s-*Gravenhage, 1888.

Koster, S.: *Hypnose in de geneeskunde.* Amsterdam, Uitg. Koloniale Boekcentrale, 1924.

Nolen, W.: *Het zoogenaamde dierlijk magnetisme of hypnotisme.* Rotterdam, W. J. van Hegel, 1886.

Reeling Brouwer: *De psychische geneeswijze naar de school van Liébault en hare techniek.* Psych. en neur. bladen, 1900, p. 10.

Renterghem, A. W. van: *Hypnotisme in de geneeskunde.* Baarn, Hollandia Drukkerij, 1908.

Rijnberk, G. van: *Een greep uit het werk van G. van Rijnberk.* Bussum, N. V. Uitg. Mij. C. A. J. van Dishoeck, 1934.

Wijsman, J. W. H.: *Hypnotismus.* Geneesk. Tijdschr. v. Ned. Indië, 1889, vol. 28, p. 183.

HYPNOSIS IN NORWAY

By

HARALD SCHJELDERUP, PH.D.

Harald Schjelderup; born 1895; Ph.D. University of Oslo; Gold Medal, University of Oslo, St. Olav Order of Knighthood; Member, Norwegian Academy of Science and Letters, Finish Academy of Science and Letters, Norwegian Psychological Association, International Psychoanalytic Association, I.S.C.E.H.; Psykologi, Oslo, Gyldendal, 1927, Nevrosene og den Nevrotiske Karakter, Oslo, Gyldendal, 1940, Det Skjulte Menneske, Oslo, Cappelen, 1961. Lasting effects of psychoanalytic treatment, Psychiatry 1955, 18, 109-133, etc.; present position, Professor and Director Psychological Institute, University of Oslo, Oslo, Norway.

RECENT PAST

Up TO A FEW years ago, hypnosis played a very minor role in Norway. To be sure, the work of Charcot, Bernheim, Liébault, and other students of hypnosis in the last half of the nineteenth century aroused considerable interest in this country, and demonstrations by professional hypnotists impressed a few medical authorities. But by the turn of the century hypnosis was very seldom used by physicians, and no Norwegian hypnotherapist achieved any national or international fame.

The question of possible dangers and abuses of hypnosis, however, soon aroused interest and debate, especially among *lawyers*. As early as 1887, a prominent Norwegian lawyer, Bernhard Getz, gave a statement about the issue. In 1896 a committee of experts preparing the Norwegian Penal Code proposed a special Section on hypnosis. With some changes the proposal was accepted. Hence Section 364 in the Norwegian Penal Code reads:

> Anybody who employs means or methods by which another person, with his consent, is put into a state of hypnosis, debil-

ity, unconsciousness or similar state, shall be punished by
fine or imprisonment up to three months.

This provision shall not prevent physicians from putting
persons into such a state for scientific purposes and for the
treatment of illness.

This old section is still law, and may be used against stage and
amateur hypnotists. However, it is not regarded as hindering the
use of hypnotic methods by competent psychologists. Experts on
criminal law have lately spoken in favor of replacing the old Section 364 with a more adequate formulation.

The interest aroused in hypnosis before the turn of the century
faded away in the first half of the twentieth century. A few Norwegian physicians used hypnosis in their clinical practice, among
them Herman Thorsen, M.D., Sigurd Dahlström, M.D., and Tor-
geir Kasa, M.D. Kasa has employed hypnotherapy during the last
forty years, especially as a means for emotional abreaction. In
general, however, interest in hypnosis was replaced by a growing
interest in psychoanalysis. Especially in the late 1920's and the
1930's psychoanalysis more and more became the object of discussion among psychiatrists, psychologists, and others interested
in the problems of mental life.

PRESENT

As in many other countries there has been a renewed interest
in hypnosis in Norway in recent years. This has manifested itself
in many ways.

In the effort to increase the usefulness of psychotherapy, a considerable number of younger *psychiatrists* have developed interest
in the therapeutic possibilities of hypnosis. In connection with a
seminar on psychotherapy in 1962, Norwegian psychiatrists for
the first time had an opportunity to participate in a course which
gave limited training in hypnosis.

Even among Norwegian *dentists* there has been a recent but
considerable interest in hypnosis and its possibility for application
in dentistry. Hypnosis was discussed as a special subject at the
Nordic Convention of Children's Dentists in 1962. However, hyp-

nodontics in Norwegian dental practice is still so new as to lack any practical significance.

While the interest in hypnosis among physicians and dentists mainly has been concerned with the possibilities of practical application, Norwegian *psychologists* have been more concerned with research in hypnosis.

The present author received his training in hypnotic techniques from Professor Paul Schilder at the neuropsychiatric clinic of the University of Vienna in 1924-1925. In the book *The Subconscious* (published in Norwegian in 1925) he discussed hypnotic phenomena at some length. In the Norwegian Academy of Science and later at the fifth Nordic Convention in Psychology, held in Bergen in 1959, the author presented preliminary results of some experiments on the time conditions of hypnotically induced dreams. The investigation was performed at the Psychological Institute of the University of Oslo. During the experiments a series of different variables could be manipulated and their effects on dreams studied. Such variables were: the kind of signal eliciting the dream, the signal for waking up, the objective duration of the dream, the main theme of the dream, etc. The content of the dream usually made it comparatively easy to control whether the duration of the dream corresponded to that allowed by the experiment.

These studies have given preliminary experimental verification to the old belief that during dreaming it is possible to experience very much in an extremely short time. Later these studies were continued within a wider frame of reference. An experimental investigation is now in progress regarding certain aspects of the fantasy process, which seems to be of importance for the highest forms of creative imagination.

Among the younger Norwegian psychologists, Dr. Arvid Åas, University Lecturer, has carried out research in hypnosis. He received his training in experimental hypnosis partly from the author, but mainly from Dr. E. R. Hilgard and Dr. A. M. Weitzenhoffer at the Laboratory of Human Development, Stanford University, USA, where he was a research fellow (1960-1962). In his efforts to find personality characteristics of the hypnotizable person Dr. Åas seems to have been more successful than most of his predecessors in the field. More specifically he investigated the relationships between certain subjective experiences as measured by a specially developed inventory, and hypnotizability as registered by objective hypnotic scales used in individual sessions. Significant correlations between subjective experiences (e.g., mental absorption as shown by altered states of consciousness and tolerance for logical inconsistencies) and hypnotizability were repeatedly found in three independent samples of subjects. The hypnosis-related experiences were analyzed in terms of content and sex differences, with a special view to possible underlying personality characteristics.

In a study of a single case Dr. Åas used the technique of hypnotic age regression in the attempt to recover language knowledge available to the subject in childhood, but later forgotten. Although there was a clear and statistically significant improvement in language knowledge during the regression, the result taken as a whole, was not particularly dramatic.

During recent years there has, as previously indicated, been a renewed interest in hypnosis among *lawyers*. This interest was particularly stimulated by the well-known Danish hypnosis murder case, and later by a Norwegian criminal case against a carnival owner, who used hypnosis on the stage. In 1959, the latter was sentenced to a fine, and the judgment was later sustained by Supreme Court. There have been other expressions of an increased interest in hypnosis among legal experts. A few years ago, the Head of Criminal Prosecution and an outstanding member of the Penal Code Committee, Professor Johs. Andenaes, wanted to see a demonstration of hypnosis at the University Psychological Institute. At this demonstration the two legal experts saw dramatic evidence of the possibility of carrying out indirect suggestions of criminal acts. The subject was given special posthypnotic suggestions, and without being aware of any wrong conduct he stole 100 crowns ($14) from the desk drawer of Professor Andenaes and wrote the police a false accusation directed against the Head of Prosecution.

The increased interest in hypnosis in Norway in recent years has most clearly been manifested among the general public. Surprisingly many articles about hypnosis have appeared in different weekly magazines. Naturally there are prejudices and misunderstandings regarding hypnosis in Norway too, but probably less than in many other countries, especially among people with academic education. One of the main reasons for this may be the fact that students, in all faculties of Norwegian universities, have to pass a preparatory examination in psychology (as well as logic and the history of philosophy). Since 1927 the textbook used has been H. Schjelderup's *Psychology* (new revised edition, *Introduction to Psychology*, 1957), in which hypnosis is discussed at some length.

With the growing interest among the younger psychiatrists, psychologists, and dentists, and with a largely positive attitude on part of the general public, the future of hypnosis in Norway must be considered as bright indeed.

IMPORTANT REFERENCES

Schjelderup, H.: Eksperimenter med tiden og fantasien. (Experiments on time and fantasy). *Nordisk Psykologi, 12:* 35-44, 1960.

Schjelderup, H.: Time relations in dreams. *Scand. J. Psychol., 1:* 62-64, 1960.

Schjelderup, H.: Hypnose og hypnosebehandling. (Hypnosis and hypnotic treatment). *Den Norske Tannlegeforenings Tidende, 72:* 451-461, 1962.

Åas, A.: Non-hypnotic experiences related to hypnotizability in male and female college students. *Scand. J. Psychol., 3:* 112-121, 1962.

Åas, A.: The recovery of forgotten language knowledge through hypnotic age regression. *Am. J. clin. Hypnosis, 5:* 24-29, 1962.

Åas, A.: A factor-analytic study of some subjective personal experiences and their bearing on theories of hypnosis. *Acta Psychologica, 20:* 196-209, 1962.

HYPNOSIS IN SWEDEN

By

Gerard Odencrants, M.D., M.A.

Gerard H. Odencrants; born 1888; M.D. (neurology and psychiatry); Fellow I.S.C.E.H., Member Swedish Doctors Society (Svenska, Läkarsällskapet), Stockholm Doctors Association (Stockholms Läkarförbund), Association for the Advancement of Psychotherapy (U.S.A.); papers on hypnosis and psychoanalysis; present position, private practise in psychotherapy, Stockholm, Sweden.

PAST

In 1785, Lieutenant C. G. Silverhielm, a grandson of Swedenborg's sister, studied animal magnetism in Paris under Mesmer and in the following year he opened a baquet in Stockholm. The Frenchman, Maisner, was also active in this country. A society was founded by C. F. Novdenskiöld for hypnotic studies and several cases of chronic diseases were cured at this time. However, the opposition to such studies and uses were great, especially when, as often occurred, it was linked with the Swedenborg doctrine. After a time, partly because of fraudulent cases, interest in hypnosis declined and studies in this field were temporarily discontinued.

In 1809, J. J. Ekman, M.D. (my great-grandfather) addressed a learned group in Gothenburg on animal magnetism. He had travelled widely in Europe and had also practiced in Paris. In 1814, Professor P. G. Cederschiöld defended the practice of animal magnetism, for in 1811, he had along with Dr. Öhrsted of Denmark, seen the usages of animal hypnosis, had studied its characteristics and then had presented himself as a magnetiser. He had published a *Journal of Animal Magnetism* which had appeared annually for some six years. In it there had often been heated debate, and this had continued for a long time. Cederschiöld had been supported in his interest by Professor

228

Sparrman, who had on journeys with Captain Cook to the South Sea Islands in the 1770's, seen how the natives treated each other with "passes." This, according to report, was an ancient Chinese procedure. He later gave up this particular interest and devoted himself mainly to obstetrics (his techniques in this field preceded those of S. Semmelweiss). Interest in animal magnetism remained but it was mainly in the theoretical field among persons interested in philosophy.

In 1887, to 1888, three books on hypnosis were published by Björnström, Huss and Wetterstrand based on ideas implicit in the program of the Nancy School. Interest during this decade was great, but in practice it was restricted to the few individuals who practiced hypnosis. A major undertaking at this time was the investigation *inter alia* of "pass effects" by the psychologist Alrutz. This was discussed in his book, *The Dynamics of the Nervous System*, Uppsala 1913. This was followed by Björkhem's (M.D.) book on *Nerve Radiation* published in 1940. About this time, interest in psychoanalysis grew and rivalled hypnosis for the interest of individuals. Exponents for psychoanalysis were Bjerre, Gejerstam, Fröderström, Billström, and others. Interest in hypnosis declined after 1930, and psychoanalysis dominated the scene. In 1942, J. Björkhem (D.D., Ph.D., M.D.) rearoused interest in hypnosis by his paper on hypnotic hallucinations. Two gynaecologists and a narcotic specialist are at present studying the applications of hypnosis to their own special fields. Psychologists have only shown a slight interest, while dentists have shown a great interest in the application of hypnosis. Individual doctors have indicated interest especially obstetricians and this general interest is on the increase.

PRESENT

At present hypnosis is used to a major extent only by a few doctors. Knowledge about hypnosis is insignificant and certain circles are skeptical about its phenomena, however, this attitude is changing as is also the case with regard to psychiatry. Law suits against doctors for misuse of hypnosis have not occurred. There is discussion at present as to whether the legal right to use hypnosis can be extended to dentists. Nowadays, only doctors may accept payment for hypnotic treatment.

The law prohibits public demonstrations of hypnosis, but this is often evaded by calling such demonstrations "psychological experiments." Individuals participating in such demonstrations are either paid subjects, or persons that have been given free admission tickets. The public has an enormous interest in anything connected with hypnosis, but for the most part has very little knowledge about it.

Academic circles have, as previously indicated, displayed a minimum of interest. Similarly, the clergy is neither interested nor does it discuss the topic. Medical teaching consists only of lectures and demonstrations given by Dr. Finer, Dr. Galambos, or myself. It is only recently that courses for pregnant women have been given.

Dental

On the subject of hypnosis and odontology, Dr. Tage Persson, a dentist at Halmstad, writes, "Although the use of hypnosis in odontology has increased considerably in different parts of the world, since World War II, its use in the Scandinavian countries has been extremely modest inasmuch as no tuition has been given at our universities or educational institutions." However, for some time supplementary courses have been arranged by and for Swedish dentists (Svenska Tandläkarsällskapet). The reason for these supplementary courses was the report submitted in 1961 by a joint committee of the Swedish Dentists' Association (Sveniges Tandläkarförbund) and the Swedish Dentists' Society (Svenska Tandläkarsällskapet). This committee, which had, *inter alia*, the task of investigating the use of hypnosis in odontological practice and the requisite training, found that hypnosis could be a valuable means of assistance. They also outlined training courses for graduate dentists. As yet, however, it has been impossible to train a large number of dentists, as these courses have mainly been of an experimental nature and it has been thought to be desirable to await the experiences reported by those dentists who have taken such courses. It is quite remarkable that this topic has aroused such great interest on the part of Swedish dentists. Such courses have always been filled long in advance.

Within the field of odontology in Sweden, hypnosis is called "suggestive relaxation" in order to emphasize that deep hypnotic trances are not necessary.

In Sweden, contrary to many other countries, a clean line has been drawn by dental organizations with regard to the right of dentists to use hypnosis for psychotherapy. They have prohibited dentists from any and all therapeutical activities concerned with the treatment of mental problems. Their committee considers that this falls within the field of psychiatry. Thus, the dentist, should not attempt to cure such habits as bruxism, tongue sucking, nail biting, etc. Relevant and significant psychological factors lie in the background of such behaviours. Should the dentist come in contact with such habits, he immediately is to contact the patient's doctor—preferably a psychiatrist.

As suggestion plays an important part in the relationship between dentist and patient, it is of the greatest importance that dentists be so informed in order that treatment be facilitated. The dentist achieves better results with a cooperative patient.

The Royal Medical Board in Sweden (Kungl. Medicinstyrelsen) has adopted a wait-and-see attitude toward hypnosis (suggestive relaxation) possibly because of the precaution taken by dental organizations against any of their members doing psychotherapy. Dental organizations have required their students to agree to this stipulation (i.e., against doing psychotherapy) before admission to the practical courses in hypnosis is allowed. Such a requirement can only benefit the patient.

Since in odontology there is little need of deep trances, dental organizations in Sweden have, as previously mentioned, used the name "suggestive relaxation." With the interpretation implicit in the name "suggestive relaxation," the use of hypnosis will never be routine. Rather it will be seen as a valuable aid which should only be used when definitely indicated. One should neither exaggerate the beneficial aspects of hypnosis as many fanatics do, nor underestimate it in the prejudiced manner of the skeptic.

Several doctors have published works on hypnosis. Of these now active, Dr. Bjorkhem has, as previously indicated, written books on nerve radiation and hypnotic hallucinations, while Dr. Finer is at work on the problem of hypnosis and pain. Several dentists are also working on this latter problem. I myself have written several papers on the uses of hypnosis and have lectured to doctors, dentists, and laymen.

The usual misconception about hypnosis is that one puts a person into a deep sleep, asks him about past events that may be relevant, and that the patient is then cured. Many people are, as a result, afraid of revealing something that they wish to conceal or of coming under the influence of another person's will. Possibly hypnosis is desired because they wish to remember forgotten events.

IMPORTANT REFERENCES

Bjerre, P.: Studier in Själsläkekonst.
Lennmalm, F.: Svenska Läkarsällskapets Historia 1808-1908.
Nachmansson, E.: Animal Magnetism. 1926.

HYPNOSIS IN THE UNION OF SOVIET SOCIALIST REPUBLICS

By

M. S. Lebedinskii, M.D.[*]

Lebedinskii, M. S.; physician and psychiatric consultant; Aphasia, agnosia and apraxia, Kharkov, 1941, Characteristics of behavioral breakdown upon paralysis of the right cerebral hemisphere in Problems of Contemporary Psychiatry, *Moscow, 1948,* Notes on psychiatry, *Moscow, 1959.*

IN THIS paper we aim to outline briefly the history of the therapeutic use of hypnosis in the USSR, our theoretical positions, the current research, and the practical application of hypnosis. Treatment by hypnosis had attracted the attention of the Russian medical profession, especially of psychiatrists, even in the last century.

RECENT PAST

In pre-revolutionary Russia, many psychiatrists devoted serious attention to the use of hypnosis in medical practice. We consider it extremely important that the phenomena of hypnosis attracted the attention of Russian physiologists. Between these two research groups, and the directions of their work, there existed a close tie which became traditional in Russian medicine. This fact played an important role in the growth and development, in our country, of a consistent physiological-clinical approach to the problems of hypnosis.

An extremely important place in the development of hypnosis in Russia is occupied by V. Danilevskii, one of the foremost Russian physiologists. Danilevskii, in referring to his own work in the area of hypnosis, wrote that, fundamentally, it was directed at overcoming the mysticism with which much of the research of

---

*Translation by Vera Kosin, Pullman, Washington, U.S.A.

scientists in this area was permeated at that time. He considered it necessary, for this purpose, to show that the phenomenon of hypnosis was inherent, in some form, not only in human beings, but also among animals, and that these two forms of hypnosis are not mutually antagonistic. He wrote: "Even at present, authorities on hypnosis state that the phenomena of hypnosis are characteristic only of humans and that animal hypnosis has nothing in common with human hypnosis. . . Such a sharp distinction of psychic manifestations is losing ground gradually. The time will come soon when such a point of view will be referred to as mystic."

Danilevskii studied hypnotic phenomena in animals, just as Richet, Beard, and others did before him. However, the theoretical positions of Danilevskii differed sharply from the positions of his foreign predecessors, as well as from those of Professor Geibel (Kiev, 1876), who had conducted similar experiments. In 1889 V. Danilevskii reported on his studies of hypnotic phenomena in animals, and on his interpretation of the relationship between hypnosis in animals and in humans, at meetings of the medical society in Kharkov, and also at the physiological psychiatry congress in Paris.

It must be said that at this congress the physiological explanations of the Russian scientist found few sympathizers among those in attendance. In Russia, to the contrary, his point of view found support not only among leading doctors and physiologists, but also wide popular support. In 1881 one of the influential newspapers—"*Russkaya Rech*" — wrote that the Russian reader must regard hypnosis "as the natural result of specific conditions of the organs of the central nervous system."

Of great influence upon the formation of physiological concepts concerning hypnosis were the investigations of I. M. Sechenov. Of especial importance were Sechenov's studies devoted to the problem of cortical depression, as they pointed out that different stimuli can affect the organism under certain conditions in accordance with the earlier effect of the same stimulant. Later, I. P. Pavlov worked out this question within the concept of the delayed response. Actively fighting the anti-physiological explanations of hypnosis was the well-known Russian physiologist I. R.

Tarkhanov. In his brochure dedicated to the question of hypnosis, published in 1886, he wrote: "The main purpose of this brochure is to show that in connection with the basic characteristics of hypnosis which appears to be mystifying, the power of suggestion . . . find adequate explanation in psycho-physiological facts already known to science, and there is no need for new, audacious and fantastic hypotheses." N. V. Vvedenskii, another outstanding Russian physiologist, also addressed his interest to the question of hypnosis and its physiological basis.

At the time the Russian physiologists were working out a physiological concept of hypnosis, a clinical psychological basis for it was being actively investigated in the clinic of S. S. Korsakov, a Russian psychiatrist. A good deal was accomplished in this area by a colleague of Korsakov's who had similar ideas, A. A. Tokarskii. A. A. Tokarskii devoted a series of studies to the problems of hypnosis, and played an important role in the development of hypnosis in Russian science. He was a confirmed materialist (as was V. Danilevskii, whom we mentioned earlier). Understandably, the author of one of his obituaries wrote: "Tokarskii considered his stand in opposition to idealism not only his personal affair, but an obligation to society." Along with the theoretical questions of hypnosis, A. A. Tokarskii devoted much attention in his research to the application of hypnosis in clinical practice. He accomplished a great deal in this area.

Of course, there is no opportunity to present here, even in condensed form, all that has been inherited from Tokarskii's research. We shall mention only a small portion. First of all, Tokarskii's persistent goal of limiting hypnosis to the field of medicine is worthy of note. He insisted that only medical doctors had the right to hypnotize persons. He spoke out sharply against all attempts frequent at that time, of turning hypnosis into a spectacle or using it to propagandize anti-scientific concepts.

Due, undoubtedly, to the influence of S. S. Korsakov and A. A. Tokarskii, as well as the entire medical community, in 1890 the Medical Council of the Ministry of the Interior in Russia forbade "public seances of hypnotism and magnetism," as well as their use by non-medical men.

While vigorously promoting the use of psychotherapy, including hypnosis, in medical practice, Tokarskii also devoted much attention to the possible harmful effects on patients from errors in its application by doctors. Tokarskii emphasized in particular the necessity of preparing a patient (through an explanation of the nature of hypnosis, etc.) prior to placing him under hypnosis. Tokarskii and like-minded individuals contributed much time and effort to popularizing the use of hypnosis in medical practice. The principal issue was not the isolated application of hypnosis, but rather, about psychotherapy as a whole, including hypnosis as a part of it. Actually, this is the prevailing point of view of the entire Soviet medical profession.

A. A. Tokarskii took into account the role of the medical community in the development of Russian medicine, and in 1889 delivered a report on the particulars of the application of hypnosis in medical practice at the third conference of Russian physicians. Following this, the presentation of papers on hypnosis, and on psychotherapy was frequently repeated at such meetings. Parenthetically, it can be said that the close connection between psychotherapy and general medicine, with broad clinical application, was characteristic of the development of psychotherapy in this country.

Later, reports on hypnosis were made frequently at conferences of psychiatrists, and in our country psychiatrists are the foremost champions of the use of hypnosis in general medicine. Let us note the reports at the first and second conferences of Russian psychiatrists. At the first conference of neuropathologists and psychiatrists in 1911, a report on psychotherapy was given by the well-known psychiatrist B. S. Greidenberg. In developing the views of Tokarskii, and evaluating the positive significance of the application of hypnosis to medical practice, Greidenberg emphasized especially the necessity of taking into account the influence of hypnosis on the consciousness of the awakened patient. Such a principle of a psychotherapeutic complex is accepted by our psychotherapists to this day. Other outstanding Russian psychiatrists had devoted much attention to various problems of hypnosis during the past century. We refer here to V. I. Iakovenko, an outstanding figure in the area of social psychiatry, particularly in the organization of psychiatric services. In 1888, in one of his works he wrote about the necessity of carefully individualizing the suggestion formula for the patient during the hypnotic condition, and about the principles of constructing such individualized formulae.

Of tremendous influence in the formation of Russian and Soviet psychotherapy was the work of V. M. Bekhterev—a leading psychiatrist, a neuropathologist, physiologist and anatomist, as well as a leading public figure. In the area of psychotherapy, V. M. Bekhterev paid especial attention to the nature of the suggestion during the hypnotic state. Bekhterev categorically refuted those concepts according to which hypnosis was nothing more than a form of neurosis, and that the hypnotic state, like a pathological condition, can be harmful in and of itself. V. M. Bekhterev regarded the hypnotic state as a specific variation of normal sleep, as totally harmless, and a state that may be induced in healthy as well as neurotic patients. The defense of this interpretation of the hypnotic condition by such a highly regarded scientist as Bekhterev played an extremely important role in solidifying scientific understanding of hypnosis, and of the appropriateness of its application in the treatment of neurosis, and many other illnesses. V. M. Bekhterev played an influential part in the broad acceptance of medical hypnosis in medical practice.

Not having the opportunity here to delve into the contributions of other doctors and physiologists in the field of hypnotherapy in pre-revolutionary Russia, let us scrutinize more carefully what was done in this area of our interest by I. P. Pavlov. Pavlov's research elevated this field of knowledge from a mere collection of empirical data, and gave it an authentic theoretical basis (thus assuring its status) and won for it wider acknowledgment and trust as an accepted therapeutic method. I. P. Pavlov's research gave an opportunity to study anew the essence of the hypnotic state, its significance in therapy, and the mechanism of its therapeutic effect. A new approach is also provided by Pavlov's research concerning the nature of the hypnotic suggestion, which is inextricably linked with hypnosis in man, but not identical to it, as is sometimes incorrectly claimed.

Of tremendous importance to the theory of psychotherapy in general, and hypnosis in particular, is the Pavlovian concept of a two-signal system. A *word* (or words) play a decisive role in hypnosis, or in the course of suggestion. I. P. Pavlov wrote: "*Words*, as a result of the life experiences of an adult, are closely linked with all internal and external stimuli which enter the cerebral hemispheres. *Words* keep sending signals concerning these stimuli, keep replacing them, and therefore can elicit all those behaviors and reactions of the organism which characterize such stimuli." Pavlovian teachings concerning the relationship of conditioned and non-conditioned reflexes, and those teachings concerning the role of the cortex in regulating the functions of the organs, equip Soviet psychotherapists for correct, scientific solutions to the theory and practice of hypnotherapy. According to Pavlov's studies, hypnosis in a person is a partial sleep, i.e., an incomplete sleep, varying in depth, but not encompassing all sections of the brain, and affecting the involved areas in different degrees. This interpretation of the hypnotic state is exceedingly important for both theoretical and practical reasons. In part, it is associated with a point of view which examines the hypnotic state in its close relation to both a natural sleep and to the state of wakefulness. The latter should not be regarded unduly as being opposite to or contrary to the condition of hypnosis. The awareness of a person in varying degrees of hypnosis to some extent retains the quality of wakeful consciousness, as well as the basic characteristics of personality and the level of its development. As Pavlov indicated, it is still not possible to reflect accurately and completely, within any one classification, all of the many hypnotic states that can be seen in man, but such variations should be taken into account. At the same time, those hypnotic conditions which I. P. Pavlov induced in animals (with characteristic symptoms, as described by him), could and should be correlated with those evident in humans in the hypnotic state brought on by suggestion. Especially in recent years, a number of investigators, applying physiological methods — i.e., electroencephalography, plethysmography, the method of formation of conditioned reflexes, etc.—showed the possibility of objectively characterizing various phases of the hypnotic state in man in particular, as well as the classical expressions of paradoxical and ultraparadoxical phases, as described by Pavlov. Identification of the phases of hypnosis is of great significance, especially for the evaluation of the strength of verbal stimuli which may be used in suggestion during the hypnotic state.

The Pavlovian interpretation of the relationship between the states of wakefulness and sleep is of considerable importance. I. P. Pavlov wrote that there is no absolute contradiction between the two. From this concept he derived his understanding of hypnosis as being the result of the division of the cerebral hemispheres into sleep and wakefulness areas, and the state of hypnosis being that of partial sleep in terms of the relationship between the secondary and the primary signal system. Such physiological interpretations showed the scope of verbal effectiveness in the process of suggestion.

The views of I. P. Pavlov were developed and corroborated by important facts gained by his many students and other Soviet investigators who agreed with his position. We shall mention only a small part of the relevant research. (We shall not cite here the relevant studies of foreign investigators.)

Interesting experimental materials were gathered in a series of studies by A. O. Dolin *et al.* Together with his co-authors and colleagues, Dolin showed, specifically, that suggestion can, in accordance with its content, affect the chemical processes of a person's organism. This was convincingly demonstrated by showing that if a person in a deep hypnotic trance was given pure water, but told that he was drinking sweet syrup, there was in a number of cases, a reflex rise in the sugar content of the blood. Control tests, for the purpose of this study, were made in which the subject was given sweet syrup but told that he was drinking pure water, and in these circumstances there was no evidence of a rise in the blood sugar content. The effect of the *words* temporarily repressed the biological reaction. By this means, and in complete accord with the teachings of I. P. Pavlov, it was shown that suggestion, capitalizing on a person's former life experiences with conditioned reflexes, can affect metabolic processes.

Important facts about the influence of suggestion on somatic processes during the hypnotic state were gathered over a period of many years of research by K. I. Platonov, one of the first Soviet psychotherapists an outstanding student of V. M. Bekhterev, and a follower of I. P. Pavlov. Among the many facts established by Platonov, let us note for example, the data which demonstrated the effect of suggestion on the condition of the digestive system of the subject. Platonov and his colleagues showed that through the influence of suggestion, the feeling of nausea, in many cases, could lead to severe and total contractions of the stomach, and affect hormonal activities, etc.

Of great import are the works of K. M. Bykov and his many students and colleagues. The theme of Bykov's works and the studies in the laboratories directed by him was the examination of the functions of the brain, their relation to the environment of the organism and the interrelationship between internal and external environments. K. M. Bykov did much to advance and develop Pavlovian teachings regarding the influence of the cerebral cortex on the organism as a whole. Understandably, his investigations gained great importance in both the practical development and theory of hypnosis.

In further presentation of our interpretation of the many issues and problems involved in hypnotherapy, we shall try to present in greater detail the role of Pavlovian teachings in our theory and practice of hypnosis. Of course, there still exists much about hypnosis that calls for future investigation and discovery, but even so, at the present time it can be stated that the therapeutic application of hypnosis has a scientific basis. The positive therapeutic value of hypnosis can, in a large percentage of cases, be considered fully proven in medical practice.

PRESENT

Before turning to a presentation of the problems involved in the application of hypnosis in our country, we shall examine the more or less characteristic attitude toward the hypnotic method of Soviet psychotherapists and physicians, admitting the existence of individual variations to this point of view.

In medical practice, in our country as in others, hypnosis is used as a tool for suggestion, and a method for healing by the actual hypnotic condition as a state of peculiar somnalescent inhibition. We rarely use the technique of hypno-analysis. Hypnosis, just as psychotherapy on the whole, can play either a subsidiary role or a primary role in the total treatment of a patient. In most cases, we look upon hypnosis not as an isolated method, but actually as one element within a program of treatment, exclusively psychotherapeutic, or, when necessary, in combination with surgical, and other therapeutic methods of treatment.

For example, hypnosis may be used as an anesthetic during surgery. Occasionally in other procedures, suggestion via hypnosis is applied in combination with various medicinal methods for the elimination of pain. It is used where medicinal methods alone are not adequate. At one time in our country many women were delivered without pain by the use of hypnotic suggestion, applied just before or during delivery. The first attempts at the alleviation of pain during delivery by this method were described in the last century. In recent years hypnosis for this purpose has been gradually replaced by prophylactic methods for pain relief (K. I. Platonov, I. Z. Velvovskii), and through the use of drugs. Advances in anesthesiology have been widely accepted within medical institutions, and in view of the free medical services which are available to our whole population, hypno-anasthesia is falling into disuse. In individual instances however, special reaction to a drug demands special preparation of the patient by psychotherapy which involves the use of hypnosis. Such an approach must frequently be considered, especially in pediatrics. It is applicable also in dentistry. In many cases of this kind, we think the use of psychotherapy merely as an expedient method for the alleviation of pain is too confining. Psychotherapy should not be limited to hypnosis. Therefore, we often do not distinguish too clearly between the use of hypnosis solely as a subsidiary method which complements other therapeutic approaches, and the truly therapeutic application of hypnosis *per se*.

The exaggerated fear of injections can be a danger signal of a tendency toward arousal of pathological fears in general. We believe that in such cases the doctor should be concerned about the total reaction of the patient. In such cases psychotherapy must, when possible, solve the problem of assuring successful overall therapy of the patient as one who is also suffering from phobias. In this case, we believe, psychotherapy should not be limited to hypnotic suggestion alone.

Let us now turn to the issue of whether the hypnotic state in itself can be regarded as therapy. We think that the answer to this question must be in the affirmative. But, this point of view of the therapeutic value of the hypnotic state is closely connected with an understanding of the advantages that accompany the hypnotic state. Tokarskii wrote: "One must accept as proven the evidence that hypnotic sleep is a means of soothing and strengthening the nervous system to a degree greater than in a normal sleep." This proposition cannot be doubted. Thirty minutes—an hour—spent in the hypnotic trance, even without the benefit of suggestion, in most cases produces an obvious therapeutic effect.

We believe that the above fact is largely explained by the following quotation from I. P. Pavlov: "When a dog in a harness (Pavlovian) goes into a hypnotic trance, the induced depression becomes associated with the total environment and bears directly on the pathological focus. Then a beneficial interaction takes place. I believe that this is the crux of the matter. Establishment of contact between a general depression with a specific condition of the pathological focus is essential." It is in this way that Pavlov explains why the prolonged sleep of the dog in the kennel does not cure the animal of the experimental neurosis, though the shorter hypnotic sleep in the harness brings about therapeutic results. Of course, the hypnotic state of the dog in its harness and the hypnotic state accompanied by direct suggestion in man are not identical; nevertheless, we believe it to be beyond question that Pavlov's concepts apply in both instances. In the hypnotic sleep the patient remains under the influence of the therapist, with attention specifically directed toward the pathological foci, with the sum total of psychotherapeutic skills being brought to bear upon him during and before the induction of the hypnotic trance. The above process is also associated with influences of the total situation which include the patient's knowledge about the doctor himself, and about the hypnotic method as an effective therapeutic treatment. Thus, the hypnotic condition affects the patient in great measure by the many conditioned reflexes which had already been formed. When the patient is brought into the hypnotic trance for therapeutic reasons, especially pleasant conditions are created for a positive effect. By this means, we think, a therapeutic effect is realized from the hypnotic sleep even in the absence of immediate suggestion. The degree of this effect on the patient is determined: by the peculiarities and the general condition of his nervous system, his relationship to the physician, the conditions of treatment, the methods used in treatment, and previous psychotherapeutic influence.

Speaking of the mechanisms of the therapeutic effect of the hypnotic state, taken in and of itself (aside from the heightened susceptibility to suggestion now present), it is reasonable, we think, to take into account another proposition, voiced by I. P. Pavlov during his "Wednesdays" (seminars). "If a dog with a phobia, accidentally, during experimentation, goes into a hypnotic trance, then the phobia disappears, is cured, i.e., if you are conducting an experiment (excluding the affected foci of the nervous system) and the dog goes into a hypnotic state as a result of the hypnosis, the phobia is gradually alleviated, and disappears. The complication lies in the fact that the illness was in the first place brought about by an excessively exaggerated use of the principle of inhibition, while the hypnotic state, in our opinion, *is* itself a state of inhibition. You see, inhibition is cured by means of inhibition . . . when you increase inhibition too much, you get a concentration of inhibition, and consequently, an intensification of inhibition. When the hypnotic state is induced, however, there is a weak inhibition of a diffuse type present, and this is not the state of intensified inhibition which originally lead to the phobia. One can imagine that weak inhibition is a therapeutic condition leading to improvement—to a normal state of inhibition." These words of I. P. Pavlov substantiate the therapeutic significance of the hypnotic state, at least in a number of cases.

Acknowledging the therapeutic possibilities of the hypnotic state we do not at the same time, endorse either its indiscriminate use or any particular time duration for its application, but rather act differentially in each case. In particular, we have seen in some patients with hysteria indications of a negative influence stemming from excessively prolonged hypnotic sleep, e.g., a loss of contact with reality characteristic of those suffering from hysteria as well as an aggravation of some pathological tendencies, etc. In some patients, a prolonged hypnotic sleep apparently creates a straining of the inhibitions, and gives rise to unpleasant sensations, which sometimes interferes with further treatment by this method.

Many psychotherapists use prolonged hypnotic sleep as a means of treatment for some types of patients. Specifically, this type of treatment was carried out with successful results on patients suffering from hypertension.

Of utmost importance for hypnotic treatment of a patient is the existence of the most optimal conditions for effective therapeutic suggestion. Of course, the application of the method of prolonged hypnotic sleep in medical treatment, as well as the use of suggestion, are, at the present time, somewhat limited by the use of psychopharmacological medication. But, it would be quite incorrect to think that these means are eliminating psychotherapy and the medical application of hypnosis. They, psychopharmacological techniques, contribute to creating more favorable conditions for psychotherapy, and particularly facilitate hypnotization and heighten its effectiveness when combined with psychotherapy as a whole. In appropriate cases, the combination of psychopharmacological methods with total psychotherapy is especially effective when the goals are the permanent elimination of fixed nervous disorders of psychogenic origin.

As it has been said earlier, the most basic aspect of the hypnotic state, and the primary reason for a doctor's choice of this method of therapy is the patient's heightened degree of susceptibility to suggestion. Russian, Soviet, and foreign authors gave much attention to the nature or essence of suggestion. Let us pause to consider the corresponding points of view of two—V. M. Bekhterev and I. P. Pavlov.

Bekhterev wrote: "In essence, suggestion is a direct grafting of the differing psychic states of one person to another—grafting which occurs without active participation of the recipient." Bekhterev differentiated suggestion from persuasion, from the influence of a command, and from imitation. This differentiation, is very important, and to Bekhterev's credit must go the discrimination between these forms of influence by one person upon another. At the same time, of course, in the practice of psychotherapy, we cannot set them totally apart. Suggestion in psychotherapy shades off into persuasion, and vice versa. A command or order, in psychotherapy is expressed in direct suggestion, etc.

Bekhterev was also concerned with the necessity of differentiating between suggestion carried out in accordance with a goal acknowledged by the patient, and suggestion exercised without an established goal. In psychotherapy, we are always concerned with the application of suggestion in accordance with a plan directed toward the resolution of the problem as the doctor sees it. Such a plan may be with or without the patient's cognizance of the suggestion involved, through persuasion, by way of a more devious route, or by means of the doctor's general behavior during hypnosis or at other times. We believe that any form of suggestion used by the doctor must be closely tied in with persuasion. Suggestion must in no way depart from psychotherapeutic principles. The power of suggestion must only augment that which the patient will comprehend with the help of the doctor. Persuasion must, in many cases, prepare patients for suggestion, and must enhance the meaningfulness and effectiveness of the latter. The context of suggestion, during a patient's hypnotic sleep, must not differ in any way from that given the patient in the wakeful state. We believe that nothing must be included in the doctor's suggestion that would be incomprehensible to the patient. The doctor, in his therapeutic procedures, has no right to impose or strengthen belief in superstitions, miracles, or mysticism. Although by comparison, Bekhterev's understanding of suggestion is greater than that of other authorities, it too lacked a physiological basis, and does not get to the crux of this phenomenon. This was accomplished by I. P. Pavlov.

Pavlov wrote that in hypnosis, in the healthy sound cortex, the positive tonus is lowered because of the radiation of inhibition. Suggestibility is based on the transformation of cells of the cerebral cortex into a condition of inhibition. When words of the doctor are directed at such a cortex, these words concentrate the stimulatory process in the appropriate area—a process which is accompanied by negative induction. The latter, because of lowered resistance, spreads over the entire cortex and, as a result of this, the power of suggestion tends to be isolated from other influences, and consequently acts with special force. Of course, it must be kept in mind, as pointed out by I. P. Pavlov, that one can only delineate certain phases of the hypnotic state. Pavlov even wrote that some degrees of depth or intensity of the hypnotic state are almost indistinguishable from wakefulness. Also, the force of the influence of suggestion may vary extensively. It is obvious, of course, that the force of suggestion is dependent not only on the phase (depth) of the hypnotic state but also upon other factors. Of utmost importance is the patient's degree of readiness for suggestion from *this* doctor, the patient's readiness to accept a specific suggestion, and his willingness to follow it. The conditions of suggestion, the state of the patient at the specific moment of suggestion, as well as the type of his nervous system are all relevant. Of significance is the true correlation between that which is being suggested and the life situation of the patient, as reflected in his biography, his temperament, his motivations, his reaction to illness, etc.

We think that it is incorrect to take the position that there is a single level of suggestibility. It is imperative, in our opinion, to take into account that the level of suggestibility can vary in relation to the subject matter of the suggestion even within the same hypnotic sleep of a given patient.

It is well known how difficult and almost impossible it is to bring to fruition realization of a suggestion which, by its context, is absolutely unacceptable to the patient's moral-ethical standards.

The degree of suggestibility depends to a certain extent on whether the suggestion is given individually or in a group of patients. V. M. Bekhterev was a strong supporter of group hypnosis. Its advantages were also recognized by V. A. Giliarovskii. Without doubt, in a group, susceptibility to hypnosis as well as suggestibility, both in the hypnotic and in the wakeful state is generally heightened. But not infrequently, a patient left alone with his doctor, accepts the psychotherapeutic procedure more calmly, and because of this, his suggestibility is heightened. Of course, the doctor, concentrating on one patient, can apply hypnotic variations most suitable to that particular person. This, too, can raise the effectiveness of the suggestion. Often individual and group sessions of hypnosis can and must be combined.

It is well known, and much has been written about it, that leading a person into the hypnotic state is not always successfully accomplished. Without doubt, there are people who can never be hypnotized by anyone. A limited number of people can be led into a deep hypnosis. The susceptibility to hypnosis of some people is markedly dependent upon their relationship to the hypnotist, the mode of hypnotizing, and upon their attitude at the onset of the trance. In many cases, the ease with which the hypnotic state can be elicited increases considerably with repeated sessions. V. M. Bekhterev wrote that persons especially susceptible to suggestion, and incapable of resistance, can be led into the state of somnambulism. K. I. Platonov, relying on his extensive experience, emphasized that the ability to be led into the somnambulistic phase may change depending on circumstances. It is difficult to say why a person, at times, loses this ability. However, this possibility should always be seriously considered by the doctor. The lowering of susceptibility may be brought about by psychological causes and such other reasons, as toxic factors, infections, etc. It may be considered an established fact that, for example, alcoholism frequently increases susceptibility. In a number of cases it has been reasonably well established that a cranial trauma heightens hypnotic susceptibility. A series of experiments carried out by Soviet investigators showed a connection between susceptibility to hypnosis, the type of nervous activity, and the interrelationship of signal systems. One could think of people who are of the artistic type (according to Pavlov), with a predominance of the primary signal system, as being more susceptible to hypnotism.

In recent years a number of Soviet investigations have demonstrated the possibility (in a number of cases) of modulating rather exactly—in one individual, within the duration of a given hypnotic sleep—the depth of the trance. This is done by changing the formula of the verbal suggestion, with the depth of the hypnotic sleep being measured by special physiological tests.

K. I. Platonov remarked that the form and tone of verbal suggestion are reflected by the depth of the hypnotic trance in no small measure. Thus, an energetic and curt enunciation of the word *sleep,* for a number of experimental subjects, was quickly reflected by a significant change in the plethysmograph; while a slow enunciation of the words *fall asleep* and *awaken* were followed by a correspondingly slower reaction of the blood vessels.

Sometimes a doctor must consider the hypnotizability of a patient before he attempts inducing the hypnotic state. Usually, the doctor puts such a question to himself because he fears failure. Frequently, psychotherapists, before attempting hypnosis, try various tests of the patient's receptiveness to suggestion, we are not however in favor of this practice. We take into account the fact that in the majority of cases the doctor can induce hypnosis either on the first attempt or upon repetition, even though it be a light hypnosis. Furthermore, if the doctor is not trying to portray himself to his patient as a magician (and this of course is not tenable), if he does not intend to hide from the patient the peculiarities of hypnosis (its scientific basis, or the possibility of replacing this psychotherapeutic method by another equally successful psychotherapeutic treatment) then an experienced doctor is not placed in an uncomfortable position by an occasional unsuccessful attempt at hypnotism. For this reason we do not try to bring into our practice the testing of a patient's susceptibility to hypnotism (or as a means of heightening suggestibility) by introducing suggestion while he is awake. We know that suggestibility, or lack of it during the waking state (with suggestion directed usually at motility) is a far from accurate measure of susceptibility to hypnosis. In view of all this, it is important for a doctor to know which patients he can rely on for successful therapy through hypnotism.

Many psychotherapists in our country have studied this problem. B. N. Birman, in particular, noted the frequent failures in attempted hypnotic treatment of patients suffering from obsessive neuroses. Other authors, too, have written about this. However, it is well to take into account that obsessions occur with various types of neuroses (and psychoses), and in patients with greatly varying types of nervous disorders. It is also worthwhile to note that V. M. Bekhterev had recognized great possibilities in treatment by hypnosis of some patients suffering from obsessions.

As outstanding an authority on the problems of psychotherapy as P. Janet wrote about the difficulties of inducing the hypnotic state in those afflicted with epilepsy. But even with this statement, experience does not allow unqualified agreement. Many patients with epilepsy are extremely susceptible to hypnosis, and this tendency can be used with notably successful results in treatment designed to influence the pathological characteristics of personality.

One of the leading Soviet psychotherapists, Iu. V. Kannabikh, wrote that the psychotherapist meets with great difficulty in attempting to hypnotize patients suffering from reactive depression. However, experience shows that this is not always true. It is likely that such a difficulty is more applicable to those patients suffering from endogenous depression.

Frequently, psychopaths are difficult to hypnotize.

We believe that in attempting to decide on the advisability of attempting hypnotism, guidance must be taken not only from the diagnosis of the illness, but also from the results of extensive clinical and physiological testing.

Generally, it is difficult to rely on the success of hypnotic suggestion with patients who are disturbed or tense for one reason or another. We consider it proper before attempting hypnosis to alleviate anxiety and tension through discussion, and with the assistance of drugs, when it seems advisable. Currently, the use of drugs has become expedient because we have so many effective tranquilizers and somniferous drugs. Of course, before attempting hypnosis it is necessary to be sure that the patient harbors no apprehension or misinformation about this treatment. While the value of clinical-psychological criteria of hypnotizability is only relative, nevertheless, the information it provides can be extremely meaningful to an experienced doctor, and can help considerably in deciding whether hypnotism should be tried, and when. In many cases the difficulty of determining beforehand the degree of hypnotizability of a patient calls for an appropriate variation in the form of the suggestion to be used at the very beginning of hypnotic treatment. This is true in both the individual case as well as in group therapy.

Many specialists in our country, as well as abroad, willingly use the method of narcohypnosis, which markedly increases the proportion of patients successfully hypnotized, as well as affecting favorably the depth of the induced sleep.

Out of the concept of the close relationship between hypnotic sleep, natural sleep, and drug-induced sleep, arises the possibility of their being brought closer together in hypnotherapy. Some of our psychotherapists, just as psychotherapists of other countries, apply the method of transforming physiological sleep into a hypnotic-suggested sleep, with success. During the past few years in the USSR a series of studies have been devoted (M. E. Teleshevskaia, and others), to the therapy by suggestion of certain conditions, primarily those of a hysterical type, when the patient is in an incomplete sleep induced by hexonium. Such a procedure is patterned after the work of P. Schilder and his colleagues. In practice, this method showed several important possibilities. This approach is especially expedient in the treatment of fixations. This method of treatment was effective in many cases where other psychotherapeutic and medicinal approaches had failed. Hexonal (pentothal, hexobarbital) usually is introduced slowly (2-4 cc of 10% solution) until a state of mild stupor occurs. It is in this setting that insistent, directive, and energetic suggestions are carried out. Frequently it is possible to achieve marked success during one, two, or several sessions. This method of narcohypnosis is specifically different in that the patient retains his mobility, and to some degree his active participation.

Where it is difficult to induce the hypnotic state, and when the latter is desirable, Soviet psychotherapists do not reject the use, in small doses, of somniferous drugs (usually barbituates) before attempting hypnotism, thus taking advantage of a drug-induced somnolence. This method of hypnotism has been used in our country for a long time. A. A. Tokarskii, following the work of Voisin, used chloroform as an aid in inducing the hypnotic state. For a slightly different reason, morphine was used to alleviate pain in a patient just before hypnotism was attempted. V. M. Bekhterev, and others, wrote about combining the use of suggestion and narcotics.

The total effect attained by the application of this latter method is, we think, of theoretical as well as practical interest. It demonstrates, on the basis of a method which closely resembles an experiment, a relationship between suggested and drug-induced sleep, a relationship, and reciprocity in the action of non-conditional and conditional activities, which specifically arises as a result of verbal stimulants. Anyone who has tried this combined method of inducing hypnosis cannot but be convinced that the need for drugs is lost quickly. Often a single application is adequate, and the patient himself has no further need of a soporific effect to reinforce suggestion. This, as well as many other facts, shows that the conditioned reflex is capable of reinforcing the unconditioned effects of drugs on the organism, i.e., on the central nervous system, and on the psyche—especially during the induction of the somnolent state. In I. P. Pavlov's laboratories it was shown that the repeated introduction of sleep-inducing chloral hydrate into the colon of a dog eventually resulted in a reaction in which the dog fell asleep following the introduction into the colon of warm water without the admixture of chloral hydrate, i.e., through the mechanism of the conditioned reflex. I. P. Pavlov also noted that a dog which has been hypnotized several times in the (Pavlovian) frame or harness would fall asleep when placed there, even before the experimental manipulations had begun. Psychotherapists know well that when humans are in familiar surroundings, the hypnotic condition is also realized more readily. A patient who has been hypnotized several times will sink into a hypnotic state, sometimes, even without suggestion, simply because of the influence of the surroundings and the situation connected with previous experience.

The following must be added to this discussion: we became convinced through personal experience that in those cases when the use of a drug prior to oral suggestions did not show results, (subjectively or objectively) and when attempts to induce hypnotism by suggestion alone also failed (and when the experiment required that the patient be unaware of a second drug dosage) the use of oral suggestion added to the drug intake (of the same quantity as in the first trial) now resulted in a hypnotic state. This type of observation also demonstrated the similarity between physiological sleep, medicinally induced sleep, and the hypnotic sleep. Such observations also demonstrate that the effect of somniferous drugs can be "subthreshold," and not revealed until a supplementary factor is added which exerts influence through the psyche of the patient.

On the other hand, in the presence of negativism on the part of the patient toward the hypnotic method of treatment, that dose of drugs which, without the negative factor, would be fully adequate for somnolency, now, together even with the factor of suggestion, may be ineffective. We believe that what we have presented corroborates the principle, especially important to the psychotherapist, that the role of the psychological factor in the effectiveness of drugs is very significant for its success or failure.

Proof of an interrelationship between drug application and suggestion is evidenced by the fact that during hypnotic sleep, which has been attained through narcohypnosis, suggestion can check the effect of the drug. Withdrawn quickly out of the hypnotic state (narcohypnosis), the patient even after only a few minutes of the initiation of the sleep can, under the influence of a specific suggestion, feel no sleepiness, and in fact be fully awake.

In practice, the application of somniferous drugs for the hypnotism of those patients who are not readily susceptible to hypnosis, must often be acknowledged as useful.

We think the narcohypnotic method is valuable in the presence of an ambivalent attitude toward hypnosis by the patient. Sometimes the patient is extremely eager for hypnotic treatment, but at the same time the process of hypnotism arouses apprehension, in spite of reassurances from the doctor with regard to this unfamiliar procedure. The application of somniferous drugs can quiet this anxiety and, in this way, help in the hypnosis of the tense or excited patient. At the present time, drugs for the preparation of a patient for hypnosis can be chosen easily. Sometimes the hypnotic sleep is delayed by a patient's entrenched habit of taking a long time to go to sleep. Here too, drugs may be of value. This is especially true at the beginning of therapy (most frequently in cases of insomnia), when a patient has acquired the habit of relying on somniferous drugs. There are many variations that account for a lowered susceptibility to hypnosis which it is reasonable to overcome with the aid of the combined method involved in narcohypnosis.

Sometimes reservations may be expressed concerning drugs (the use of which in routine medical practice is usually not concealed from the patient) and their use may lower the effectiveness of future suggestion, by having a negative influence on the relationship between doctor and patient, and thus on the total success of the treatment. Observations show that the total picture obtained depends upon the conduct of the doctor. As we have said already, we do not subscribe to the type of behavior wherein the doctor tries to impress the patient with his supposedly unusual powers regarding hypnosis, or creates an aura of mysticism. Particularly with regard to the hypnotic method, we always explain its essence to the patient from a materialistic point of view, i.e., from the Pavlovian position. With this approach it follows that the use of drugs cannot damage the authority of the doctor, or this method of treatment.

Regardless of whether we use drugs or other non-verbal techniques to induce hypnosis, we see the basic virtue of the medical use of the hypnotic state as essentially a treatment by suggestion, primarily characterized by a close relationship between doctor and patient. It may be considered that the success of suggestion, particularly as expressed in the ensuing hypnotic trance, reinforces the patient's hopes for future suggestive influence, and heightens suggestibility.

Taking this into account, let us look into some of the problems of hypnotic treatment. We believe that successful attempts at hypnotic treatment depend to a great extent upon the attitude of the patient toward his doctor. From this point of view we examine the nature of the rapport. The roots for the rapport were planted, to a large extent, before the influence of suggestion and the hypnotic state were attempted. The nature of the rapport is largely dependent upon the doctor-patient relationship. In connection with this it is desirable to consider the possibility of transmitting the feeling of rapport to another person. Contrary to the belief, formerly held by many specialists, transfer of rapport is not a simple process. The doctor who has induced hypnosis originally, can arouse a degree of acquiescence to the suggestive influence

of another doctor, but he cannot always assure, by means of transferred rapport, the same effectiveness to the suggestion of the
other doctor, as had been true for him. The selectivity of the rapport, the role played by the immediate surroundings, the interrelationship between the patient and his original hypnotist, the
doctor to whom the rapport has been transferred, are of course,
all important matters. The degree of this selectivity is, to no small
extent, dependent upon the patient's relationship with the doctor.
Rapport can be understood from a psychological point of view as
a dependency (fixation) of the patient upon his doctor, and physiologically, as a dominant physiological mechanism, described by
A. A. Ukhtomskii as forming in the patient, and directing his
attention, feelings, and thoughts, toward the doctor. This fixation or dominance grows from the very first meeting of the doctor-
psychotherapist and patient.

Facts established during experimentation with animals have acquired great importance, both in grasping the essence of the hypnotic state and in understanding the mechanics of inducing hypnosis in man. The psychotherapist should realize that in the experiments on animals done by Pavlov and his colleagues, it was
shown that the hypnotic state in animals may be induced primarily through weak, monotonous, and repeated stimulations. However, sometimes the hypnotic state may appear quickly, resulting from strong stimulation. These observations during experimentation help in an understanding of its physiological nature—
an understanding which has been reached through experience
by many doctors.

Among the important problems of medical hypnosis the role of
the depth or phase of the hypnotic state must not be overlooked.
Much research has been devoted to this problem by our scientists,
as well as by foreign investigators. V. M. Bekhterev especially,
noted that light hypnosis can be utilized for medical therapy with
significant effectiveness. Every specialist knows that the depth
of the hypnotic state varies, but that it is important to recognize
the attained depth in order to adjust the suggestion accordingly.
The hypnotic state, in any degree, heightens suggestibility, i.e.,
the receptiveness of the patient to the oral influence of the doctor.
Various objections have been raised against the proposition of the

heightened suggestibility found in a hypnotic state. We believe that experience does not allow us to consider these objections as valid.

Of course, a state of a deep hypnosis promises (as a rule but not invariably) a high degree of susceptibility to suggestion. A deep hypnotic state in itself is proof of high susceptibility, and a readiness of the patient to submit to the hypnotic treatment and to the therapeutic medical ministrations of the doctor, especially of that particular doctor. Deep inhibition of the analyzers of the external and internal environments during the condition of deep hypnosis, inductively strengthens "foci of wakefulness" in the cerebral cortex, i.e., strengthens rapport, and intensifies the effectiveness of the verbal suggestion. Frequently, as previously stated, the attained hypnotic state through suggestion is documentation of the patient's faith in the hypnotic treatment, and consolidates the authority of the doctor in the eyes of the patient, which in turn strengthens his influence on the patient. At the same time, there can frequently be seen an incomplete post-hypnotic persistence of the effect of the suggestion on the patient, who is in the somnambulistic phase of hypnosis.

Disparity between the depth of the hypnotic state and the effectiveness of suggestion depends on a number of facts. It is worth noting first, as has already been mentioned, that the degree of suggestibility of any given individual varies in accordance with the subject matter. Specifically, the patient may be highly receptive to suggestion in general, but difficult to put to sleep through suggestion. Then there are patients who may be put into a deep trance readily, but when directed in this state toward the symptoms of their illness, or its causes, will submit to suggestion in different ways, in varying degree and for different reasons. This apparently is especially true as a result of the different attitudes to the symptoms on the part of the patient, the different meanings they may hold for him, and the firmness with which he holds on to them, etc. In the previously noted divergence of the effectiveness of suggestion, an obvious role was played by the presence or absence of the ability on the part of the patient to go to sleep. The type and condition of the nervous system has a bearing on this problem.

As is known, the question of the possibility of identifying the depth of the hypnotic state and the classifying of the various levels of hypnosis has occupied many investigators. Russian scientists too, have given this matter much attention. The classification of V. M. Bekhterev suggests three stages of hypnosis: light, medium, and deep. B. N. Birman, a colleague of I. P. Pavlov, preferred to speak of two basic hypnotic phases: hypotaxis or a light hypnosis, and the somnambulistic phase. K. I. Platonov uses a schema, regarding the depth of the suggested sleep, developed by E. S. Katkov. This schema delineates, as does that of V. M. Bekhterev, three basic stages of hypnosis. But at the same time, in this schema, each of these stages is divided in turn, according to basic physiological criteria, into three levels. This classification attracts attention because it describes more fully the hypnotic phases. At the present time it is probably more reasonable to use classifications which do not attempt to subdivide the hypnotic state extensively. But even the use of simplified schemas does not obviate the necessity of identifying, through as detailed a clinical and physiological examination as possible, the depth of the hypnotic state. Much has been accomplished by Soviet scientists in this direction during the last few years. In such an examination various physiological methods are used: electroencephalography, plethysmography, the formation of conditioned reflexes, etc. For example, through examinations of this type (V. E. Rozhnov, I. V. Strelchuk, et al.) it was established that with the deepening of hypnosis the percent of conditioned and nonconditioned reactions characteristic of the paradoxical and ultra-paradoxical phases (according to Pavlov) noticeably increases. The blink reflex was used for the purposes of differentiating the degree of depth of the hypnotic trance, and it was shown that during the deepest trances, the blink reflex disappears entirely. Through a series of physiological studies by Soviet scientists, different expressions of similarity and dissimilarity between sleeps of varying depth, induced by suggestion, naturally, or medicinally, were achieved. The problem of electroencephalographic indices reflecting the depth of hypnosis has been studied by M. P. Nevskii *et al.* The theoretical significance of this type of investigation is indisputable. In practice, we think, it is undesirable to burden a hypnotized patient with various tests, and we prefer to rely to a large extent on clinical observations followed by subsequent interrogation.

Acknowledging the possibility of effective therapy through even a light hypnosis, we still must take into account fully the specifics of each variation of the hypnotic state, with all of its peculiarities, and identify them within the limits of the knowledge available to us at the present time. It is in accordance with these specifics that the medical treatment is planned. The state of deep inhibition does not allow the use of a highly involved suggestion, since its content may be incomprehensible to the patient. On the other hand, in light hypnosis, one should take into account the associations of that area which forms the object of the doctor's suggestions, with other areas of consciousness. In such instances, one must exert a broader influence on the psyche of the patient, bringing the suggestion, in its forms and content, closer to the explanation or resolution of the patient's problem.

In the USSR therapy through hypnosis is carried out individually or with groups of patients. As has been shown by many of our authors, especially V. M. Bekhterev, the effectiveness of suggestion can be heightened in group hypnosis. To the suggestive influence of the doctor is added the interacting influence of other patients. The susceptibility to hypnosis of patients is often greater in a group. When some level of hypnotic sleep is attained, most of our psychotherapists continue group suggestions with the suggestion calculated to influence equally all persons in the group (similar to individual hypnosis). While working with the group, the doctor also comes up to each patient, and quietly, so that he alone will hear, makes a suggestion designed for him alone. Whether the hypnotic suggestion is carried out individually, or by the group, we usually consider it imperative to precede it by a satisfactory mutual acquaintance between patient and doctor. The meeting must take place privately. It is important to remember the necessity for the doctor to know each patient for a correct assignment of the patient by the doctor into the right group, and for the assurance of an adequate individual approach when the patient is in the group. It is also important to remember that during the initial meetings of a doctor with the patient, the patient also becomes better acquainted with the doctor. This contact should increase a patient's faith in his doctor, and thus pre-dispose him to participation in group therapy.

In those cases when a group is selected on the basis of a single criterion, and when all the patients are equally in need of relief from the same problem (e.g., alcoholism or smoking) treatment in a group is frequently begun. Later individual psychotherapy may be performed in accordance with the individual need. It is worthy of note, however, and many investigators have written about this in our country, that problems and habits which are apparently alike, may have altogether different roots. Thus, for example, alcoholism may have different origins and different manifestations. In conducting group hypnotherapy, this cannot be overlooked, especially when initial failures in treatment are noted. It goes without saying that the structure of the oral suggestion, the subject matter, the timing, the intensity of the directive, the phrasing of the directive, etc., are all important.

Very important is the gradual and sequential statement of the problem. Various psychotherapists handle this in different ways. We think that this must be handled in accordance with: the nature of the illness, the individual involved, the particular nervous system, the nature of the syndrome, the interrelationship of the individual symptoms, and the attitude of the patient toward each of these factors.

A number of psychotherapists devote attention to the nature of the prognosis and how it should be formulated during the hypnotic state. The doctor is not always, of course, able to predict what he can attain during treatment. Sometimes it is reasonable, at first, to formulate fairly carefully, the problem of treatment, and its goal. While the doctor must remain invariably optimistic during the suggestion, excessive promises can arouse a deep disappointment in the patient, both toward the doctor and toward the value of the treatment. Great tact is required, at this point, on the part of the doctor. Sometimes it is wise to first formulate something that is easily and quickly attainable, while speaking more generally about future goals.

Frequently, the psychotherapist using hypnosis must decide whether to direct the suggestion toward the underlying causes of the illness, or towards its symptoms, i.e., its manifestations.

This must be decided in various ways, depending upon a number of circumstances. If the cause is evident to both the doctor and the patient, then, of course, it is reasonable to direct the suggestion there. It is not wise to treat with scorn, when deciding on the subject matter of the suggestion, a so-called symptomatic approach to therapy. Sometimes it is possible, with sufficient permanence (or on first attempts less permanently) to relieve the symptoms. This is usually done to impede or stop the progress of the illness, and in this way create a positive effect on the illness as a whole. Besides this, even a small amount of initial success through psychotherapy, gives the doctor an opportunity to: increase the value of his treatment, reinforce the hope of the patient, and raise the effectiveness of his suggestive influence and treatment for the future. Sometimes it becomes extremely important to select objectives for the first suggestions which lend themselves more readily (in the doctor's judgment) to influence, but which, at the same time, are sufficiently significant symptoms in the patient's eyes. This of course poses a problem of no minor difficulty. Frequently, for example, of great importance to the patient, yet a problem that is relatively easy to alleviate, is insomnia. With hysterical patients, it is always necessary to begin with the alleviation of nervous fits, paralysis, aphonia and mutism, if these are present.

In sorting out those specific symptoms characteristic of the illness, which must be the primary targets of suggestion, we usually approach with care those which are most markedly expressed, and which are, therefore, most difficult to overcome. Patients will often react more violently in the hypnotic state than in the waking state when painful areas are touched upon. Specially directed research has shown that frequently suggestion is not realized exactly (as intended by the doctor) but is altered by the patient to some degree. This change is often a result of contact between the individual and the suggestion, almost as if it were a compromise. Such peculiarities in expression of the realization of the suggestion must be fully analyzed and used as a guide in the structure of future suggestion.

Suggestion during the hypnotic state is not used by us exclusively as a method of sedation and inhibition. At some stages of therapy, with some patients, this use is only of limited significance. We look upon suggestion also as a method which stimulates and activates. In this respect we are close to the view of E. Kretschmer. We combine in a complex psychotherapeutic system the activating method of suggestion during the hypnotic state with other activating methods, such as, for example, the method of training nervous processes with the goal of effectively strengthening and increasing the direction and activity of a patient in overcoming various pathologic symptoms.

We feel that the number of hypnotic sessions should be limited with the idea of gradually preparing the patient for treatment in a waking state, so that he will not need hypnotherapy nor ultimately any treatment. Excessive use of hypnotism can lead, sometimes, to the formation of an inordinate dependence of the patient upon the psychotherapist, and to the desire for hypnosis (for a specific state) regardless of its therapeutic effectiveness.

A number of investigators in our country have studied the question of the nature of rapport and post-hypnotic amnesia. In these studies it has been shown that the rapport depends on the formation of a focus of excitation in a depressed cortex (I. P. Pavlov). But the nature and the area of the zones of inhibition, under the influence of various conditions, can change during hypnosis. It may be considered proven in connection with this, that the intensity in selectivity of the rapport is always relative at any depth of the hypnotic state. Rapport is a two-fold phenomenon: the hypnotized patient receives the words of the hypnotist but still has a capacity for internal reaction. Upon examination, the relative strength of the rapport is also indicated by the fact that the hypnotized patient can, to a certain extent, receive and interpret the words of a third person, in the absence of an expressed reaction to them. These facts must be considered when providing the environment for the hypnotic session. An evaluation of the situation in clinical practice demands special attention to external stimuli. The selectivity of the rapport, and its expression, may vary with conditions.

As a result of a series of studies, we also consider post-hypnotic amnesia as a relative matter. According to Pavlov's "Wednesday" seminars, despite a patient's apparent total amnesia regarding a session it is still possible to activate partial recall by means of leading questions. It should not be overlooked that after hypnosis, patients frequently state that they have forgotten all suggestion, but at the same time can recall certain feelings or emotions they felt during the trance, as, for example, the fear that they could not awaken, etc. This specific form of amnesia which appears in relation to the hypnotic state is not connected exclusively with the somnambulistic phase of hypnosis. Frequently a light hypnotic state may also leave a patient without recall of what had been suggested. Such partial amnesia relates both to that part of the suggestion which later is exhibited in the patient's behavior, as well as to the unrealized part of the suggestion, i.e., independently of the potential activity of trace reactions and from the possibility of trace reactions in the future. Of importance here is whether the amnesia was suggested by the doctor although this fact, alone, does not decide completely the type or character of the amnesia.

Some research has noted that during physiological (natural) sleep, a person can, sometimes, learn that which has been told him, and then can remember it well upon awakening. This occurs without his knowing how he came by that knowledge. Similar phenomena are also observed in some patients. Certain variations of so-called post-hypnotic amnesia can to a certain extent be classified as characteristics of this kind of memory. During examination a close connection may be found between the phenomena of post-hypnotic amnesia and the phenomena of suggestion as the latter is being interpreted by the patient. One of our patients groaned loudly while in the hypnotic state. The groan coincided with the moment of the closest approach of the suggestion to the area of disturbance, i.e., the point which caused the patient the greatest suffering in his illness. When the trance was withdrawn, we asked him why he groaned. He remembered the fact of groaning, but could not remember during what part of the suggestion it took place. He stated that at some given moment he was "suffering gravely." This was said with an evident display of emotion, and with an expression of pain on his face. It should be noted that at this point the patient (to whom amnesia had *not* been suggested, as is frequently done by psychotherapists) began to remember less affective and less vivid moments present in the suggestion. By this means, we have been able to observe the presence, in a series of patients, of an emotional episode which was present in the course of post-hypnotic amnesia. In many cases, amnesia is connected with a unique and temporary divorce of the emotional turbulence from its subject matter. Such behavior occurred in the case described above.

Let us not pause any longer on those problems which occupy investigators and practitioners of hypnotherapy in the USSR. It would be impossible to discuss them all. Let us rather go to several other kinds of problems found in the practice of hypnotherapy in this country. But again, we can only mention them briefly.

The use of hypnosis for therapeutic purposes is widely accepted throughout the USSR. This method is considered effective here and by applying it one is frequently able to reduce the time needed for successful psychotherapy. Experience shows that when psychotherapy is properly practiced, i.e., when there is a correct combination of hypnotherapy with other psychotherapeutic and therapeutic procedures, lasting positive results can frequently be attained. The hypnotic method is used widely by our psychoneurological dispensaries and medical stations.

We utilize psychotherapy and the hypnotic method, particularly in clinical departments. Here it is used by specialists in psychotherapy (principally psychiatrists) and other doctors (obstetricians, dermatologists, internists, etc.) specializing in the clinical area to which a patient's problem has been referred, and for which he is being treated.

The hypnotic method is widely used in the USSR in the treatment of neuroses, less frequently, but still to some extent, it is used with psychoses. V. F. Snegirev, an outstanding Russian obstetrician-gynecologist of the last century, directed attention to the importance of psychotherapy in the treatment of gynecological illnesses. In the treatment of alcoholics, post-cranial trauma, etc., the method of hypnotherapy is often successful when combined with other methods. In individual cases, hypnosis is used in the treatment of neurological (organic) illnesses. In the clinical picture of organic illnesses of the central nervous system considerable space is given to functional stratification which can be removed by suggestion during the hypnotic state. Specifically, such therapy was used with those suffering from certain forms of aphasia. Of course it might be argued that the application of this method here was only secondary. The use of psychotherapy, including hypnotherapy, is becoming widely applied in the clinical practice of internal medicine. Reasonably good results have been obtained in the treatment of many cases of bronchial asthma, hypertonia, and malfunctioning of the cardiovascular system and the digestive system. Frequently, psychotherapy is very necessary when the basic treatment of a somatic illness is terminated or nearly terminated, but certain characteristics persist in the form of neurotic reactions. Some patients recovering from myocardial infarcts or coronary spasm can be cited as examples.

Hypnosis is also frequently used in obstetric clinics and in gynecology. Positive results have been attained in treating toxicosis and uterine bleeding in pregnant patients. Our psychotherapists and gynecologists have achieved a high percentage of improvement in cases of an inadequate or totally absent milk supply in nursing mothers.

Willingly, and with success, our specialists in dermatological psychotherapy, include the use of hypnosis in their treatment of skin diseases. Dermatologists use the hypnotic method in the treatment of eczema, neurodermatitis, various types of pityriases, urticaria, psoriasis, etc.

K. I. Platonov and others used hypnotherapy with some success in a few cases of endocrine disorders. Many psychotherapists occasionally use hypnosis successfully in their treatment system for stuttering.

We have obviously not enumerated all the clinical areas where psychotherapy can be useful and in which Soviet doctors specifically apply hypnosis as an element in a therapeutic system. It is taken for granted, that regardless of the types of illness in which the hypnotic method is used therapeutically, that it has been combined with other methods of psychotherapy and other methods of treatment wherever it is feasible and reasonable to do so. We never place psychotherapy in contraposition to other medication or methods of treatment; we do not separate them from each other. Only rarely is the hypnotic method *per se* used as the sole method of treatment. The psychotherapeutic phase of the combined type of therapy consists, as a rule, of a consolidation of several methods.

The majority of psychotherapeutic specialists in the USSR come from among psychiatrists. A psychotherapist who is capable of carrying out the many high-level psycho-therapeutic skills required by those suffering from the neuroses or psychoses, must be a qualified psychiatrist. In our country, basically, it is these specialized psychotherapists who take upon themselves the theoretical and practical problems of psychotherapy, as well as the burden of training future psychotherapists.

The application of psychotherapy to other types of illnesses demands adequate competency on the part of the doctor to problems of related clinical specialists. Of course, the obstetrician, the gynecologist, the dermatologist, and others who use hypnosis in the treatment of their patients, must also be adequately trained in the problems of psychoneurology, and psychotherapy (which includes hypnotherapy). When such specialists are not present, combined treatment is done here frequently by psychoneurologists together with other specialists—internists, endocrinologists, etc.

There is still much to be accomplished in the preparation of specialists in the area of psychotherapy. At the present time such training is taking various avenues. In our country, future doctors become acquainted with the elements of psychotherapy in medical institutes when they are being instructed in this area. Psychotherapy is also taught here in institutes for the professional improvement of physicians, as well as in specialized courses organized at scientific research institutes.

HYPNOSIS IN THE UNITED STATES

By

JOHN G. WATKINS, PH.D.

(See p. 3 for biographical note)

PAST

THERE WAS evidence that the early Indians in this country employed trance states as part of their religious ceremonies, and as a therapeutic device in the practices of the medicine men. In addition, the Eskimos apparently became involved in auto-hypnotic states during the long periods of waiting and loneliness required by the search for food in the Arctic wastes. Williams, in LeCron's text *(Experimental Hypnosis, N. Y., MacMillan, 1952)*, describes in considerable detail the cataleptic-like seizures of the medicine men among the Indians of the Arctic Circle which "justify the assumption that they are hypnotic." It is probable that the hypnotic state is practiced as part of both religion and medicine in primitive tribes throughout many parts of the world, and hence is not peculiar to the early men of the North American continent.

From an historical standpoint the United States cannot be said to have made any significant contributions prior to the twentieth century. The great names come primarily from England and France, and what little was done in this country in the 1800's represented a "spilling over" into the United States of thinking and practices developed in other areas.

The Zoist, a journal on hypnosis established by Elliotson in England, published papers in the early 1840's describing the surgical removal of tumors under "mesmeric trance" by several American physicians. In 1860, a lay hypnotist, Phineas Quimby, assisted a surgeon by hypnotizing a patient who was being operated upon for removal of a nasal polyp. Perhaps of greater significance was the influence of Quimby on Mary Baker Eddy, the founder of Christian Science. Mrs. Eddy came to Quimby as an invalid, and after treatment by "magnetism," became rehabilitated and embarked upon her career of developing a drugless, healing religion. It is noteworthy that Mrs. Eddy went to considerable lengths to deny that Christian Science had any relation with hypnosis. Most workers in the field of hypnosis, however, would view Christian Science as a method of treatment by suggestion.

The popularization of hypnotic treatment which followed the work of Liébeault, Bernheim, Charcot and Janet in France was transferred to this country, and a number of practitioners during the so-called "balmy" days of hypnotism treated all and sundry ailments by hypnotic suggestion. A few treatises were written on the subject in the United States. However, they did not contribute anything new, but rather presented history and practices from other countries and described methods of inducing the hypnotic state and giving therapeutic suggestions.

Thus the United States did not contribute to causes of the period of "boom and bust" which characterized the development of hypnosis in the 1890's, but did participate in it and reflect the trend which existed on the European Continent. The misuses, failures and subsequent loss of scientific interest in the technique occurred at the same time in this country. By 1905 the medical profession was largely disillusioned. Only a few outright "quacks" plus a very few courageous researchers were still working with hypnosis.

In regards to the latter, specific credit should be given the studies of Boris Sidis, psychologist (*The Psychology of Suggestion.* N.Y. D. Appleton and Co., 1921), and Morton Prince, psychiatrist, both of whom were ardent investigators of abnormal psychological phenomena. One of the classic studies of this period was that of the multiple personality case, "Sally Beauchamp," which was presented by Prince (*The Dissociation of a Personality.* N. Y. Longmans-Green, 1906. Reprinted N. Y., Meridan, 1957). In reading his detailed report about this dissociated girl one is struck by the remarkable modern-ness of Prince's techniques and theories. A number of hypnoanalytic methods, which apparently were not used again until the works of Erickson and Wolberg appeared some thirty to forty years later, were employed by Prince. And many of his theoretical formulations, concerning the nature of dissociative reactions and the role hypnosis plays in studying them, lie close to modern-day thinking. We must conclude that both Sidis and Prince were "voices crying in the wilderness," men ahead of their time, whose works were ignored then because the world was in the midst of another cyclical swing away from the excesses of hypnotic use which has so often in the past brought its temporary discreditation.

RECENT PAST

During the 1920's and early 1930's a few pioneering investigators began to study hypnotic phenomena by controlled laboratory experiments. These included N. C. Nicholson who, working in the physiological laboratory of the Johns Hopkins University Hospital, investigated resistance to ergograph fatigue during hypnosis. Further studies by Griffith Williams failed to confirm Nicholson's findings that hypnotic suggestion could significantly overcome fatigue effects. P. C. Young, working at the Harvard psychological laboratory in 1922, also failed to find significant suggestive effects on fatigue during the hypnotic state as measured by dynamometer grip. G. H. Estabrooks investigated tests of suggestibility, following up studies of two earlier British researchers, F. Aveling and H. L. Hargreaves. Stalnaker and Riddles studied the hypnotic recall of early memories, and Huse became concerned with the ability of hypnosis to facilitate the recall of recently learned material. Investigations of post-hypnotic amnesia were undertaken by Strickler, Coors, and Patten.

Other published reports of this time included studies on hypnotic dissociation by Messerschmidt, on conditioned reflexes initiated under hypnosis by Scott, on the correlations between hand levitation and eye closure by Jenness, and on hypersuggestibility as related to trance states by Krueger. These do not represent an exhaustive list of investigators of this period but are presented to indicate some of the studies made and the topics which interested researchers of that day. Most of these people were university psychologists who worked in laboratory settings. Many of them were students or associates of Clarke Hull, Professor of Psychology at Yale University, who is also known for his basic contributions to the field of learning. Hull, deserves great credit as being one of the first psychologists of recognized academic stature who dared to study intensely hypnotic phenomena at a time when such a subject was not respectable in most universities. In 1933, Hull published a book (*Hypnosis and Suggestibility,* N.Y., London, D. Appleton-Century, 1933) summarizing the research of these investigations and others. This book still stands as the most important work of the period and is a basic reference to early scientific research in the field of hypnosis in this country.

After the work of Prince there was little interest in the United States in clinical applications of hypnosis. It remained to a series of papers by Milton Erickson to reinitiate attention on the part of psychiatrists to the potentialities of hypnosis in psychotherapy. In these stimulating studies, Erickson reported on many unconscious dissociative phenomena observed under clinical treatment situations. He also experimented widely with new and unusual hypnoanalytic devices. In general, his approach, although psychoanalytically oriented, and at times in collaboration with psychoanalysts, did not aim primarily for the attainment of insight such as characterizes psychoanalytic therapy. Rather, it has been Erickson's contention that through the skillful use of hypnotic suggestions administered with psychodynamic understanding, significant changes in the inner character structure of patients can be achieved without the need for conscious, intellectual understanding. Perhaps his approach could be described as hypnodynamic, suggestive therapy. Erickson appears to have been one of the first clinical investigators who emphasized the relationship with the patient, and who developed non-directive and patient-centered induction techniques.

PRESENT

It remained to Brenman and Gill, two psychoanalysts at the Menninger Clinic, to begin the serious integration of hypnosis with psychoanalytic theory and method. In their earlier work (*Hypnotherapy.* N.Y., Inter. Univ. Press, 1947) they surveyed history and theory, described several methods of induction and considered various methods of therapy ranging from the suggestive, through the abreactive to the hypnoanalytic. Studies conducted in the clinical situation at Menninger's Clinic were discussed. Later (*Hypnosis and Related States: Psychoanalytic Studies in Regression*. N.Y., Int. Univ. Press, 1959) this same team summarized their more advanced studies and thinking. They attempted formulation of comprehensive theories about the nature of the hypnotic state which would harmonize research findings about hypnosis with accepted psychoanalytic theory and practice. Lindner presented a detailed case study involving hypnoanalysis and followed this with several other contributions in this area.

The first text on hypnoanalysis *"per se"* was published by Wolberg (*Hypnoanalysis*. N.Y., Grune and Stratton, 1945). A wide variety of hypnoanalytic techniques were described and illustrated through the presentation in detail of a case treated by hypnoanalysis. Later, Wolberg expanded his methods to a two-volume general text on all medical hypnosis. However, in spite of the contributions of these pioneers in hypnoanalysis, few psychoanalysts to date have been willing to reconsider their classical Freudian orientation to include hypnosis and hypnoanalytic approaches to treatment.

During World War II war neuroses were generally treated in the American Army by drug-induced abreactions, most battalion surgeons being unacquainted with hypnotic techniques. However, a few reports such as those published by Kardiner (*The Traumatic Neuroses of War*. N.Y., Hoeber, 1941) and others indicated that interest in hypnotherapy was still alive in certain Army medical circles.

The only book published at this time which was devoted entirely to the use of hypnosis in the treatment of war neuroses was one by Watkins (*Hypnotherapy of War Neuroses*. N.Y., Ronald, 1949). The work describes induction techniques and many different hypnotherapeutic approaches. This was followed by a number of case studies with verbatim reports illustrating hypnotherapeutic techniques ranging from post-hypnotic suggestions, to abreactions, to rather complex hypnoanalytic procedures.

Special attention should be directed to the contributions of Jerome M. Schneck, psychiatrist, and Milton V. Kline, psychologist. The record (some references are given at the end of this chapter) of these two, individually and in collaboration, is both significant and prolific in the areas of scientific research and clinical application. Schneck, as a psychoanalyst, has had considerable influence in inducing some analysts to reexamine their classical analytic positions regarding hypnosis. His writings include not only numbers of clinical and experimental papers on a wide variety of topics but also the writing and editing of various texts summarizing research and clinical practice. As the Founding President of the Society for Clinical and Experimental Hypnosis he was a key figure in the early organization of hypnosis specialists into scientific societies.

Kline, as a co-founder of SCEH, was closely associated with Schneck during the formative years of this Society. His writings, although also punctuated with numerous significant clinical contribution, were comprised more of controlled experimental studies and textbooks summarizing the entire field of hypnosis. During the latter part of the 1950's, Kline's contributions emphasized the development of theoretical formulations concerning the nature of the hypnotic state and its manifestations. As Founding Editor of the *Journal for Clinical and Experimental Hypnosis*, he exerted significant influence on the development of scientific research through his selection and publication of many outstanding papers. During the early 1950's Long Island University became a center of hypnosis research and the first home of the Institute for Research in Hypnosis.

During the past decade within the United States, there has been a phenomenal increase of attention toward the applications of hypnosis. Although this interest is held by both professionals and laity, it has been the curiosity and demand of the general public which has often forced members of the healing arts professions reluctantly to reexamine many preconceived ideas about its nature and usefulness, attitudes which had become firmly entrenched by professional education.

Life and *Look* magazines and the *Reader's Digest* (U.S. magazines with large circulations), to mention but a few, have published popularized articles regarding hypnosis. These were often highly enthusiastic accounts of "miracle cures." Public interest was whipped into a high enthusiasm, bringing hordes of people to their physicians, dentists and psychologists demanding treatment by hypnosis. Often these demands were met by resistance, the "pooh-poohing" of the merits of the hypnotic modality, or even pontifical statements regarding the dangers and hazards involved. Such resistance reflected both the previous ignoring or negative teachings about hypnosis which has been typical of medical, dental, and psychological education, and also the fact that most of the practitioners, having had no training in this modality, did not wish to disclose their lack of understanding about its use.

More recently, a number of articles have appeared (primarily initiated by one writer) aimed at stressing the dangers and misuses of hypnosis. These seem to have stimulated as much over-alarm as did the earlier articles over-enthusiasm. It is difficult to achieve a healthy balance of mature moderation in this sensitive field.

While the public interest, through such popular articles, has been stimulated to new peaks, the approach of the pertinent professions has been marked with more caution and conservatism. This is especially true of the official societies in medicine, psychology and dentistry.

ATTITUDES

Medical

In 1958, the American Medical Association (A.M.A.) investigated the clinical use of hypnosis. Nine consultants (seven physicians and two psychologists), who were recognized as authoritative contributors to the field, were asked to assist the A.M.A. Council on Mental Health in the formulation of official policy related to hypnosis. The conclusions of this study were published by the Council in the *Journal of the American Medical Association* following their approval in 1958 by the A.M.A. Board of Trustees and the House of Delegates.

Major conclusions of the Report were as follows:

1. Hypnotic techniques should be used within the scope of the professional training and competence of the physician or dentist who employs it.
2. A physician should use hypnosis in undertaking only

such procedures as he would be qualified to undertake without it.

3. Hypnosis should be used on a highly selective basis in accordance with specified indications and contraindications.

4. It should be used in association with other techniques, never becoming a single technique used under all circumstances by any physician.

5. It should be employed only by professionally qualified individuals who have received proper training in its use.

The Report warned against its use in entertainment and by untrained individuals. The lack of suitable training facilities was noted, as well as the limitations of short-term seminars and institutes in the field. A number of suggestions were made regarding training. The Report recommended that psychiatric departments within medical schools assume the responsibility for offering competent and thorough instruction, not only to psychiatric residents, but to selected physicians in other fields for whom the use of hypnosis was indicated. Much emphasis was placed on the need for adequate study of psychopathology and psychodynamics with attention directed to the all-too-frequent stress given to methods of induction. The Report encouraged an expansion of research in medical hypnosis.

Although the public clamor for hypnotherapy remains high, and although the A.M.A. has officially endorsed the medical use of hypnosis, urging that it be taught in medical schools, the training institutions have been slow in following these recommendations. Courses have been offered in such schools as Seton Hall, Pennsylvania, and the University of California at Los Angeles. However, the overwhelming majority of medical schools have continued to ignore this report and its recommendations. A recent questionnaire circulated to deans of medical schools disclosed that only five out of some thirty-nine reporting institutions were currently offering any instruction in hypnosis.

Although several thousand physicians have received some training in this treatment modality, their education has been primarily through short-term seminars, institutes, and workshops which have been offered either by traveling groups of lecturers or by professional societies devoted to the study of hypnosis as part of their annual conventions. The two main traveling, teaching groups were the "Hypnosis Seminars" led by Milton Erickson and the "Hypnosis Symposium" under the guidance of Leslie M. LeCron.

A rather curious anomaly is that the greatest interest among physicians has been in the non-psychiatric specialties. Obstetricians, surgeons, anesthesiologists, pediatricians and dermatologists, as well as many general practitioners, have flocked to take courses. While official A.M.A. policy points rightly to the responsibility of psychiatry, the psychological specialists of medicine, for assuming leadership and providing adequate training to the other branches of medicine, the attitude of the majority of psychiatrists has been one of ignoring and resistance. Very few have prepared themselves to work in the hypnotic modality, while apparently many, influenced by the emphasis devoted to the psychoanalytic approach in the United States, dismiss hypnosis with the same arguments used by Sigmund Freud and his daughter Anna in their early writings. Often quoted are the statements by these early authorities to the effect that, "hypnosis by-passes the Ego," or "hypnosis is a method of treatment by suggestion which brings only temporary alleviation of symptoms," etc. Those who are familiar with modern-day research findings and thinking know that such criticisms need not be valid when the modality is used in the more sophisticated and enlightened manner now possible. However, the influence of these great writers and their associates has apparently prevented many present-day psychiatrists from re-examining their positions regarding clinical hypnosis.

The greatest resistance to the use of hypnosis comes from the Freudian psychoanalysts, even though it was Freud, himself, who wrote in one of his papers (Turnings in the ways of psychoanalytic therapy. Collected papers. Vol. II, N.Y., Hogarth Press and the International Institute for Psychoanalysis, 1948): "It is very probable too, that the application of our therapy to numbers will compel us to alloy the pure gold of analysis with the copper of direct suggestion; and even hypnotic influence might find a place in it again as it has in the treatment of war neuroses."

Although the specialty of psychiatry as a whole has not paid much attention to the field of hypnosis, it should be noted that a number of the most outstanding contributors to the area are psychiatrists. At the present time there are signs that the psychiatric profession is showing somewhat increased interest. Its official organization, the American Psychiatric Association, has issued reports encouraging the assumption of greater responsibility in training and development of hypnosis on the part of its members.

Perhaps the medical specialty which has given hypnosis the greatest attention is obstetrics. This interest was spurred by research findings indicating the potential harmfulness to the newborn by the excessive use of anesthetics during labor. In addition, the work of Grantly Read in painless childbirth stimulated interest in drugless-approaches to the pain problems of labor and delivery. It was Read's contention at first that his methods did not involve hypnotic suggestion, a position which he subsequently modified. Although the majority of obstetricians still do not use hypnosis, nor are trained in hypnotic procedures, nevertheless, most of them are familiar with the possible use of such methods, and perhaps at least ten per cent have employed them at one time or another. Kroger and others have shown the value of group conditioning methods in preparing pregnant mothers for the use of hypnosis during labor.

There are a number of physicians who have taken courses in clinical hypnosis but who fail to use it even though they believe in, and respect, its therapeutic possibilities. Some of these practitioners find themselves unsuited to the inter-personal relationship demands which are stimulated by the hypnotic situation. Others feel that the amount of time required for the induction of many patients preclude its effective use by the busy clinician.

Dental

During the years immediately following World War II interest in the applications of hypnosis to the practice of dentistry began to appear. Although there had been isolated reports, even back into the eighteenth century, of tooth extractions under hypnotic trance, and while a few of the present leading hypnodontists were beginning their early work prior to the War, the significant impetus for this movement appeared first about 1947 and almost simultaneously in the State of Minnesota and in New York City.

In Minnesota the movement was sparked by the teaching of two professors of psychology, Thomas O. Burgess of Concordia College, Moorhead, Minnesota, and William T. Heron of the University of Minnesota at Minneapolis. Through both individual teaching and clinical workshops some 300 dentists in Minnesota and adjoining states were trained in hypnodontic techniques within two or three years. This group organized an association known as the American Society of Psychosomatic Dentistry.

In New York City a group was formed at about the same time known as the Hypnotic Study Club for Dentists. The initiative for the early instruction and formation of this movement came from two dentists who had been interested for some time in the applications of hypnosis to the practice of dentistry, Jules H. Weinstein and Aaron A. Moss. Weinstein had been actively utilizing hypnosis in his dental practice since about 1925 and was an ardent campaigner for the restriction of hypnosis from the entertainment stage to the professional clinical situation. Moss, who later became the first Treasurer of the I.S.C.E.H. became known for his teaching and for the first textbook in hypnodontia (*Hypnodontics*. N.Y., Dental Items of Interest Pub. Co., 1953).

From the historical point of view, it might be noted here that the profession of dentistry was first in the stimulation of interest in hypno-anesthesia, preceding the general utilization of this procedure by the medical profession. Approximately a hundred years earlier the discovery of chemo-anesthesia and its first utilization in the practice of dentistry was announced by dentists Morton and Wells. This initiated its subsequent use by the medical profession.

Officially, the American Dental Association (A.D.A.) has been slower to give its approval to the applications of hypnosis than have the American Medical Association and the American Psychological Association to their members. The A.D.A. Council on Dental Education has considered the matter of dental hypnosis following presentations concerning its value and utilization by several well-known hypnodontists. However, as of the date of this publication, neither the A.D.A. nor its Council has taken any action designed to recognize the uses of hypnosis in dentistry. The only national official recognition of its dental uses and the right of the dentist to employ this modality has been the Report of the A.M.A.

The Michigan State Board of Dentistry has made it legal to use hypnosis in dentistry, but has not spelled out regulations concerning its proper employment. It is difficult to regulate professional practices legally until they have first been generally taught in accepted training institutions.

A few dental schools have occasionally offered isolated courses or workshops in hypnodontia, especially during the years 1957 to 1960. These were seldom taught by regular faculty members, but usually involved short-term, post-graduate institutes taught by visiting instructors and sponsored or accredited by the dental schools.

Following the Report of the A.M.A., which stressed the dangers in using hypnosis and affirmed that all teaching should be done under the supervision of the psychiatric departments of medical schools, dental schools tended to show a reticence at offering or sponsoring such courses. At the present time almost no dental schools are training dentists in hypnodontia. Dentists who wish instruction in methods must acquire these in the various short courses, seminars and workshops given by professional societies.

Through the instruction offered by the societies previously mentioned, plus training units offered by the American Society of Psychosomatic Dentistry, a number of dentists (probably several thousand) have had exposure to hypnotic methods. Few have developed the experience and skill to employ these routinely, and hence, because of the time involved such methods are often reserved by these for the occasional recalcitrant patient whose unusual fears of the dental situation make it impossible to perform needed dental procedures without hypnotic relaxation. Several dentists specializing in pedodontia have found hypnotic methods of great use in handling fearful children.

Among the major professions which utilize hypnotic techniques at the present time there is the least progress in the dental field. The teaching, interest and enthusiasm here is being maintained by a small number of pioneers who have been active in the respective hypnosis societies. Further progress probably awaits some gesture of official acceptance or approval by the A.D.A. followed by a renewed interest on the part of the dental schools.

Psychological

During the past two decades the character of American psychology has undergone considerable change and expansion. In 1940 there were less than 1,000 members of the American Psychological Association (A.P.A.). As of the present writing, there are over 20,000. Prior to World War II psychology was primarily an academic and research discipline. Occasionally, demonstrations of hypnosis were given in courses on abnormal psychology by a few professors who were studying the phenomena. Such demonstrations were generally motivated by scientific interest in the unusual psychological aspects of hypnotic suggestion. Little or no applications were stressed. Clinical utilization was almost nonexistent, even as the clinical use of the psychologist, himself, was as yet not common.

As a consequence of the need for more psychological services in Army Hospitals during the Second World War, and in the hospitals and clinics of the Veterans Administration after the War, a great interest was stimulated in the clinical employment of psychologists for both diagnostic and therapeutic purposes. Standards were raised. Clinical training was sponsored. Ethical practice codes were written, and in many States legislation was enacted legalizing the role of the psychologist as an applied behavioral scientist and defining his activities in relation to those of the medical practitioner. The present-day use of hypnosis by psychologists must be evaluated in the light of this recent, dynamic change in the organization and activities of psychologists as scientists and as practitioners.

For many years the A.P.A., the official spokesman for American psychology, paid no attention to hypnosis or the activities of its members in this field. As various psychologists began to attend courses and to utilize hypnotic techniques in their clinical practice, articles appeared in the professional journals of the A.P.A. The dangers of unskilled and unethical use of hypnosis became

increasingly recognized until finally, in 1959, the A.P.A.'s Board
of Professional Affairs was given the task of evaluating the state
of hypnosis as employed by the psychological profession and of
making appropriate recommendations for its regulation. In November of 1959 the Board issued its Report which recognized the
activities of psychologists in the "practice, teaching and study of
hypnosis," "noted with satisfaction the high level disciplinary program of the Society for Clinical and Experimental Hypnosis"
(SCEH) and gave its approval to the American Board of Examiners in Psychological Hypnosis by recommending that A.P.A.
members whose competence in clinical or experimental hypnosis
had been certified by that Board be appropriately listed in A.P.A.
Directories. The American Board of Examiners in Psychological
Hypnosis (ABEPH), which will be described more in detail later,
was a societal-sponsored certification board, designed to indicate
applicants whose high level of competence had been investigated
and certified. In 1960, the Report of the Board of Professional
Affairs was subsequently approved by the A.P.A. Board of Directors and then by the A.P.A. Council of Representatives after
certain modification in requirements for certification. Thus, psychology became the first of the major professions which recognized a certifying board and a level of approved competency in
the field. Since that time an increasing number of announce-
ments and articles referring to activities of psychologists in the
field of hypnosis has appeared in official journals of the A.P.A.

In 1960, and again in 1961, the A.P.A. sponsored one-week
"Post-Doctoral Training Institutes" in hypnotherapy. Several university psychology departments have offered courses in hypnosis
at the graduate school level, the University of California at Los
Angeles, Stanford University, Washington State University, the
University of Michigan, Roosevelt University, and the University
of Chicago, to mention a few. In spite of these exceptions, the
traditional academic departments of psychology have shown as
much resistance to the teaching of hypnosis as have the medical
schools. The study on education in hypnosis by Moss et al., which
was previously mentioned and referred to at the end of this chapter reported that only eight psychology departments are currently
offering such courses.

While the Pre-War interest in hypnosis was primarily on the part of academic psychologists engaged in teaching and research, since 1945 the impetus has come from clinical psychology. Many clinicians, searching for more rapid methods of treatment have focused their attention on integrating various other psychotherapies with hypnosis. There is increasing recognition that hypnosis is not an isolated therapy but is most effectively employed in conjunction with psychoanalytic and other psychotherapies. This tendency to bring hypnosis into closer relationship with other recognized approaches promises to modify extreme attitudes of acceptance or rejection and permit its integration with other psychologic methods.

In the scientific societies devoted to the study of hypnosis, such as the American Society for Clinical Hypnosis and the Society for Clinical and Experimental Hypnosis, psychologists are overwhelmingly in the minority, ranging from only five to fifteen per cent of the total membership. However, within these organizations they have exerted influence disproportionate to their numbers, primarily because the few psychologists associated with these societies have been prolific producers of published contributions. Perhaps half of the significant books and articles relating to scientific hypnosis has originated from psychologist members.

Of note is the recent trend for interest in hypnosis to involve new contributors. For more than a decade the articles published in the field were primarily by the small group of active, psychologist investigators affiliated with the national hypnosis societies. Beginning about 1960, articles concerning hypnosis and research studies involving the use of hypnotic techniques began to appear in journals which had previously published no literature relating to this field. Such research studies were often carried out by psychologists within government agencies and by professors of psychology in major universities. New names, many of them well known and respected in other fields of psychology, began to appear as authors of papers related to hypnosis. Although most psychologists have not had training in hypnotic techniques, and although the contributions in the field stem largely from a relatively few investigators, the number of scientists concerned is expanding. It may be that the official acceptance and approval of work in hypnosis by the A.P.A. has stimulated more experimental psychologists to develop interests in this direction. Growth here is slow and conservative but appears to be more soundly motivated and devoid of the exhibitionistic fanfare which has so often characterized its introduction into clinical fields.

Other Professional Disciplines

There are no other professions at present in this country which have evinced significant attention toward the field of hypnosis, and membership in the national hypnosis societies is not open to professionals of other disciplines. However, isolated individuals from certain other areas have shown interest in the field, and when able to secure training, have found uses for the modality.

Optometrists concerned with the fitting of glasses, and especially contact lenses, are confronted with patients exhibiting resistance and anxieties. Many of these have difficulty in adjusting to glasses, just as do some patients to prosthetic devices such as artificial limbs. Hypnosis can sometimes be of help here, and a few optometrists have employed hypnotic methods. However, there is no provision for training members of this discipline.

A few law enforcement officials have experimented in the use of hypnosis in crime detection and especially in lie detection. There have been suggestions for its employment in the field of military espionage and counter-espionage. A few teachers have experimented with hypnosis as a method for improving learning and retention, but as yet no systematic studies of its possibilities in the field of education have been made. There has been an occasional veterinarian who has studied hypnosis and reported uses in the calming of disturbed animals. This represents an attempt at applying findings from studies made in the field of animal hypnosis.

Finally, it should be mentioned that various clergymen have shown interest in hypnosis and have sought enlightenment concerning it, not so much to practice hypnotherapy as such, but rather to understand better the emotional reactions to religious ritual, services and practices. Some men of the cloth (priests, ministers and rabbis) are also psychologists or physicians, and have turned their training in hypnosis achieved via the medical and psychological professions toward studies pertaining to their religion. A number of papers have been published concerning the relation of hypnosis to religious rituals.

In general, the public interest is higher than professional interest, but with the exception of Marcuse's paper-bound summary published by Penguin in 1959 *(Hypnosis, Fact and Fiction)* few scientifically sound books have yet been published to inform the lay public about hypnosis.

RESEARCH

As noted earlier, Hull compiled and evaluated most of the objective scientific research published prior to 1933. Weitzenhoffer undertook the difficult job of extending this coverage from the years 1933 to 1953. Since that time occasional bibliographies have been published by SCEH, and by Crasilneck and Hall, but essentially students will have to go to the original sources which are largely the pages of the *American Journal of Clinical Hypnosis* and the *International Journal of Clinical and Experimental Hypnosis.* The editorship of the latter *Journal* has passed from Milton Kline to Frank B. Kirkner, Chief Clinical Psychologist of the Veterans Administration Hospital in Long Beach, California (1960-1961) and then to its present editor, Martin Orne, M.D., Ph.D., Department of Psychiatry, Harvard University. Occasional articles have appeared in other medical, dental and psychological Journals which may be located through the *Medical Medicus Index* and *Psychological Abstracts,* but these reference sources cannot be counted upon to give thorough coverage. In fact, as noted by Moss, Logan and Lynch, the number of entries related to hypnosis reported in *Psychological Abstracts* has declined considerably since 1957, a trend which is not in keeping with the actual number of papers published. It should be noted that some fifteen Ph.D. dissertations pertaining to hypnosis have been reported recently by major universities. Two works should be cited as good reference sources, the first, edited by LeCron entitled *Experimental Hypnosis* and subtitled "A Symposium of Articles on Research by Many of the World's Leading Authorities" does contain a number of provocative papers and studies. The other, edited by Kline *(Clinical Correlations of Experimental Hypnosis)* is in press at the time of this writing. It is a serious attempt to bring together modern research findings and theory.

Until recently, the overwhelming majority of published research studies were carried out in isolated centers and largely by a few dedicated pioneers in the field. A large number of contributions by a relatively small number of writers was the rule.

However, we now see research reports emerging from a number of centers, often university psychology departments. Some of these contributors are relative newcomers to the field of hypnosis. Noteworthy of attention are the studies by Weitzenhoffer and Hilgard and Associates at Stanford University, Shor at Harvard University, and London at the University of Illinois. The Stanford research group has developed the first carefully standardized scale of hypnotic susceptibility *(The Stanford hypnotic susceptibility scale, forms A and B.* Palo Alto, Calif., Consulting Psychologists Press, 1959), an instrument which will be helpful in making available validating standards for other research studies. Studies pertaining to the field of animal hypnosis have been summarized by Marcuse at Washington State University. At the University of Texas, Southwestern Medical School, Crasilneck and Associates have given especial study to the problems of hypnotic control of pain. At Harvard University, Barber has attempted a theoretical formulation of the effect of hypnosis on pain. Barber has also called critical attention to the lack of objective controls found in so many past experiments in this field. (Experimental controls and the phenomena of hypnosis. *J. Nerv. Ment. Disease, 134:* 493-505, 1962.).

If there is any significant new trend beginning in the research area in hypnosis it is the appearance of sophisticated studies with increased attention to research design and controls such as those by Blum at the University of Michigan, by Reyher at Michigan State College and Reiff and Scheerer *(Memory and Hypnotic Age Regression.* Int. Univ. Press, 1959) in their investigations of hypnotic regression at the University of Kansas.

Some foundations are beginning to make funds available to support research. The annual conventions of the national societies have featured research studies which have then usually been reprinted in their respective journals. Both organizations have offered prizes, awards, and recognitions aimed at stimulating scientific contribution.

Controversies About the Nature of Hypnosis

Hypnosis is a topic about which many controversies have revolved, but two will be mentioned here as being foci of considerable attention by scientific investigators in the United States. The first, involves the extent to which anti-social or criminal behavior can be induced by hypnotic suggestion. This controversy has extended over a long period of time. It includes early studies by Estabrooks, Wells, Brenman, Rowland, and Watkins which concluded that anti-social behavior can indeed be induced under hypnosis, and experiments by Erickson and Wolberg who arrived at the opposite conclusion. Summaries of this controversy published by Weitzenhoffer and Young (in LeCron's text) have tended to arrive at the conclusion that such behavior can be induced when the situation has been misrepresented to the patient through hypnotic hallucinations so that the subject thinks he is performing an act in line with the beliefs of his own conscience. They do not find that definite and controlled evidence has yet shown that subjects can be "forced" to violate directly, and without distorted perception, their own personal views of right and wrong. This controversy continues, even though the statement has been widely published in this country that no one can be hypnotized against his will nor be forced to perform acts which are against his conscience. It may well be that this is a good position to be upheld before the public which might otherwise become unduly alarmed and resistant toward hypnotic treatment and experimentation.

The second controversy is more basic to the field, namely, the reality of hypnotic phenomena. Investigators like White (A preface to a theory of hypnotism. *J. Abnorm. Soc. Psychol.*, 36: 477-505, 1941), Sarbin (Contributions to role taking theory: Hypnotic behavior. *Psychol. Rev.*, 5: 255-270, 1950), and Barber have taken the position that such phenomena as hypnoanesthesia, hypnotic regression, etc., are not genuine, but artifacts based upon the subject's desire to please the hypnotist by playing such roles as he defines for them to play. They hold that with rigorous controls these phenomena either cannot be elicited, or that they are only symptoms which can be induced equally in the fully conscious state. These investigators have challenged a large number of the reports of other experimenters. Pattie is among those authorities who have produced considerable evidence of the reality of hypnotic phenomena. This same writer (The genuineness of some hypnotic phenomena. Chap. 6 in *Hypnosis and its Therapeutic Applications*, R. M. Dorcus (Ed.) N.Y., McGraw Hill, 1956) has summarized the conclusions of a number of studies by various other experimenters.

LAWS

As the number of practitioners employing hypnosis in clinical settings and the number of researchers in universities has increased in this country, attention has been forced upon the ethical and legal problems raised. The SCEH has adopted an Ethical Practices Code which defined in general terms restrictions and controls proper in the use of hypnosis. The hypnosis boards have undertaken to enforce this ethical code among their own diplomates.

However, little yet exists in the way of established legislation regulating the practice of hypnosis. The State of Oregon (since 1908) has forbidden the public demonstration of a person in a "mesmeric or hypnotic trance" and thus has had control over stage demonstrations by charlatans. Several attorney generals have ruled that the practice of hypnosis is a part of the practice of medicine, a ruling not acceptable to psychologists. A few cities have adopted a code which requires that the use of hypnosis be restricted to physicians, dentists and psychologists. And at the present writing there are cooperative efforts to enact more state laws restricting its use to competently trained practitioners in the major professions. The trend indicates that such legislation will soon be enacted in key states, and in time may become general throughout the country. Both national hypnosis societies have created legislative committees which are studying the situation and preparing to make recommendations. The great public interest in hypnosis has brought about an occasional presentation of movies, television, and radio productions in which hypnosis was demonstrated or made part of a story. Reports are on record of actual harm which has happened to susceptible viewers who have observed hypnotic demonstrations on television. Constructive counter-actions have been initiated by responsible quarters in the hypnosis movement.

The Committee on Hypnosis of the A.M.A. has produced television films of an educational nature which have been shown on national networks. These illustrated ethical and unethical uses of hypnosis. Of recent note is the conclusion of an agreement between SCEH and the National Broadcasting Company whereby the scripts of programs related to hypnosis will be reviewed at the Director's office in consultation with the Society. The seeking by broadcasters of reputable expert consultation in this sensitive area is a constructive move. In addition, both the American Psychological Association and the American Psychiatric Association have made representations to the broadcasting companies when programs involving the questionable use of hypnosis have been released. It is to be anticipated that there will be a continuing increase in ethical control by professional and scientific organizations.

Additional Considerations
(a)—The Case of Bridey Murphy

In 1955, Bernstein, a lay hypnotist, published a book entitled: *The Search for Bridey Murphy* (N.Y., Doubleday, 1956). In this work a series of interviews with a young housewife under deep hypnosis were described. It was maintained that the subject had been "regressed" back to a pre-birth period a century earlier, to an existence in Ireland. Under this regressed state she revivified her presumed earlier life as "Bridey Murphy." The incidents she described seemed most realistic, and her description of the place and time authentic. The published report of the case implied a belief in reincarnation and strongly contended that under hypnotic regression such earlier lives could be contacted.

This case intrigued the lay public, and the work became a best seller. Newspapers and magazines took up the matter and published articles about "Bridey Murphy" together with interviews of experts in the field of hypnosis concerning their attitudes about this situation.

Kline edited a survey of professional thinking on the topic (*A Scientific Report on the Search for Bridey Murphy.* N.Y., Julian Press, 1956). It was generally concluded that patients under hypnosis will often fantasy and fabricate in ways designed to please their hypnotist, and that in this case the subject was giving to the hypnotist what he wished. One of the national magazines investigated the early life of the subject and reported that as a small child she lived close to an Irish nurse, named Bridey Murphy, who used to regale the child with stories about "the auld countree." With that, the matter stopped as far as professionals were concerned. The incident, however, focused national attention on hypnosis, revealed some of its potential misuses, and in the course of the controversy, stimulated more professionals to look into the area. It also increased public interest and demand for hypnotic services.

Additional Considerations (b)—Societies

Because of the enormous professional and lay ignorance concerning hypnosis unreasoning prejudices and fears about this modality tended to develop in both circles. The early pioneers who dared to experiment in this area found themselves often isolated and subject to the rejection of colleagues. Academic experimentalists had to endure ignoring by their universities and sometimes even official prohibition of their activities. Great educational institutions, which prided themselves on academic freedom, did not always extend this freedom to include the study of hypnosis. Likewise, early clinical workers in the field frequently bore the brunt of active attack or tacit disapproval on the part of professional colleagues, often to the detriment of their practices and their livelihoods.

In addition to the traditional "boom and bust" cycles which had characterized the history of hypnosis, the one other recurring fact was the obvious need (from the time of Mesmer) felt by all serious students in this field for scientific and professional respectability. The struggles of Braid and Elliotson in England to secure acceptance of their articles by *Lancet,* the official medical publication, and by Liébault in France for university recognition, are only typical of the recurrent problem experienced by all pioneers in this sensitive and controversial area.

It was natural that there would develop a strong tendency for early workers to turn toward each other for mutual recognition, encouragement and protection. This need initiated the organization of clubs and societies devoted to the study of hypnosis. These may be divided in this country into two major classes: those which were organized around the interests of a single profession (dentistry) and those which were multi-disciplinary in character and aimed at bringing together physicians, psychologists and dentists, the three major professions which had concerned themselves with hypnosis.

The Society for Clinical and Experimental Hypnosis (SCEH)

This Society was established in 1949 by some twenty-five pioneering workers, mostly psychiatrists and psychologists. Later, its membership was opened to dentists and to non-psychiatric physicians. A New York psychiatrist, Jerome Schneck, became its first President, serving from 1949 to 1955. The Society's second President (1955-1958) Bernard B. Raginsky, M.D. was from Montreal, Canada. Raginsky became later the Founding President of the I.S.C.E.H. It was during Raginsky's presidency of SCEH that the Institute for Research in Hypnosis, the Hypnosis Boards, and I.S.C.E.H. were organized by the Society. He played a most significant administrative role in this period of active development as well as being a prolific contributor to the literature in hypnosis and psychosomatic medicine.

Succeeding presidents of SCEH included Roy M. Dorcus, Ph.D., (1958-1959), psychologist and Dean of Life Sciences at the University of California at Los Angeles, Jacob H. Conn, M.D., (1959-1961) professor in the Psychiatric Department at the Johns Hopkins University Medical School, and Dr. Milton V. Kline, (1961-1963), psychologist.

In 1954 the Society began publication of the *Journal for Clinical and Experimental Hypnosis* under the editorship of Milton V. Kline. It also undertook to publish occasional monographs, bibliographies, and to encourage exchange and communication between workers in the field.

In the summer of 1958, the Executive Council of SCEH instructed its research and training branch, the Institute for Research in Hypnosis, to incorporate within its charter *The American Board of Clinical Hypnosis* with three autonomous sub-sections: *The American Board of Medical Hypnosis* whose first president was Jerome Schneck, *The American Board of Hypnosis in Dentistry*, whose first president was Jacob Stolzenberg, and the *American Board of Examiners in Psychological Hypnosis* whose first president was Milton Kline. These were organized with the objective of providing a high-level of certification for experienced workers which would be comparable to the requirements of other specialty boards in medicine, dentistry and psychology.

The American Board of Clinical Hypnosis was incorporated in the State of New York with the "consent" of the State Commissioner of Education to whom the Institute was responsible. It was not the policy of these Boards to evaluate the clinical or research competence of their candidates as such, but rather to certify those already recognized clinicians and scientists who could demonstrate high levels of proficiency in the use of hypnotic techniques within their respective areas of operation. The recognition accorded the American Board of Examiners in Psychological Hypnosis by the American Psychological Association has already been noted. At the present date of publication the medical and dental boards have neither been approved nor disapproved by the American Medical Association and the American Dental Association. They continue to function as independent boards operating outside the structure of the A.M.A. and A.D.A. The principle of "certifying boards" has been controversial, and a number of workers in the field of hypnosis have challenged the desirability of such organizations.

Controversy in the Ranks

The tendency of hypnosis workers to draw together into societies was soon met by a counter-tendency, that of disagreeing, dividing and forming splinter groups. By their very nature, leaders in the hypnosis movement often tend to be prima donnas. This is not to criticize nor disparage those outstanding scientists and clinicians who have through yeoman efforts developed this discipline to its present position, but rather to point out that since the hypnotist must use his own personality and prestige as the foundation of his induction approaches, leadership in this field obviously tends to fall toward those who can develop commanding character traits and who are sufficiently motivated and internally integrated as to withstand the barbs of rejection and criticism. Only those who could persevere in their programs in spite of isolation and adverse community attitudes could make the contributions and achievements which carried them to top positions of recognition by their associates.

It was, therefore, not surprising that strong differences of opinion began to appear within the various societies. Controversies developed over matters of training, education, standards of competency, ethics, and society administration as well as over matters of theory. These affiliations and splits did not within the hypnosis movement become inter-disciplinary. Thus dentists, surgeons, obstetricians, psychologists and psychiatrists tended to make their identifications on their respect for each other as individuals, for their competencies, achievements and published contributions, and their mutuality on views regarding the above factors related to training, education, etc. Inter-professional quarrels, such as have often characterized the relationships between psychiatry and psychology, did not tend to become activated within the hypnosis movement. During the fractionation of hypnosis societies, the lines of demarcation were generally drawn along other than disciplinary lines.

Psychologists and physicians did not each form separate societies related to their respective disciplines, but dentists did. The development of dental hypnosis was marked by great fluidity of societal organizations in those groups devoted primarily to dental hypnosis.

As noted earlier, the group of dental practitioners which centered in Minnesota founded *The American Society of Psychosomatic Dentistry*. This organization later expanded its membership to include medical practitioners and became *The American Society of Psychosomatic Dentistry and Medicine*. Its official Journal *The American Journal of Psychosomatic Dentistry and Medicine* was edited by Phillip Ament. This group has been active under the teaching and leadership of Ament and Irwin S. Shaw in developing teaching programs and certifying instructors for the teaching of dental hypnosis.

The original New York group underwent a number of changes. Originally called the *Hypnotic Study Club for Dentists* it reorganized first as the *American Society for the Advancement of Hypnodontics* and later changed the name to the *American Hypnodontic Society*.

In 1954, a number of dental study groups in the Midwest united to organize the *Academy of Applied Psychology in Dentistry (AAPD)* which published (for one year) under the editorship of Irving Secter the *Journal of Hypnosis and Psychology in Dentistry*.

In 1955, the American Hypnodontic Society temporarily relinquished identification as a national organization to become a chapter of the AAPD. In 1959, it withdrew from AAPD and revived its identity as the American Hypnodontic Society.

In addition to the above national organizations in dental hypnosis numerous city study clubs and local academies for dentists interested in this field have maintained autonomous or semi-affiliated relationships with the national groups. The plethora of dental societies interested in hypnosis and the controversies (largely administrative) which often raged between them brought no unity of voice from dental hypnotists in their continuing negotiations for recognition by the A.D.A. Accordingly, in 1961 under the initial presidency of the L. M. Staples of Boston, a Council of Societies in Dental Hypnosis was formed with the objective of uniting into a common effort all organizations concerned either fully or partially with the problems and recognition of dental hypnosis.

While the decade from 1947 to 1957 was marked by much change and maneuvering within the field of dental hypnosis, the

SCEH during this period remained the one national organization which aimed at uniting hypnosis workers within the three disciplines of medicine, dentistry and psychology. However, in 1957, disagreements and controveries began to trouble this national organization. The single most divisive issue developed over training and the rate of expansion in the promulgation of clinical hypnosis. Within SCEH one center of members were most mindful of the "boom and bust" history of hypnosis. They felt that its sound and orderly development required that such high standards be maintained that the scientific respectability of its workers could not be questioned in other circles, and that training should be conservatively given, over substantial periods of time, and only to selected individuals of high potential competence. They emphasized that this time hypnosis must earn an accepted and continuing place among reputable life sciences.

Another group of workers, primarily centered around Milton Erickson, M.D., called attention to the lack of available training throughout the country. They held that the benefits of clinical hypnosis were such that there should be an active stimulation of "grass-roots" interest and that the values of hypnosis should be transmitted as soon as possible to all physicians, dentists and psychologists throughout the country. To implement their viewpoint they organized a traveling, teaching group known as "Hypnosis Seminars" chaired by Erickson and including Irving Secter, Seymour Hershman, Edward Aston, and during its earlier stage, Leslie M. LeCron and William S. Kroger. During the period of 1955 to 1961 this instructional team held three day "seminars" in dozens of cities and gave brief but intensive periods of teaching to several thousand professional students. They emphasized the benefits of hypnosis, tended to be unimpressed by its reported dangers, and did not believe it essential that its students have intensive background study in basic psychology, psychopathology or psychodynamics. They held that the average physician, psychologist or dentist could, with this minimal three-day training, be trusted to use hypnotic techniques in his practice or research in a primarily beneficial way.

In answer to this, the original center of members within SCEH called attention to the literature existing which indicated dangers and anti-social behaviors (P. C. Young: Antisocial uses of hypnosis. Chap. 16 in *Experimental Hypnosis*. L. M. LeCron (Ed.) N.Y., MacMillan, 1952) that could be initiated in hypnosis. They emphasized that hypnosis represented a very complex, sensitive psychological state and that intervention by even an otherwise well-trained physician into his patient's "psyche" by hypnotic methods was not wise unless this doctor had received full training in precautions and contra-indications and was well grounded in the "psychodynamics" of unconscious human behavior.

The focal point of this controversy came to a head at the 1957 spring meeting of SCEH. The "Seminars" had trained a relatively large number of students in the Midwest, centered around Chicago, and application was made by this group for admission to the Society. A bitter controversy arose over the adequacy of training of these applicants. This controversy was not fully resolved, and the application of this group were not accepted.

The differences of opinion and bitterness of this controversy erupted later in the same year with the formation of a new national hypnosis organization. In May of 1957 twelve group leaders, sympathetic to the view that training must be more rapid and made more broadly available, held a group interview by coast-to-coast telephone hookup. During this telephone conference the formation of *The American Society of Clinical Hypnosis (ASCH)* was initiated and formalized in October of that same year by representatives of about twenty local city groups. Milton Erickson was elected as the Society's first President. In July 1958, the Society published the first issue of its official journal, *The American Journal of Clinical Hypnosis*, with Erickson as its editor.

In 1959 Frank Pattie, Professor of Psychology at the University of Kentucky succeeded Milton Erickson as President of The American Society for Clinical Hypnosis. He was followed in 1961 by Herbert Mann, M.D. of San Jose, California.

The organization of the American Society for Clinical Hypnosis signalled the beginning of a three-year period of great controversy and bitterness as the two national hypnosis organizations, SCEH and ASCH, began aggressively to compete with each other for professional recognition and public approval. At the outset ASCH acquired a considerably larger membership. It had an active, traveling, training program (Seminars), and during its formative states did not require as high qualifications for membership. Large numbers of physicians and dentists took the Seminars and afterwards joined the "American Society." This gave the ASCH certain natural advantages such as the economic benefits to be received from a large number of dues-paying members. The Society was better able to finance its publications, journal and newsletter, and to provide more and better public relations materials. Its first annual scientific meeting was held in Chicago in October 1958. The Society concentrated on the organization of a large number of city sections. At one time it reached a membership of well over two thousand. ASCH presented the public image of itself as the largest, and hence the most representative, of the hypnosis societies.

SCEH, with its higher membership requirements at this time, its belief in long-term education as a requirement for such membership, and its implied disapproval of the short-term, seminar-type of instruction, could not compete with ASCH in numbers of members. Although it also became larger, its growth was at a much slower rate. It, however, maintained the advantage of including among its membership a much larger proportion of the contributing and publishing scientists. Accordingly, SCEH concentrated on presenting the public image of high quality and scientific respectability. During this period the ASCH Journal was faced with the problem of securing more scientific manuscripts for publication, while the SCEH Journal had greater difficulty in obtaining adequate financing for the publication of its issues.

There was much jockeying for the favor of key individuals, with resignations and counter-resignations, accusations and counter-accusations characteristic of the inter-social conflict. Charges of unethical conduct were made, and personal attacks were initiated. Men who had previously collaborated with each other in scientific publication ceased to work together. New groups and individuals found themselves indecisively wavering between affiliation with the respective camps.

Certain natural pressures began to be exerted on both groups which brought a modification of policies and practices tending to minimize their differences. As public and professional interest in hypnosis waned, the demand for seminar-type training lessened. At the same time there was the initiation of a few longer-term courses in some universities and medical schools. ASCH reorganized its Seminars program into a non-profit scientific foundation, while SCEH, through its Institute for Research in Hypnosis, became more active in organizing "Training Centers" in key cities aimed at presenting longer-term courses in line with its prevailing philosophy about education.

The extremely high membership requirements which characterized the earlier years of SCEH were lowered, while, at the same time, ASCH raised its own earlier lenient requirements until the basic standards in both organizations became comparable. SCEH, as noted earlier, became active in the international organization of hypnosis through I.S.C.E.H. and advancing its scientific acceptance through affiliation with the American Association for the Advancement of Science (1961). ASCH did not undertake to organize another "international" organization but did expand its influence beyond the United States by securing the "affiliation" with it of a number of hypnosis societies in other countries, notably Japan and South America. It also moved to increase its scientific acceptance by becoming a member of the World Federation for Mental Health. Many workers in hypnosis became members of both organizations. There was a cessation of attacks on each other, and by 1962 the two organizations were following somewhat parallel but non-interacting paths.

One other factor has had a recent significant influence on the scene of American hypnosis, that of the *Committee on Mental Health, Sub-Committee on Hypnosis of the A.M.A.* This Sub-Committee was chaired by Harold Rosen, M.D., a psychiatrist, formerly an officer in SCEH who has made significant published contributions to the field. This Committee took a number of positions which were in opposition to key policies of both SCEH and ASCH and which were not acceptable to various other professional groups. It opposed the ASCH short-term seminar type training and disapproved of the SCEH-sponsored certification boards. By maintaining that hypnosis was a "psychiatric technique" to be taught exclusively in the psychiatric department of medical schools and under psychiatric supervision, its program (Am. Psychiat. Assoc. Committee on Therapy. Regarding hypnosis: Statement, Washington, D.C., 1961) did not receive the whole-hearted support of either the psychological profession or the non-psychiatric physicians. Finally, through its chairman, it embarked on an education program in the press, national journals and television, aimed at alerting the medical profession and the public to the "dangers" of hypnosis. This Committee's policies, thus, were isolated from the trends and practices of both of the major national hypnosis societies who included among their joint membership almost all the serious scientific and clinical workers in the field. These ultra-conservative policies do not appear, as of present writing, to have furthered the Committee's stated objectives of stimulating hypnosis education within medical schools. Rather, the effect has been to frighten the public and many physicians about the use of hypnosis and to initiate a much greater wariness concerning its clinical employment. As a result, the demand for public services and for professional education in hypnosis has declined. The actions of this Committee do not appear to have had any effect either way on the gradual increase in university research studies.

FUTURE

A projection of present-day trends justifies the following predictions relating to the future of hypnosis in the United States:

1. Growth of interest in hypnosis will continue but at a slower pace. There will be a gradual incorporation of training, control and experimentation in hypnosis into the traditional society institutions of universities, medical and dental schools, and legislation relative to the regulation of hypnosis in the public interest will be enacted. Such movements will meet with continuing, but diminishing resistance.

2. The "boom days" of great excitement over hypnosis, of high public enthusiasm and interest in lay articles on hypnosis, and of the flocking by professional people to courses and institutes of training are over.

3. Hypnosis will lose its flavor of "uniqueness" but will be more integrated into the general body of medical and psychological theory and practice.

4. Workers in this field will tend increasingly to identify themselves as psychiatrists, internists, dentists, psychologists, etc., who sometimes use hypnosis, rather than as "hypnotists."

5. In the clinical field emphasis will be on its more selective use, and on investigation concerning its contra-indications.

6. Research studies will move toward better research design rather than the enthusiastic reporting of uncontrolled observations.

7. Controversies regarding societal organization and structure will decline with relatively more energy being put into the validation of research findings and the development of greater sophistication in clinical practice.

8. Attention will turn from induction techniques toward attempts to understand more the nature of hypnotic states.

9. Increasing emphasis will be given to the relationship between hypnotist and subject and to its comparison with other human inter-personal relationships.

10. Only those will continue in working with hypnosis who have surmounted their original awe and enthusiasm at the unusual aspects of its manifestations and who have become more deeply interested and dedicated toward understanding basic human nature. In this respect the numbers of workers in the field may decline but the competence of those remaining will increase.

IMPORTANT REFERENCES

A.B.E.P.H.: The American Board of Examiners in Psychological Hypnosis. *The American Psychologist, 16:* 203-205, 1961.

American Medical Association: Report of medical use of hypnosis. *J.A.M.A. 168:* 186-189, 1958.

Blum, S.: *A Model of the Mind.* New York, Wiley, 1961.

Bowers, Margaretta K., and Glasner, S.: Auto-hypnotic aspects of the Jewish Cabalistic concept of Kavanah. *J. Clin. & Exp. Hyp., 6:* 3-23, 1958.

Crasilneck, H. B., and Hall, J. A.: Physiological changes associated with hypnosis: A review of the literature since 1948. *Int. J. of Clin. & Exp. Hyp.*, 7: 9-50, 1959.

Erickson, M. H.: An experimental demonstration of the psychopathology of every day life. *Psychoanal. Quart.*, 8: 338-353, 1939.

Kline, M. V. (Ed.): *Hypnodynamic Psychology.* New York, Julian Press, 1955.

Kline, M. V.: *Freud and Hypnosis.* New York, Julian Press and The Institute for Research in Hypnosis Publication Society, 1958.

Kroger, W. S.: *Handbook of Medical Hypnosis.* New York, Lippincott, 1962.

Lindner, R. M.: Hypnoanalysis as a psychotherapeutic technique. In *Specialized Techniques in Psychotherapy.* G. Bychowski and J. L. Despert (Eds.) New York: Basic Books, 1953.

London, P.: Hypnosis in children: An experimental approach. *Int. J. Clin. & Exp. Hyp.*, 10: 79-91, 1962.

Marcuse, F. L.: Animal hypnosis and psychology, Chap. 4 in *Hypnodynamic Psychology*, edited by Milton V. Kline. New York, Julian Press, 1955.

Moss, C. S., Logan, J. C., and Lynch, Dorothy: Present status of psychological research and training in hypnosis: A developing professional problem. *The American Psychologist*, 17: 542-549, 1962.

Raginsky, B. B.: The use of hypnosis in anesthesiology. *J. Pers.*, 1: 340-348, 1951.

Raginsky, B. B.: Temporary cardiac arrest induced under hypnosis. *Int. J. of Clin. & Exp. Hyp.*, 7: 53-68, 1959.

Schneck, J. M.: *Studies in Scientific Hypnosis.* Baltimore, Williams & Wilkins, 1954.

Schneck, J. M. (Ed.): *Hypnosis in Modern Medicine.* Springfield, Ill., Charles C Thomas, Publisher, Rev. ed., 1963.

Society for Clinical and Experimental Hypnosis: The Ethical Code. *Newsletter of S.C.E.H.*, 1959, Vol. 2, No. 3, 5-7.

Society for Clinical and Experimental Hypnosis: Summary of Existing Legislation. *Soc. Clin. Exp. Hyp. Newsletter*, 2: 7-13, 1961.

Weitzenhoffer, A. M.: *Hypnotism: An Objective Study in Suggestibility.* New York, John Wiley and Sons, 1953.

Wolberg, L. R.: *Medical Hypnosis, Vols. I & II.* New York, Grune & Stratton, 1948.

NATIONAL ADDRESSES

Societies

The Society for Clinical and Experimental Hypnosis (SCEH)
The U. S. Division of I.S.C.E.H.
> Administrative Offices:
>> 200 West 57th Street, New York 19, New York

The American Society of Clinical Hypnosis (ASCH)
> Administrative Offices:
>> 4206 West Irving Park Road, Chicago 41, Illinois

The American Society of Psychosomatic Dentistry and Medicine (ASPDM)
> Secretary-Treasurer:
>> Eugene G. Lerner, D.D.S.
>> 2177½ Seneca Street, Buffalo, New York

The American Hypnodontic Society
> Administrative Offices:
>> 2 East 63rd Street, New York 21, New York

Journals

The Journal of Clinical and Experimental Hypnosis (renamed since January 1959, *The International Journal of Clinical and Experimental Hypnosis*).

Published by SCEH on behalf of both SCEH and ISCEH.
> Editor: Martin Orne, M.D., Ph.D.
>> 74 Fernwood Road, Boston, Massachusetts

Newsletter of the Society for Clinical and Experimental Hypnosis
> Editor: Margaretta K. Bowers, M.D.
>> 4 Grove Street, New York 14, New York

The American Journal of Clinical Hypnosis
Published by ASCH
> Editor: Milton H. Erickson, M.D.
> 32 West Cypress Street, Phoenix, Arizona

Newsletter of the American Society of Clinical Hypnosis
> Editor: Leo Wollman, M.D.
> 2802 Mermaid Avenue, Brooklyn, New York

The Journal of the American Society of Psychosomatic Dentistry and Medicine
Published by ASPDM
> Editor: Philip Ament, D.D.S.
> 964 Delaware Avenue, Buffalo 9, New York

NAME INDEX

SUBJECT INDEX

307